MATTHEW
BOULTON
AND THE SOHO MINT

TO MY FAMILY

MATTHEW BOULTON

AND THE SOHO MINT

Copper to Customer

SUE TUNGATE

BREWIN BOOKS

BREWIN BOOKS
19 Enfield Ind. Estate,
Redditch,
Worcestershire,
B97 6BY
www.brewinbooks.com

A CIP catalogue record for this book is
available from the British Library.

ISBN: 978-1-85858-723-3

Printed and bound in Great Britain
by Page Bros Ltd.

Contents

Notes

THIS book covers Soho Mint during Matthew Boulton's lifetime only. Names in use during the eighteenth century, for example: Sumatra, Bengal, Bombay (now Mumbai), Ceylon (now Sri Lanka) and Madras (now Chennai), are used, with the exception of Parys Mine, Anglesey, which Boulton often spelt as Paris. Original spelling has been retained in transcriptions of archival material, though some punctuation has been added.

The Soho Mint produced coins, tokens and medals. A coin is a piece of metal to be used as money which conforms to a standard approved by a government or ruling authority, whereas tokens were produced for private individuals or organisations, and did not necessarily represent the value of the metal they contained. Medals were in general made to celebrate public events, and were sold to collectors.

The weight measurements in the eighteenth century consisted of tons, hundred weights (cwt), quarters (qtr), stones (st), pounds (lb), ounces (oz), and grains. 1 grain = 0.0648 grams; 1 gram = 15.43 grains; 1 ounce (av) = 28.35g; 16 ounces (oz) = 1 pound (lb); 2240 lb = 1 ton. One ton is roughly the equivalent to a metric tonne; 1cwt = 50.8kg.

Length measurements used are inches, feet, yards and miles. 1 inch = 2.54cm; 1 foot = 30cm; 1 yard = 91cm; 1 mile = 1.6km.

Monetary values are given in (£) pound, (s) shilling and (d) pence. For example: £300 2s 5d, but in original documents the values may be written as 300£ 2/- 5d or in other notations.

References to **MS** documents all come from the Archives of Soho at the Library of Birmingham. References to **AD1583** come from the Cornwall Heritage Trust.

Most images were taken by Sue Tungate with kind permission of the various curators (Birmingham Assay Office, Birmingham Museum and Art Gallery, Avery Weighing Museum and the British Museum). 'Gold' images are gilt copper, except for the Nottingham medal.

MB = Matthew Boulton
MRB = Matthew Robinson Boulton (Matt)
BM = British Museum
BMAG = Birmingham Museum and Art Gallery
Assay Office = Birmingham Assay Office

Chapter One

Matthew Boulton
and Coining

Introduction

MATTHEW Boulton (1728-1809) was responsible for revolutionising minting practices in the late eighteenth century, by setting up the first steam-powered coining press in the world at Soho Mint, Birmingham. This contributed to solving the currency shortage, which threatened to derail industrial progress. In addition to the large coinage orders for the British Government and the East India Company, Soho Mint produced tokens and foreign coins, and around sixty different medals. During Boulton's life time, he made around one hundred and fifty designs of coins, medals and tokens, in fourteen languages, including English, Latin, Sumatran, Arabic, Persian, Welsh, French, Italian, Sanskrit, Portuguese, Russian, Hindi, Bengali, and Gaelic. The manufacture of nearly 600 million items meant that he had a huge influence on design, production and distribution; the practices and technologies he initiated spread across the world.

In order to assess the contribution made by Boulton and his team, the following questions should be answered: Why did Boulton become involved in coining? His famous Cartwheel two pence remain the largest and heaviest British copper coins in general circulation. Why were they made by Boulton and not by the Royal Mint in London? Where did the copper, iron, and steel, used as raw materials at the Soho Mint, come from? How was Boulton connected to the copper mining industry in Cornwall and Anglesey? What technical problems needed to be overcome to make a functioning mint, and who was involved in building it and making its products? How were the dies and blanks formed? How were the coins ordered, commissioned and designed and how much influence did Boulton himself have on the designs? How were his products sold and distributed all over the world? What lasting influence did he have on minting?

How did Matthew Boulton manage to reform coinage in the eighteenth century, while continuing to work at many other activities?

This book describes the processes involved, from mining the **copper**, to the final delivery of the product to the **customer**. Boulton's organisational role in the entire process was vital; from obtaining the raw materials, to the design, production, marketing and distribution of the finished product. The Soho Mint needed his application of scientific and technical knowledge to new industrial processes, and his artistic and business skills in marketing.

Who was Matthew Boulton?

Much has been written about Matthew Boulton, a Birmingham entrepreneur, manufacturer, engineer and scientist, and a generally well-liked figure. He was linked to many other key players of the eighteenth century through his social and business contacts. Profound changes were taking place, and he made noteworthy contributions to economic growth and globalisation, introducing new forms of industrialisation, including the transformation of power supplies. His interests were wide ranging, and apart from his manufacturing businesses, he campaigned for the extension of the canal system to Birmingham, the establishment of the Birmingham Assay Office in 1773, and worked with various local and government committees. He sought improvement in all things; techniques, organisation, land enclosure, education, science and manufacturing. Boulton was a co-founder of the Lunar Society, whose members included: Josiah Wedgwood, Erasmus Darwin (grandfather of Charles), James Keir, James Watt, William Withering, and Joseph Priestley.[1] Boulton was made a Fellow of the Royal Society of Edinburgh in 1784 and of the Royal Society of London in November 1785.[2]

Birmingham was already a centre for highly-skilled metal-work in the sixteenth century, and by the time Matthew Boulton was born in 1728, the town was becoming a hub of early industrialisation. The growth of industry was promoted by a stable government and security, despite a series of wars in the eighteenth century. Boulton was twelve years old when the War of the Austrian Succession (1740-1748) broke out and seventeen during the Jacobite Revolution of 1745. By the time Britain was emerging as a major colonial power in North America and India, after beating France in the Seven Years War (1756-1763), he had established, what was in its time, the most famous manufacturing business in the world at Soho Manufactory. He developed the steam-engine with James Watt during the American War of Independence (1775-1783). His Soho Mint was most affected by the events of the French Revolutionary War (1792-1802) and the final part of his working life ended with his death in 1809 during the Napoleonic Wars (1803-1815).

---

1 J. Uglow (2002) *The Lunar Men: Friends who Made the Future* Faber and Faber, London.
2 The Royal Society Repository GB 117, Reference Number EC/1785/12.

Boulton was a member of the important mercantile class who belonged to a network of economic activity, and his contemporaries included many of the first industrialists. He started work in the family button and buckle works in Birmingham in the 1740s and he inherited the business when his father died in 1759. Boulton's first wife, Mary Robinson, also died the same year, and he had then married her sister Ann. His second wife died in 1783. With his wives' inherited wealth and a relatively prosperous background, Boulton could have chosen to be an 'idle gentleman' but he was more interested in doing something useful with his life. He wrote:

'I am partial to Trade in as much as it extends a man's powers of doing good and I would rather be distinguished as the greatest Manufacturer in Europe than as a Count of the Holy Empire'.[3]

Most transactions in the eighteenth century took place within networks of personal trust, with complex webs of credit to pay for goods and carriage. Therefore, Boulton's personal reputation was important to his businesses. Links, including partners, suppliers, customers and friends, as well as rivals, were significant in obtaining commissions. He was the ultimate networker; when lobbying for the establishment of the Birmingham Assay Office in 1773, he received valuable advice from the Earl of Dartmouth and claimed to have approached a total of forty peers to guide the application through parliament.[4] Lord Shelburne, Sir Joseph Banks, Benjamin Franklin and John Motteux of the East India Company, were influential friends, who all helped in extending the steam-engine patent, and in setting up the Soho Mint. His contacts also included bankers and other influential members of the establishment such as Charles Jenkinson (1729-1808), President of the Board of Trade (1786-1804), who was made Baron Hawkesbury in 1786, and later became Lord Liverpool in 1796; William Faulkener, Secretary to Privy Council on Coin; and Thomas Howard, Lord Effingham (1747-1791), Master of the Royal Mint from 1784-1789. Boulton also had meetings with William Pitt (1759-1806), the Prime Minister from 1783.[5]

His Soho Manufactory in Handsworth, two miles from the heart of Birmingham, became a centre of excellence in metal working from the 1760s on. Clever designs were used, enabling many products to be assembled from a relatively small number of components, each of which was manufactured in quantity. Boulton engaged well paid skilled craftsmen who used labour-saving devices, which enabled them to be more productive. Standardised methods of manufacture were introduced wherever possible, and machines such as fly presses

---

3 MS 3782-13-36 Item 27, MB (Soho) to MRB (Germany) 18 December 1788.
4 J.V. Beckett (1986) *The Aristocracy in England 1660-1914* Blackwell, London p229.
5 MS 3147-3-10 Item 5, MB (New River Head) to James Watt (Birmingham) 5 March 1786; MS 3147-3-10 Item 6 MB (London) to James Watt (—) 15 March 1786.

were used to make goods cheaply. Employees were organised in a variety of workshops, each with a manager responsible for a particular area of production.

Boulton's pattern books from the Soho Manufactory showed 1,470 different articles for the toy and other metal trades. 'Toys' were small metal objects such as buckles, snuff boxes etc. for personal use. The ormolu, silverware and other goods produced there greatly influenced taste and fashion of the period, and helped raise the reputation of goods produced in Birmingham. By 1765 Boulton had brought all the functions of a modern business, including research, design, advertising and marketing under his control. Merchants were selling his goods in America, Germany, France, Spain, Russia, Italy, Holland and Sweden as well as in Britain.[6] Eventually, there were around a dozen businesses under the Soho umbrella, including steam engines, metal plate manufacture and a copper warehouse, run by Boulton, generally in association with others.

Figure 1:1 1798 Soho Manufactory from Stebbing Shaw (1801) *History of Staffordshire.*

The manufactory's principal building is shown in the centre, with the workshops of Rolling Mill Row to the right, and the mill pool in front. The Soho Mint was built to the left behind the buildings shown. The key workers were housed at the Manufactory, and a water wheel powered much of the machinery. Boulton's workforce generally respected him as an enlightened employer.[7] He had a patriarchal attitude, but treated his employees well, employing medical men

---

6 N. Goodison (1974; amended 2002) *Matthew Boulton Ormolu* Christies, London pp404-406.

7 MS 3147-3-6-17, MB to J. Watt 12 March 1782; MS 3782-12-5 Letter Book, 26 December 1780-19 August 1783; Items 164 and 172, MB (Soho) to James Watt (Cusgarne) 26 March 1782 p273; 6 & 10 April 1782 p289.

regularly to care for them.[8] This attitude was partly profit driven and self-interest, but made for a good working atmosphere.

In the 1770s Boulton played a key role in making James Watt's condensing steam engine project a reality, providing the finance, the skilled workmen and the drive to extend Watt's original patent until 1799. Many of Boulton's suggestions for important technical improvements in steam engine design can be seen in his correspondence with Watt. He also understood the commercial opportunities offered by an engine that could produce a constant rotary motion. In 1783, Boulton discussed reports of him being credited with its invention alongside Watt.[9]

Unlike most of his other ventures, Boulton controlled the Soho Mint virtually single handed, though it shared contacts and agents with other businesses at Soho, which reduced overheads. Key workers could be moved easily from one section to another. Boulton was heavily involved in its design and the choice of personnel, including engineers, engravers, clerks, craftsmen and apprentices. There was little input from his partner James Watt (1736-1819), but his son, Matthew Robinson Boulton (1770-1842) became involved, once he reached his majority. Set up from 1788, the Soho Mint was able to compete with the state monopoly in coining at the Royal Mint, which was dominated by old practices and hereditary rights. Boulton applied modern industrial methods to minting, introducing a completely new coining process without losing the support of his workers. Antagonism to innovation, both technical and organisational, was common elsewhere, especially at the Royal Mint.[10]

The Team at Soho Mint
Very experienced engineers and workmen were required to design and build the new Soho Mint. John Rennie (1761-1821), early in his career as an engineer, provided drawings and estimates for the building, which was under construction by January 1788.[11] In the same year, he rebuilt the rolling mill at Soho, run by Thomas Kellet, which was able to expand to roll metal for the mint. William Murdock (1754-1839), one of Soho's most trusted and reliable employees, came to work at the Soho Mint in 1789. He had supervised the erection of steam engines since September 1779, generally in Cornwall. After the rotary engine was developed, around 1784, Murdock had discussed plans with Boulton for applying steam power to coining.[12] Boulton continually praised his work, saying that the

---

8 MS 3782-12-59 Items 174 and 180, William Cheshire (Soho) to MB (London) 8 November 1798, 5 December 1798.

9 MS 3147-3-7-7, MB (London) to James Watt (Birmingham) 16 April 1783.

10 D. Sellwood, 'The Trial of Nicholas Briot', *British Numismatic Journal*, 1986, 56, pp108-23.

11 G. Demidowicz, 'Power at the Soho Manufactory and Mint', in M. Dick (ed.) (2009) *Matthew Boulton: A Revolutionary Player* Brewin, Studley pp122-123.

12 MS 3782-13-120, Mint Inventions and Improvements Volume 1, Folder 8, Conference held at Soho House, with William Murdock, James Watt, John Southern, Peter Ewart, James Lawson and Matthew Robinson Boulton, 7 January 1810.

firm needed *'more Murdocks, for of all others he is the most active man and best engine erector I ever saw'.*[13]

Important contributions were made by James Lawson (1760-1818), who had been employed along with Murdock in Cornwall from 1779 as an engine erector and draughtsman.[14] By 1789 Lawson was supervising the installation of Soho Mint machinery, and in 1790 was involved in drawing up the steam-powered coining press patent.[15] By mid-1790 Boulton had a fully working steam-powered mint which cost upwards of £5,000, with two engines and an annealing stove, as well as presses. Lawson was also an expert in die multiplication and responsible for important modifications to the coining process, developing an automatic layer-in which placed coining blanks onto the coining press.[16] Later he directed the erection of Soho's steam-powered machinery at the Royal Mint.[17]

Another engineer, Peter Ewart (1767-1842) had been educated at the University of Edinburgh. He had worked intermittently for Boulton, starting as an apprentice to Rennie.[18] He was *'a good mechanick, an excellent millwright, and an ingenious honest man'* and helped to develop the mint equipment, introducing a new method of cleaning the blanks.[19]

John Southern (1761-1815) worked as an assistant to James Watt, answering letters about technical problems, from at least 1781. He became head of the Drawing Office at Soho from 1796 to 1803, and was also involved with the Soho Mint.[20] In 1798, Southern was in charge of installing new coining presses with an improved design. He was also concerned with plans for providing the Russian Mint in 1799,[21] the Danish Mint in 1805,[22] and by March 1806 was drawing up plans to supply up-to-date equipment to the new Royal Mint.[23] His father and three brothers also worked at Soho.

The mint's team also included Boulton's London bankers, William and Charlotte Matthews, and competent clerks who coordinated the orders for copper, payment of wages, dispatching coins and so on. Accounts at Soho's Birmingham Warehouse were kept by Zaccheus Walker, Boulton's brother-in-law and chief clerk from at least 1760, whose son, Zack Walker Jnr was born 1768,

13 MS 3147-3-8-36, MB to James Watt 8 November 1784.
14 MS 3782-12-66-1-57; MS 3782/13/43/1-113, James Lawson files 1782, 1783, 1785, 1786, 1789-1799.
15 MS 3147-3-14-11, MB (London) to JW (Soho), 16 July 1790.
16 David Vice and Richard Doty, *The Conder Token Newspaper*, 1/3, 15 February 1997 and 1/4, 15 May 1997.
17 MS 3782-3-116-124, Setting up the Royal Mint 1805-1822.
18 MS 3782-12-66-106, John Roberts (Soho) to MB (London) 27 January 1788.
19 MS 3782-12-66-2, James Lawson (Soho) to MB (London), 27 June 1789; Item 4, 6 July 1789.
20 MS 3782-12-66-58-104 February 1788 to December 1799; MS 3782/12/66/118-119; MS 3782-13-43-114-135 November 1800 to May 1815.
21 MS 3782-12-66-102, JS (Soho) to MB (—) 27 May 1799.
22 MS 3782-13-43-120, JS (—) to MB (—) 6 January 1805.
23 MS 3782-13-43-122, JS (Soho) to MRB (—) 21 March 1806.

shortly before his mother died. James Pearson was also a cashier and bookkeeper from 1776-1815. Boulton also needed translators for the foreign orders and to correspond with his agents abroad; for example, Andrew Collins translated the German and French correspondence. He also had agents in Cornwall; Thomas Wilson worked on Boulton's behalf in the copper mining industry from 1780 until at least 1803.

John Roberts, who kept the household accounts from 1787-1791, seems to have had initial responsibility for paying the wages of the workers at the Soho Mint. He complained in May 1789 that: *'No one at present seems to have the active management of the mint'*.[24] However Zaccheus Walker was able to supply some details.[25] Fuller Mint records were kept from February 1791 when Boulton's son, Matthew Robinson Boulton (Matt) took over responsibility for day-to-day management, though the major decisions were left in Matthew Boulton's hands.[26] Matt was followed by William Brown, Boulton's confidential clerk from the end of 1791, who joined Soho as a bookkeeper. Brown earnt £300 per annum by July 1800. William Cheshire, employed from 1796, was paid 100 guineas per year. He acted as an amanuensis and private clerk to Boulton in 1805, 1808 and 1809.

Steam-engine erectors such as Lawson were only paid 10s 6d per week in 1779 with bonus payments for special work, a similar rate to John Busch (Bush or Bouch), the die forger.[27] But Lawson's wage rose more rapidly. By August 1791 he was earning £63 per year 'over & above his Board' and was paid an extra three guineas for 'Experiments on Coinage'.[28] Later, Lawson's pay rose to £250 and then to £300 per annum plus 1% commission by 1800. Similarly, Southern's pay increased, and he became a partner in 1810 after Boulton's death. Murdock was paid a little more initially, 15s per week, around £40 per year in 1779, but by 1800 was on the same salary as Southern. He was offered a partnership in 1810, but did not accept.[29]

Boulton also needed skilled engravers for making highly detailed dies. These included foreigners such as Jean-Pierre Droz, Rambert Dumarest, Noel-Alexandre Ponthon, Augustin Dupré, and Conrad Heinrich Küchler, but also local engravers John Westwood, John Gregory Hancock, John Phillp and Thomas Wyon. Most were paid per die produced, but Boulton claimed that Droz had cost him over £1,000 and produced nothing useful.[30]

Boulton had on-site specialists in die forging, cutting, and annealing: John Busch, John Peploe and Joseph Harrison, and additional individuals were drafted

24 MS 3782-12-66 Item 111, John Roberts (Soho) to MB (—) 7 May 1789.
25 MS 3782-12-74 Item 172, Zaccheus Walker (Birmingham) to MB (London) 19 January 1789.
26 MS 3782-3-13, Mint Day Book 8 February 1791-16 May 1795.
27 AD1583/1/3, Balance Sheet, James Lawson in account with Boulton & Watt c1784.
28 MS 3782-3-13, Mint Day Book 1791-May 1795, p8, 13 August 1791.
29 J. Griffiths (1992) *The Third Man: The Life and Times of William Murdoch (1754-1829)*, Deutsch, London.
30 MS 3782-13-36 Item 47, MB (London) to MRB (Amsterdam) 13 July 1790.

as needed from other areas of the Soho concerns, to build the coining presses.[31] Many of the workmen belonged to family groups, for example; Thomas Harrison had started working at Soho as a 'toy maker' from 1766, with his brother, Joseph Harrison, as a whitesmith from 1767. Joseph worked as a principle assistant in the steam engine business from its early years, and travelled around as an engine erector. He helped to set up the temporary mint for a Sumatran coinage in 1786, and became chief foreman of the engine yard at Soho in 1790. William Harrison joined as a smith, making coins and medals in 1790 and later Mrs. Harrison was also working at the Mint. John Jerome, apprenticed in 1790, came to join his father John, and other relatives Joseph, Thomas and Timothy Jerome, working at Soho Mint.

Apprentices, women, carriers and outside suppliers were also used. Many of the unskilled operations such as loading blanks into the coining press were automated, but casual workers, usually as girls and women, were required for certain jobs such as packing coins when large orders needed to be dispatched. Mint workers had to be dependable and honest, so it was important to select suitable individuals.

Coins

A coin is a piece of metal to be used as money which conforms to a standard approved by a government or ruling authority. Coins originated in Lydia (in modern Turkey) around 600 BC and were originally made from electrum, a natural gold-silver alloy, with the face value theoretically equal to their intrinsic value, so production was determined by the availability of precious metals. By the fourteenth century this came mainly from Bohemia, Austria, Serbia and Sardinia, but later from Guinea and the Gold Coast via the Africa Company of Merchants. It was difficult to make coins of one metal only as it was impractical to use gold or silver to make very small value coins, and if base metal such as copper was used for high value coins, they were usually too big and easy to counterfeit. Therefore, different metals were usually used for different value coins.[32]

Gold coins were in use in Celtic Britain in the second century BC, remained in Roman Britain, but disappeared from circulation around 425 AD. From the late seventh century silver coins known as sceattas began to be used. These were superseded by silver pennies and halfpennies, issued from the time of Offa of Mercia (757-796). By 956 AD, one currency was valid throughout Britain with the standard set at 240 pennies to 16 ounces (oz) or one pound weight (lb) of silver. Regal coinage was issued from the Tower of London from 1279 by the Royal Mint which achieved a monopoly on coining in the sixteenth century. Over time, the range of denominations increased. High value coins, gold sovereigns, worth

---

31 MS 3782-12-108, Item 53, Mint Notebook, 1788, p10 and p52.
32 C. Howgego (1995) *Ancient History from Coins* Routledge, London, p1.

twenty shillings, or one pound sterling (£), were issued by Henry VII (1457-1509) from 1489, but the last sovereigns (£1 coins) were made in 1603 and were not made again by the Royal Mint until 1817.[33] Other high value gold coins were made, including the unite and the laurel from James I's reign, and the guinea, from 1663 until 1814. The rises in the price of gold relative to silver caused the value of the guinea to increase, at times, to as high as thirty shillings. The highest value gold coin ever issued in England was the five guineas piece, introduced by Charles II in 1668 and last issued in 1777.

A shilling was worth twelve pennies, and was denoted by 's' (from roman 'solidus', a gold coin introduced in 301 AD. The solidus remained the standard gold issue of the Roman and then the Byzantine Empires until 1092). Pennies were denoted by 'd' (from 'denarius', the standard Roman silver coin, struck between 211 BC and c.AD 240). Silver pennies were essentially the only coin struck in England until the 1270s, but gradually fell in purchasing power after that. Halfpennies (½d), struck in silver, were very rare until Edward I (1239-1307) issued large numbers. Copper farthings (¼d) were first introduced during the reign of James I (1603-1623), and copper halfpennies from 1672. Under Newton's direction from 1717, the Royal Mint produced £30,289 worth of copper coins over seven years, with halfpennies being predominant. Around one thousand tons of halfpennies and farthings were struck up till 1775, which sufficed until greater calls for small change were caused by the expansion of industry. After 1775 no more copper coins were made by the Royal Mint until 1821.[34]

In the eighteenth century, the official monetary unit, the pound (£), did not actually exist as a coin, but was represented by a gold guinea with a value stabilised at 21s in 1717. Gold coins were usually of good quality, and generally struck in sufficient quantities by the Royal Mint. Re-coinages of gold were carried out in 1734 and again in the 1770s when old gold coins were melted down, including those dating back to Elizabeth I. Matthew Boulton was involved in the later re-coinage as an exchanger of gold coin.[35] But a few 'hammered' gold coins were still in circulation despite efforts to remove them.

Silver shillings and sixpences were produced in sufficient numbers until the reign of George II (1727-1760). But for the next fifty-five years they were made in very low numbers. There was no shortage of silver bullion (ingots) but the market price for silver was above what the Royal Mint was authorized to pay.[36] Any good quality silver coins were likely to be converted into bullion and exported.

---

33 G. Selgin (2008) *Good Money: Birmingham Button Makers, the Royal Mint, and the Beginnings of Modern Coinage 1775-1821* The University of Michigan Press, Ann Arbour pp8-18.

34 H.A. Seaby and P.J. Seaby (1949 edn) *A catalogue of Copper Coins and Tokens of the British Isles* B.A. Seaby Ltd. London.

35 D. Symons (2009) Talk at conference: *Where Genius and Arts Preside: Matthew Boulton* 3rd-5th July 2009.

36 G. Dyer & P.P. Gaspar *The Dorrien and Magens Shilling of 1798* British Numismatics Journal Vol. 52 (1983) pp198-214.

The grossly underweight silver shillings in circulation were effectively a token coinage. To make up for the lack of change, silver 'pieces of eight' or eight reales from Spanish bullion, mined in their American colonies, were used freely.[37]

By the 1780s, the main regal coins in use were the gold guinea, silver shilling, and copper halfpenny, though half crowns (2s 6d) and sixpences (6d) were also sometimes used. Silver pennies and halfpennies had ceased to be practical from the reign of Charles II on.[38] The guinea was used for large value transactions, though all monetary values were given in pounds (£), shillings (s) and pence (d). This system, with twenty shillings or 240 pennies to the £, was retained until decimalisation of the regal coinage in 1971. Post decimalisation, there are now 100 pence to the pound and 1p equals 2.4d.

For small value transactions, the copper halfpenny was mainly used by working people, but copper farthings were not common.[39] The Royal Mint had never really considered that minting copper was part of its remit, so poor quality control meant that copper coins of the same denomination were not necessarily of uniform size or weight. Those in circulation were often worn, with indistinct images, which meant that they were easy to counterfeit. Even when new copper coins were supplied, they were often melted down and used to make lighter weight counterfeits, in particular in Birmingham.[40] There were no copper pennies until Boulton's issue of 1797 from the Soho Mint. Due to the lack of official coins, a variety of other unofficial small change was available in Britain, including a range of tokens, foreign coins, and counterfeits.

Another problem was that all newly-minted coins had to be collected from the Royal Mint at the Tower of London, as no arrangements were made for distributing them round the country.[41] Copper coins were not accepted in large numbers to pay customs and excise, or exchanged for gold at the Royal Mint. If increased quantities were made available, small value coins tended to end up in London, and consequently there were many complaints so the Royal Mint stopped coining. However other areas further away suffered from a great shortage of small change. Boulton thought that this needed to be remedied, to avoid limiting economic activity.

Even by the early eighteenth century, two thirds of Government revenue came via small cash purchases in the form of customs duties on imports, and excise on home produced articles. More and more people were dependent on a money wage, as barter trading and subsistence farming decreased, especially

---

37 H.E. Manville (2001) *Tokens of the Industrial Revolution: Foreign silver coins countermarked for use in Great Britain c1787-1828* British Numismatic Society Special Publication No. 3 Spink, London.

38 C.E. Challis (ed.) (1992) *A New History of the Royal Mint* Cambridge University Press, Cambridge p17.

39 H.A. Seaby and P.J. Seaby (1949 edn) *Catalogue of Copper Coins and Tokens of the British Isles*.

40 G. Selgin (2008) *Good Money* pp20-22.

41 The Royal Mint moved to Llantrisant in South Wales from December 1968 and the Tower Hill Mint finally closed in 1975. Information from www.royalmint.com.

after further parliamentary enclosures of common land between 1750 and 1780. Burgeoning urban populations generated unprecedented demand for low denomination coins for the purchase of goods and services. Daily necessities, such as beer, sugar, tea and tobacco, were bought in a variety of retail shops or from itinerant sellers. By 1785 London had 21,600 shops.[42] The population was also increasing, especially in towns: in 1792 the *Universal British Directory* estimated that Birmingham's population was 60,000, around eight times larger than in 1700.[43]

Employers had increasing difficulty in finding sufficient coin to pay their employees. The *Birmingham Gazette* noted that a workman in Birmingham received on average 9s or 10s per week in 1787, while the agricultural wage was around 7s 6d per week as late as 1793, though women were more poorly paid.[44] The wages at the Soho Mint were better, where some experienced workers were earning up from 18s to £1 10s per week.[45] Workmen had very little likelihood of ever seeing any gold coins, and were forced to accept poor quality shillings in their pay which might buy only sixpence worth of goods. They might receive counterfeit pennies or halfpennies in their change.[46] Boulton thought this situation needed to be remedied.

Why did Boulton become involved in coining?
Why did Matthew Boulton set up the Soho Mint when he could have been at the point of retirement? He was after all in his late fifties when he first started to build it and sixty-nine years old when, after many setbacks, he finally achieved his regal coinage contract in 1797.

Apart from a possibly profitable business opportunity, one of his motives was to reform the coinage in order to defeat counterfeiters, and to improve the reputation of Birmingham goods. He also wanted to make more copper coin available to pay his workers. He had other reasons too, such as using up the copper surplus, and enhancing his own reputation.

Boulton had been interested in coinage reform from at least the 1770s. He wrote to Lord Dartmouth, First Lord of Trade and Secretary of State for the Colonies, on 10 November 1772, suggesting that the Legislature should consider the poor condition of coined and paper currency.[47] He also contributed to the investigations into the Royal Mint in September 1782 when the Home Secretary, Lord Shelburne, (Marquis of Lansdowne from 1784), appointed Samuel Garbett (1717-1803) and his son Francis (1742-1800) to report on the Royal Mint.

42 P. Matthias (2004) *Official and Unofficial Money in the Eighteenth century* British Numismatic Journal Vol. 74 pp68-83.

43 Anon, *Universal British Directory of Trade and Commerce and Manufacture*, London, 1792, p202.

44 H.W. Dickinson (1936) *Matthew Boulton*, Cambridge University Press, Cambridge, p139.

45 S. Tungate (2013) *Workers at the Soho Mint* in: S. Baggott, M. Dick and K. Quickenden (eds.) *Matthew Boulton – Enterprising Industrialist of the Enlightenment* Ashgate, Farnham.

46 G. Selgin (2008) *Good Money* pp24-29.

47 H.W. Dickinson (1937) *Matthew Boulton* p135.

Boulton wrote:

> *'My friend Mr. Samuel Garbett hath been appointed to investigate sundry important matters relative to the weight and standard of the coin, as well as whatever relates to the conduct of the business of the Mint. The Lords of the Treasury have certainly made a proper choice, for I do not think there is a man in England better qualify'd, more to be depended upon, or more proper in every respect'.*[48]

Garbett reported all his findings, including the costs of the Royal Mint, to Boulton. The report was not followed through as Shelburne's Ministry fell in February 1783, but Garbett was later involved in planning a new regal coinage with Boulton and Thomas Williams.[49]

Boulton himself said that an important motive for setting up the Soho Mint was to put an end to counterfeit coin. Patrick Colquhoun, a magistrate, had investigated counterfeiting during the promotion of the 1785 Police Bill and published his ideas in his *'Treatise on the Policing of the Metropolis'*.[50] Boulton had contributed to the report and wrote:

> *'In the course of my journeys, I observe that I receive upon average two thirds counterfeit halfpence for change at tollgates etc., and I believe that the evil is daily increasing'.*[51]

He was asked to make counterfeit gold coins for Portugal in 1794, counterfeit Anglesey tokens in 1796, and in 1801, base silver Danish coins, but refused.[52] Other manufacturers did not, as it was possible to make an excellent profit on 'currency speculation'. One merchant alone was exporting the modern-day equivalent of £1 million counterfeit coins.[53]

Boulton estimated there were 72 counterfeit halfpence to the lb, versus 46 for the Royal Mint issue. His own issue of 1799 halfpence were of much better quality, at 35 to lb weight.

Given the minting technology in general use at the time, the best defence against counterfeiting was to strike coins to a high weight so that their intrinsic value was reasonably close to their face value, to produce them from well-engraved dies that were difficult to copy well, to mark their edges in some way so that cast

---

48 MS 3782-12-108 Item 32, Report on the state of the Mint, S. & F. Garbett to *'The Right Honourable The Lords Commissioners of his Majesty's Treasury'* 23 November 1782; MS 3782-12-27 Item 259, MB to Mr. Gilbert 11 December 1782.

49 MS 3782-12-61 Item 44; Item 45; Item 47, S. Garbett (London) to MB (Soho) 2 September 1782; 22 October 1782; 5 December 1782.

50 G. Selgin (2008) *Good Money* p31.

51 J.F. Sanders (1970) *Matthew Boulton and the Copper Coinage of Great Britain* Coin and Medal Bulletin, Seaby, London p233.

52 D. Symons (2009) in: R. Clay and S. Tungate (eds.) (2009) *Matthew Boulton and the Art of Making Money* pp18-23.

53 D. Vice *A trial strike of a Birmingham counterfeiter's die* Format 37 September 1988.

copies became much harder to make, and to reproduce the dies mechanically so that each die, and hence each coin, was identical. The Royal Mint did none of this. The result was poor copper coin in circulation, with worn out halfpennies still in use and many counterfeits.[54]

Figure 1:2 Worn coin and forgery: George III halfpennies.

Employers resorted to various stratagems in order to pay their workers, including remuneration in kind, truck tokens, payment at intervals and group pay.[55] The lack of small change affected Boulton personally; he needed to be able to supply the large workforce at Soho with wages, and as early as 1771, he was having problems in finding sufficient suitable coin. A correspondent, Francis Cobb, wrote to Boulton:

'The scarcity of cash in this part & for many miles round us has been for some time past greater than I ever remember, & had it been to have saved my life don't believe I could have raised so much as to have satisfied your last week's bill'.[56]

Similarly, in 1783, Zaccheus Walker, Boulton's brother-in-law and warehouse manager, wrote: *'At present there is a very great scarcity of cash at Birm^m & Lichfield'.*[57]

The poorest workers risked having bad coin in their pay refused at local shops or only taken at a discount. Their plight appears to have been close to Boulton's heart:

'It is now too common a custom among many of the lower classes of Manufacturers and traders, to purchase these counterfeit halfpence at little more than half their nominal

---

54 W.J. Davis (1895) *The Token Coinage of Warwickshire*, Birmingham pxiii.

55 G. Selgin (2008) *Good Money* p24.

56 MS 3782-12-23 Item 194, Francis Cobb (Lichfield) to MB (London) 3 April 1771.

57 MS 3782-12-74 Item 74, Zaccheus Walker (Birmingham) to MB (London) 15 February 1783.

value, and to pay with this money their workmen & labourers, greatly to the injury of the honest part of the community, and to the detriment of Trade'.[58]

He was also concerned that it would lead to counterfeiting of gold and silver coins and a debasement of the currency. In addition, a stable coinage might reduce pressure from workers for higher wages.

Boulton believed that he could produce sufficient coinage to supply the needs of the growing industrial workforce, and that he could do it more economically than the Royal Mint.[59] He was keen to provide coins containing the intrinsic value of metal, of constant diameter, thickness and weight, and to use steam power to produce it cheaply so that it would not be worth counterfeiting.[60] He could solve the problems posed by Britain's serious shortage of small change by mechanising the process, using the Boulton and Watt rotary engine.[61]

His friend, James Keir in a memoir, said:

'it was always in Mr B's mind to convert such trades as were usually carried on by individuals into Great Manufactures by the help of machinery, which might enable the article to be made with greater precision, and cheaper than those commonly sold'.[62]

As well as wanting to improve the supply of money, Boulton was motivated by the enjoyment of innovation and the enhancement of his reputation. He wanted to perform a public service in making coin. In letters to Joseph Banks in September 1789, Boulton complained that nothing was being done by the Government.[63] He wrote:

'I took up the subject because I thought it would be a publick good, and because Mr. Pitt had express'd a wish to me of seeing something done to put an end to counterfeiting the copper coin'.

He continued:

'It is not sufficient for a copyist to immatate my coin, but 'tis absolutely necessary that it should be done at half the expence, which the bad coin hath cost our Government, as the best preventitive against counterfeits'.[64]

---

58 MS 3782-13-36 Item 37, MB (Soho) to MRB (Langensalz, Germany) 12 November 1789.
59 MS 3782-12-97, Copper coinage and government 112 a and b, Mint memorandum December 1789.
60 R. Doty (1998) *The Soho Mint and the Industrialisation of Money* pp15-16.
61 MS 3147-3-7-7, MB (London) to James Watt (Birmingham) 16 April 1783.
62 MS 3782-13-37, 'Memorandum for the Memoir of M Boulton'. Undated but accompanies a covering letter from James Keir to MRB 3 Dec. 1809.
63 MS 49 Reference 82934, Timmins Album Volume 1 Item 10 MB (Soho) to Sir Joseph Banks 14 August 1789.
64 MS 3782-21-1, MB (Buxton) to Joseph Banks (Soho Square, London) 10 September 1789.

The government repeatedly postponed a decision about a new coinage. Meanwhile from 1787, the shortage of small change had also led to the provision of tokens by individuals including the major copper producer, Thomas Williams, and the ironmaster, John Wilkinson. The Anglesey halfpence were of much better quality than those in circulation from the Royal Mint, and so became very popular and in general use.[65] Token issuers, like counterfeiters, were putting their own money into circulation to meet a very obvious need, but the big difference was that token issuers, at least the respectable ones, promised to redeem their products.[66] By the 1790s an explosion of tokens, counterfeits and similar unofficial pieces were produced and were accepted in circulation as they were all that were available and were essential to keep the economy working.[67]

When he failed to achieve the regal contract, Boulton started to make tokens for such customers, gaining much useful technical knowledge in the process. Things began to break down when some tokens themselves began to be counterfeited, and others were put into circulation with no intent to redeem them.

It was a financial crisis caused by the war with France which eventually gave Boulton his opportunity to make his first regal coinage issue in 1797, but despite his claims, these cartwheel coins were not difficult to counterfeit.[68] Counterfeiting was again rife in February 1799 when Boulton wrote to Sir Joseph Banks who was on the committee for Coin: *'The number of counterfeit money makers are very numerous in Birm^gm but ... nobody seems interested in bringing the offenders to Justice'.*[69] The design of the 1799 regal coinage made at Soho Mint included various technical improvements such as edge markings and concave blanks, which made the coins much more difficult to counterfeit.

Another reason for Boulton's development of the Soho Mint in the late 1780s, was to use up copper surpluses, in order to maintain the viability of Cornish copper mining. Many of Boulton and Watt's steam-engines were employed in Cornwall and he had shares in several Cornish copper mines, plus a large stock of copper, purchased when the mines were unable to dispose of it elsewhere. The annual premiums received for Cornish steam-engines peaked at over £9,400 in 1787 then declined sharply, due to increasing problems with sales of copper. In 1788, Boulton and Watt received around £5,000 out of £12,000 owed by the Cornish Mine Adventurers, but by 1798 only 14% of the year's total premiums due were paid. Despite collecting £30,000 in back royalties in 1799, Boulton and

---

65 D. Vice (1989) *The Soho Mint and the Anglesey Tokens of the Parys Mine Company* Format 38 March 1989.
66 J. Powell (1993) *The Birmingham Coiners 1770-1816* History Today Volume 43, July 1993 p66.
67 D. Symons (2009) in: R. Clay and S. Tungate (eds.) (2009) *Matthew Boulton and the Art of Making Money* pp1-23.
68 G. Dyer (2002) *The Currency Crisis of 1797* British Numismatics Journal Volume 72 2001, pp135-142
69 MS 3782-12-56 Item 96, MB (Soho) to Sir Joseph Banks (—) 1 Feb 1799; D. Symons (2009) in: R. Clay and S. Tungate (eds.) (2009) *Matthew Boulton and the Art of Making Money* pp13-15.

Watt were still owed over £162,000 from the Cornwall mine owners.[70] The copper industry was vital to the finances of Soho, which is why Boulton was so concerned with copper sales.

Was the Soho Mint a viable concern?

Several authors have made attempts to discuss Boulton's financial affairs, but have found it difficult to come to any definite conclusions. Like modern businesses, Boulton had cash flow problems; his capital was tied up in copper stocks, and payments for completed mint orders were not always easily obtained. In May 1793, Boulton appeared to be solvent, *'I have the satisfaction of saying that I do not owe a single guinea for copper or brass or any other metal, but have much owing to me for those materials'.*[71]

A detailed financial analysis of the Soho Mint is beyond the scope of this book. When the Soho Mint was first established, no separate record books were kept, so it is hard to assess whether it was initially financially worthwhile. Large sums were invested in its construction, and both buildings and machinery were altered many times. However, David Vice has estimated that between 1793 and 1799 in excess of £109,000 was made at the Soho Mint, making it one of Boulton's more profitable enterprises.[72] When the further regal coinage issues of 1805-1807 and contracts for the East India Company from 1803 are also considered, Soho Mint was successful financially as well as technologically and artistically.

---

70 T. Wilson to M. Boulton and J. Watt 22nd Feb 1799, in: H. W. Dickinson (1936; 1999) *Matthew Boulton* p176.

71 MS 3792-12-68 Item 43, MB (Soho) to Charlotte Matthews (London) 7 May 1793.

72 D. Vice (forthcoming) *A Numismatic History of Soho Manufactory and Mint 1772-1850* p5.

Chapter Two

Copper

ADVANCES in metal technologies were essential to the rise of industrialisation during the eighteenth century, especially in Birmingham, which was a centre for skilled metal workers. One commonly used metal was copper, which was alloyed with zinc to make brass from 1715 on in Birmingham. By 1770 there were 38 brass founders; 56 in 1788; and 71 by 1797.[73] It is somewhat surprising that Birmingham became a centre of the copper trade since it had no local supplies except for limited amounts from the Peak District. Most copper used came from Cornwall.

Matthew Boulton got his start in business manufacturing 'toys' in brass and other metals, including copper, gold, silver, pewter and steel. Boulton also used copper in making plated wares at Soho; that is copper ingots covered with silver and then rolled into sheets from which silver-plated articles were made, and in making ormolu; applying a finely ground, high-carat gold-mercury amalgam to an object made from copper. The production of ormolu enhanced his reputation as a manufacturer of high-class wares. Therefore, Boulton took a great interest in many aspects of the metal industries, including how ore was mined and smelted. It was his practical experiences with metal that enabled him to make a success of the Soho Mint.

Copper

Copper is one of the most easily worked metals after gold and silver, and was among the first to be used extensively by mankind. It was essential to the Soho Mint as other cheap metals were unsuitable for coining; iron rusted, pewter was not sufficiently robust, and brass was too hard to be easily embossed with an image. Copper, however was malleable, did not shatter, and had a distinctive hue, so that a freshly minted coin had an attractive appearance. It also had a

---

73 H. Hamilton (1967) *The English Brass and Copper Industries to 1800* Cass, London p268.

high resistance to corrosion and was relatively cheap, which was why it was used to make low value coins, being both practical and decorative.[74]

Mining had been carried out in Cornwall, Cumbria and elsewhere as early as the Bronze age, but until the 1740s, most copper used in Britain came from the area now known as Germany, and from Scandinavia. The Mines Royal Company and the Mineral and Battery Company were set up in the reign of Elizabeth I and the right of mining gold, silver, copper, tin and lead in Britain was a royal prerogative until 1689. German mining specialists provided the finances and expertise.[75] When halfpennies and farthings were minted for Charles II, copper blanks were imported from Sweden as there was not sufficient copper mined in England.[76] In 1692, Dockwra's, the most productive company in Britain, produced 80 tons of copper compared to Sweden and Norway's 1,600 tons of copper per year. However, in 1717 the English Copper Company was contracted to provide 700 tons of copper locally for coining.

Copper came mainly from Cornwall, Cheshire, the Peak District and Anglesey.[77] Copper mining in Cornwall had become increasingly important by the mid eighteenth century. But Cornish mines were prone to flooding which is why Matthew Boulton first became involved in the copper industry from 1777, providing steam engines to pump out water from the mines.

The discovery of a large lode of copper at Parys Mountain in Anglesey meant that by the mid-1780s, there was an overproduction of copper in England. Boulton tried to find new outlets for copper including its use in coinage; as the more sales there were, the better the chance Boulton and Watt had of being paid. This led to the development of the Soho Mint.

Mining Copper

Most early copper ore was obtained from open pits, but later, shafts were sunk using braces, wedges and levers, or by fire setting; that is heating rocks and then quenching them quickly with water to alternately expand and contract them, in order to crack them up. Copper ore was then extracted using picks, shovels and drills and brought up to the surface by windlasses. In Cornwall, mine captains were responsible for the organization of the workers. 'Tributers' (the miners) were paid per ton of ore, and in turn paid less skilled 'tut' workers as labourers. They bid for 'bargains' to work for a certain period, sometimes making great progress and profit when they hit a rich vein, and at other times striking only bare rock. Where possible, water wheels were used for power, but there were few

---

74 J. Morton (1983) *Thomas Bolton and Sons Limited*. Morland, Ashbourne.

75 R. Rees (2000) *King Copper: South Wales and the Copper Trade 1584-1895* University of Wales, Cardiff.

76 H.A. Seaby and P.J. Seaby (1949 edn) *A catalogue of Copper Coins and Tokens of the British Isles* B.A. Seaby Ltd. London.

77 H. Hamilton (1967) *The English Brass and Copper Industries to 1800* p108.

suitable sites, so often ore was raised to the surface 'to grass' by man powered windlasses or the horse whim.[78]

The ore was then treated by surface workers, usually women and children, by handpicking the better fractions from the rock to concentrate it for smelting. It was relatively easy to see the yellow chalcopyrite ore, which could then be crushed and separated by gravitational and flotation methods.

Figure 2:1 Chalcopyrite copper ore.[79]

Until the early nineteenth century, practically the entire copper mining region was within a 13 km radius of Carn Brea Hill, near Cambourne. Most Cornish mines were dug as deep shafts and often suffered from flooding. John Coster, a metallurgist and engineer, had developed the first true copper mine in Cornwall, at Chacewater in the early 1700s. In order to drain the mines, Coster pioneered adit drainage and erected one of the first horse-whims in Cornwall to power primitive suction pumps. He also made significant advances in assaying and dressing copper ore. Chacewater became the focus of innovation in mining technology, with early Newcomen steam-engines installed by Joseph Hornblower in 1725 to pump water from the mines.[80] Brass cylinders limited the size of early Newcomen engines but iron casting techniques, pioneered by the Coalbrookdale Company, allowed larger iron cylinders to be made. From 1765 John Smeaton was using cylinders up to 72 inches in diameter and by the time he erected a new Newcomen engine at Wheal Busy in 1775, about 600 Newcomen engines had been built.[81]

However, by the mid-1770s, due to the cost of fuel which had to be imported from South Wales, the Cornish mines were becoming less profitable.[82] The

---

78 Information from site visit to Levant Mine, Trewellard, Pendeen, Cornwall, 2009.

79 From Wikipedia.

80 Oxford Dictionary of National Biography, www.oxforddnb.com.

81 P.G. Embrey and R.F. Symes (1987) *Minerals of Cornwall and Devon* British Museum, London p26.

82 H.W. Dickinson & R. Jenkins (1927; republished 1981) *James Watt and the Steam Engine* Moorland, Ashbourne.

Newcomen steam-engine was not efficient, as every time the steam was condensed to make the pumping action, the cylinder was cooled. The Boulton and Watt (B&W) steam-engines incorporated a separate condenser and had cylinders with increased precision made by John Wilkinson, using his boring machine. Therefore, they were more fuel-efficient, and were introduced to maintain profitability. The first B&W steam-engine was in operation at Chacewater by September 1777.[83] This brought about a dramatic improvement in mine drainage and the owners, the Mine Adventurers, were able to make considerable savings in coal. For example, Consolidated Mines made a saving of over £10,000 in one year between June 1783 and June 1784.[84]

This was also vital to the fortunes of Boulton and Watt. During the late 1770s to the mid-1780s, most of their engines were being sold in Cornwall. Boulton wrote in 1782:

'I have long turned my eyes upon the mines of this county [Cornwall] as the most likely means of rewarding me for the ten years' attention I have bestowed upon fire engines, and of refunding me the money I have expended upon that subject, and likewise (what is still greater) the money I have lost getting, by withdrawing my attention from my manufactory [.........] I have set nine large new engines to work since my arrival here in September last, and have now the pleasure to see twenty-one of them going in this county, and likewise to say with truth that not one of the great copper mines in Cornwall at this time working would have existed as a mine had it not been for me and my partner'.[85]

B&W steam-engines were not sold initially as complete machines, but as designs; specialist parts, such as valves were made at Soho but the cylinders were usually made at Bersham by John Wilkinson, or at Coalbrookdale. The engines were erected by engineers paid by the Mine Adventurers. In return for the use of their patent, Boulton and Watt wanted one third of the savings in fuel made by a B&W engine, compared to a Newcomen engine. Complex tables of premiums were agreed, with a standard set at Poldice Mine during August and September 1778.[86] By the mid-1780s there were around 40 B&W engines in operation in Cornwall.

Boulton, along with James Watt and other steam engineers sent from Soho, spent a lot of time in Cornwall in the late 1770s, acting as supervising engineers and generally promoting their engine business which was initially profitable.[87] The Cornish mining industry provided a training ground for many of the important engineers of the eighteenth century and most worked for the firm of Boulton

---

83 www.cornish-mining.org.uk.
84 AD1583/11/102, Thomas Wilson c1795.
85 MS 3782 Letter Book 1781-1783 Item 259, MB to Mr. Gilbert 11 December 1782.
86 AD1583/11/66, Method of Calculating tables for Wheal Maid, Poldice Mine by standard trials.
87 MS 3782-13-96, Copper trade Volume 1 Item 5. Debts due to Messrs Boulton and Watt Dec 1780.

and Watt at some time. William Murdock and James Lawson both installed B&W engines in Cornwall. The list also included the Hornblower family, Edward Bull and Richard Trevithick, who all later used B&W designs without permission; and were taken to court for infringing Boulton and Watt's patent. Ironically the injunction against Trevithick was served in December 1796 in a pub opposite Soho Manufactory.[88] However Common Engines (as Newcomen engines were then known) remained in use for a considerable time, and many more were built as they were less complicated, and cheaper to install and maintain. Of the 2,200 engines built in the eighteenth century; only about 450 were B&W engines. The separate condenser was added to many of Newcomen's engines and also to at least 83 'pirated' engines.[89]

Boulton, with his usual enthusiasm, suggested improvements to copper mining practices, including an improved bucket system to bring the ore up to 'grass'. He also had plans made of the mines, including Poldice, Wheal Virgin, Consolidated, North Downs, Chacewater and Polgooth Mines.[90] Many of these

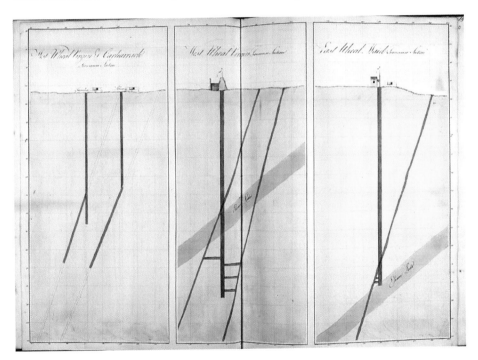

Figure 2:2 1784 Cornish mine plan showing shafts and copper lode.[91]

88 AD1583/9/55, James Watt Junior to Wilson 30 Dec 1796.

89 J. Tann (1995) *Riches from Copper: The Adoption of the Boulton and Watt Engine by Cornish Mine Adventurers* Transactions of the Newcomen Society, Volume 67 pp27-52.

90 MS 1381-1, Maps showing the shafts and adits in several Cornish Mines drawn by James Lawson c1784-5.

91 MS 1381-1-14-39, Mine plans. Carharrick, Cornwall 1784.

plans were drawn up by James Lawson, who returned to help set up the Soho Mint in 1789, along with William Murdock. Lawson also set up the new Royal Mint from 1810. In 1784 Boulton wrote:

'hitherto the Adventurers have seen through the Eye of the Captains which are not so clear as these plans are, & if these plans are fill'd up from time to time (say once a quarter) with all of the workings, the Adventurers may soon become more distinct Miners than the Captains. If I could but continue here for one Year I should become a Miner & able to remove many grievances & bad customs'.[92]

Copper miners were heavily dependent on the price of the copper ore they produced, unlike smelters who sold copper metal. By 1784, copper ore production in Cornwall had increased to nearly 40,000 tons but profitability in the Cornish mining industry had peaked in 1782, and then declined until the late 1790s.[93] Copper ore prices were also reducing in Cornwall due to competition from Parys Mine in Anglesey.

Due to lack of sales, some Mine Adventurers refused to pay premiums to Boulton and Watt. This was a serious drain on Soho's finances. In 1794 Thomas Wilson, B&W's agent in Cornwall calculated the savings made by the use of B&W engines to be from £8 to £10 a day.[94] By the end of 1798, premiums were due from at least thirteen mines and a court case, which extended until 1799, showed that the Cornish Mine Adventurers owed Boulton and Watt £268,000. They were eventually paid £106,000 for a total of fifty-seven engines which had saved £800,000 worth of coal.[95]

In 1783 Garbett wrote:

'That the Anglesea Copper Company have already very much undersold the Cornish copper. That there is reason to believe they already have it in their power to stop some of the mines in Cornwall'.[96]

Ore from Anglesey could be produced cheaply since, unlike the Cornish copper mines, the Parys and Mona mines were mainly mined from the surface as open pits, as is still impressively evident. At the peak of production in 1792, 60-80,000 tons of copper ore were produced annually in Anglesey.

In September 1787 Boulton described the mine:

---

92 MS 3782-12-73 Item 147, MB (Cusgarne) to John Wilkinson 20 September 1784.
93 MS 3782-13-93-1, History of copper trade and a vindication of price rises by Matthew Boulton 1793.
94 AD1583/11/68, Account of the State of the Principal Mines in Cornwall in 1794.
95 D.B. Barton (1961; 3rd edn 1998) *A History of Copper Mining in Devon and Cornwall* D. Bradford, Barton Ltd, Truro.
96 MS 3782-12-61 Item 49, Samuel Garbett (Birmingham) to MB (London) 17 May 1783.

Figure 2:3 Parys Mine, Anglesey.[97]

'I spent 3 or 4 days in inspecting the Anglesey Copper Mine which is a tremendous Mine for a Cornish Miner to behold. It is not like a deep Cornish mine but is an open Work like a Quarry or a Gravil Pit & worked by open day light'.

He concluded: *'Hence you see what an immense profit arises from one great work … So great that I fear all the Mines in Cornwall will be obliged to give up which will be a great loss to me'.*[98]

A contemporary account describes extensive excavations at Parys Mountain, including one: *'two hundred yards long, one hundred and fifty yards broad and twenty to forty yards deep, which gives a content of nine hundred thousand cubic yards of removed natural ground'.*[99] Even by this time the mine, over twice the size of a football pitch, was exciting interest as shown by images produced by Ibbetson and de Loutherbourg at the time.[100]

---

97 Image taken by author, August 2009.
98 MS 3782-13-36 Item 10, MB (London) to MRB (Versailles) 21 September 1787.
99 An account written by the Reverend Bingly is detailed on www.parysmountain.co.uk (accessed 5.9.2008).
100 Philip de Loutherbourg (1740-1812) was an English artist of French origin.

Figure 2:4 'The Parys Copper Mine', Anglesey 1785, by J.C. Ibbetson.[101]

Smelting Copper

Extraction of ore from a mine was only part of the procedure; it needed to be smelted to obtain copper metal. Copper was rarely found as pure crystals, but as ores such as chalcopyrite, azurite, bornite and chalcocite. The principle ore, chalcopyrite 'yellow ore' ($CuFeS_2$), contains copper (Cu), iron (Fe) and sulphur (S), but may also contain various impurities such as arsenic (As).[102]

Smelting techniques for copper were possibly first developed in Serbia, as there is evidence from sites at Pločnik and Belovode for copper slag dating to c.5500-5000 BC. For nearly 6,000 years the process, known as calcining, was to heat the crushed and concentrated ore with charcoal, burning in heaps in the open or in charcoal fired furnaces. This process was repeated, and initially could involve up to sixteen calcinings over a period of three months.[103] The earliest description in 1556 from *De Re Metallica*, by Georgius Agricola, has engineering drawings of copper furnaces and stamping mills.[104]

The introduction of the reverberatory furnace, applying heat from above, had improved copper smelting. The ore was heated to 1,200°C and converted to copper with the removal of arsenic oxide and sulphur dioxide, as poisonous gases.

---

101 Watercolour by J.C. Ibbetson, National Museum of Wales, www.labspace.open.ac.uk.

102 R. Prain (1975) *Copper: the anatomy of an industry* Mining Journal Books Limited, London.

103 R.F. Mikesell (1988) *The Global Copper Industry: problems and prospects.*

104 D. Sellwood (1994) *Early Austrian and German machine minting* Metallurgy in Numismatics 4, Royal Numismatic Society Special Publication, London pp108-111.

It produced 'blister' copper, so called because of the broken surface created by the escape of gases as the copper ingots were cast.[105] This method had first been used at Redbrook, Forest of Dean in the late seventeenth century by the Clerke family from Bristol, with their technical advisor, John Coster, previously mentioned in connection with Chacewater Mine. Here Abraham Derby may have learnt the techniques that he later applied successfully in the iron industry.[106] Unlike in a blast furnace, ore was not in direct contact with the fuel, and smelting was more efficient due to a draught caused by a tall chimney.

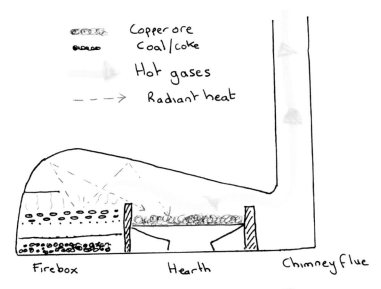

Figure 2:5 Reverberatory furnace.[107]

Sir Humphrey Mackworth was another early pioneer, setting up a reverberatory furnace near Swansea in 1698, where Cornish ore was generally smelted; he also exported coal to Cornwall.[108] The smelting works at Warrington, run by Thomas Patten (1690-1772) had twelve reverberatory furnaces by 1754, and initially supplied the Birmingham area including the Soho Manufactory. Patten also extended his activities to the Greenfield valley, near Holywell, Flintshire. Anglesey ore was smelted at Ravenhead near Liverpool until Thomas Williams took over the site at Holywell.[109]

In his notebooks and letters Boulton described the smelting process in full, and also how to set up a smelting works, calculating the costs, and staff required, including the transport of copper ore and coal supplies.[110] He also studied the

105 F. Sherwood Taylor (10th edn 1960) *Inorganic and Theoretical Chemistry* Heinemann p295.
106 H. Hamilton (1967) *The English Brass and Copper Industries to 1800* p102.
107 Adapted from Wikipedia.
108 R. Rees (2000) *King Copper: South Wales and the Copper Trade 1584-1895* p9.
109 J. Morton (1983) *Thomas Bolton and Sons Limited* p13.
110 MS 3782-12-108-27, General notebook 1780-1790.

chemistry, and though he did not understand it in modern terms, he knew from practical experience what worked:

> *'if you have one sort of Ore that contains much Iron & another that contains much Sulpher be sure & mix those 2 sorts & not melt them separately … Refine high by much Fire & last of all phlogisticate well with good Charcoal stoping the draft of air over the metal'.*[111]

It generally took 24 tons of coal to produce a ton of copper from the ore, and Boulton priced the process.[112] When he visited Williams at Parys Mountain Mine in 1787, he was also interested in the by-products of the smelting process. In a letter to his son Boulton explained: *'the Sulphur arises to ye top & is condensed in the form of flowers of Brimstone in the Condenser … This Brimstone is sold for the purpose of making Oyl of Vitriol'* [sulphuric acid].[113] There was little use for arsenic and it was discarded. The toxic waste-products left barren areas which are still found two hundred years later.

Boulton also ordered a small reverberatory furnace for Soho in March 1787. He wrote to Thomas Wilson, his agent in Cornwall for advice:

> *'I should be obliged to you if you would procure for me a Drawing of one & charge the expence to me; at the same time pray inform me what it & the Chimney will cost Building & how much Copper it will melt at one time & how many meltings it is capable of makeing p[e]r day. I should also be glad if you would tell me at what expence you think I could melt p[e]r Ton Scraps of Copper into Cake supposeing I have from ten to 20 Ton to melt'.*[114]

This furnace was 18 foot long, 12 foot wide and 4 foot deep and could contain over 3 tons in each 18-36 hour calcining. He made notes about its use.[115]

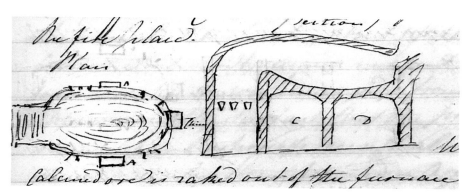

Figure 2:6 Reverberatory furnace drawn by Matthew Boulton.

---

111 AD1583/2/41, MB (Soho) to Wilson (Cornwall) 22 March 1787.
112 MS 3782-12-108-27, General notebook 1780-1790.
113 MS 3782-13-36 Item 10, MB (London) to MRB (Versailles) 21 September 1787.
114 AD1583/2/41, MB (Soho) to T. Wilson (Truro) 22 March 1787.
115 MS 3782-13-93 Item 32, Notes made by Boulton on copper and smelting 15 April 1800.

Types of Copper

In 1779, **copper metal** was selling for £90 per ton, with Anglesey producing around a quarter of the British production of 5,400 tons.[116] But just under ten years later, Boulton estimated that Anglesey was generating 4,000 tons of copper compared to Cornwall's 5,300 tons. A small amount, 900 tons, was coming from the Duke of Devonshire's mines at Ecton, Derbyshire, and 600 tons from the Macclesfield Company with a grand total of 10,800 tons of copper produced per year.[117]

The type of copper produced depended on how many refinings the ore went through at the smelting works and its subsequent processing. 'Common copper', for example, was poured into iron moulds to make slabs for the brass founders of Birmingham and the Black Country.[118] Boulton wanted the best copper for his Soho Manufactory products and continued to seek high quality metal for the Soho Mint. With his usual attention for detail, he made extensive notes on the manufacture of different grades of copper. In October 1780 he wrote:

> 'The copper smelters aim at making the first regulas not too good but to contain about 25% of fine copper. They charge their reverbatory furnace about 6 times in 24 hours and run off regulas at each charge. It runs into ▼ [water] out of a tap hole but is obstructed by a wooden pole which breaks it into smaller parts & saves pulverising. It is then roasted & then smelted again & is then called black copper'.[119]

The prices of various metals were published weekly in the Birmingham newspapers.[120] Copper could be sold as 'best or common shot, Japan, or common Battery or Brass Copper', or as 'Bowls; Tough cake; Tile; Shruff; Pot' and so on. A typical example is an order sent to Boulton in August 1789 by the Cornish Metal Company: 'Bowls (9cwt 3q 6lb); Tough cake (31 tons 10cwt 3q 6lb); Tile (130 tons 6cwt 1q 4lb); Shruff (11 tons 5lb). Shot (6 tons 19cwt 1q 21lb) at £80 6s; and Pot Metal (20 tons 3cwt 0q 19lb)'.[121]

Copper was often ordered for the Soho Mint in 'cakes' weighing between 16 and 80lb each (7-36kg).[122] These were formed when molten copper was poured by the ladleful into iron boxes 16 inches long, 11 inches wide and 11 inches deep, placed in a half-circle in front of the furnace. A contemporary account was written by Dr A. Lentin from the University of Leipzig, who spent six years at Parys Mountain in the late eighteenth century:

---

116 MS 3782-12-108-27, General notebook 1780-1790.
117 MS 3782-12-108 Item 53, Mint Book 1788 p24.
118 J. Morton (1983) *Thomas Bolton and Sons Limited* p14.
119 MS 3782-12-108-27, General notebook 1780-1790.
120 MS 3782-12-108 Item 55, Boulton's General Notebooks 1789-1795 p8.
121 MS 3782-12-90 Items 41-50, Cornish Copper Mines.
122 MS 3782-12-108 Item 53, Mint Book 1788 p87.

'While the last box is being filled, the metal in the first has solidified to such an extent that a new layer can be poured on to it without binding with the first. So the boxes are filled, one after the other, producing a number of thin cakes which are approximately 1/4 inch thick and which can be separated when they are properly cooled'.

The cakes were then rolled, stamped and numbered. 'Shot' or granulated copper was also sometimes made by pouring the molten copper into water, either from a height or directly, depending on whether feather shot or rounded shot was required.[123]

Only certain types of copper were suitable for use at the Soho Mint, due to its properties when rolled. In particular copper from Parys Mine was considered to be excellent. Boulton wanted copper that was to *'be fine, be ductile, be sound & free from flaws & in short that it be as good as that we buy of the Paris Mine Co and I must do them the justice to say it is the best I have ever used'.*[124] Anglesey copper was also cheaper than he could find elsewhere. Arrangements for supplying copper for the new Soho Mint were made with Thomas Williams in December 1787.[125] Williams stated: *'In short my uniform Place shall be only to supply the copper & get the coin done by you'.*[126]

The different sorts of copper had to be ordered well in advance and orders were very specific. In May 1792 Boulton only wanted tough cake copper: *'As all the Copper I want, is intended for Rolling & Coining, I can only use soft tough Cake, the dry Tyle Copper will not be of any use to me'.*[127]

Copper needed to be 'tough' so that it could be rolled accurately, and blanks cut for coining.[128] His preparation of copper was renowned for producing better quality coins. He was particularly concerned that they should be of a bright shiny appearance, and thus instituted specific ways of handling and rolling the metal.

Organisation of the Copper Industry

The metal industries were run by some of the first industrial entrepreneurs. Mines could be initially set up at small cost, but required constant investment to keep them functioning. Often a number of 'adventurers', including miners, land owners and entrepreneurs, took shares in the mine. In Cornwall, copper mines were run under the 'cost book' system; that is expenditure for equipment and wages was financed by 'calls' on the adventurers, who then received profits on a quarterly basis. This worked well when there was competitive demand for copper ore, but often no working capital was retained and thus mines could easily close

---

123 The Amlwch Heritage Trust has now translated Lenten's letters. www.parysmountain.co.uk (accessed 5.9.2008).

124 AD1583/1/16, Purchasing Cornish copper. Boulton to Wilson 26 January 1784.

125 MS 3782-12-73 Item 72, Thomas Williams (Anglesey) to MB (Soho) 29 December 1787.

126 MS 3782-12-73 Item 74, Thomas Williams (London) to Matthew Boulton (Soho) 5 April 1788.

127 AD1583/5/21, MB to Wilson 29 May 1792.

128 AD1583/9/10, MB to Wilson 26 February 1796.

if the adventurers refused to pay for operating costs.[129] The ores were sold on a system of ticketing whereby buyers gave a single price for each lot of ore, and the highest bid won.[130] Boulton was dependent on these sales to gain payment for the B&W steam-engines in Cornwall, and thus had a great interest in the profitability of the mines.

Copper smelting and manufacturing works required a high capital outlay and a plentiful supply of coal. Most works were concentrated in the Bristol and Swansea areas, where finance often came from wealthy merchants. Between 1737 and 1779, copper smelters became organized into cartels, with the larger smelters tending to absorb the smaller ones, and it was relatively easy for them to force low prices for copper ore on the mine adventurers. Very few smelters had direct interests in mines, and could easily shut down their works when copper was not selling well. Mine Adventurers however had to sell their ore, as expenses, such as fuel for steam-engines to prevent flooding, continued whether the mine was making a profit or not. Thus, smelters were able to fix both the price of the ore and the refined copper, and profited most from copper sales. The firms of Swansea and Bristol, known collectively as the 'Associated Smelters', under the leadership of the Bristol Brass Company, included the Mines Royal Company, Warrington Company, Cheadle Company, and Roe and Company.[131] They reacted aggressively to any incursions that threatened the status quo.

Importance of Thomas Williams of Anglesey
Thomas Williams (1737-1802), a major player in the copper industry, first became involved as a lawyer in a dispute about Parys Mine in Anglesey in 1774. This mine was jointly owned by Lord Uxbridge and the Reverend Edward Hughes. Williams initially worked on behalf of Hughes. Mona Mine, on the east side of the mountain, was worked by Charles Roe and Company until the lease ran in 1785. Here the 'Great Lode' of copper ore was discovered in 1768. Williams became the manager of the Parys Mine Company in 1778, and of the Mona Mine in 1785. Williams was a very good organizer and salesman, and was able to sell Anglesey copper cheaply.

The emergence of Anglesey came as a challenge to the Associated Smelters' control over the price of copper. From 1779, they had tried to apply their normal tactics to Thomas Williams, a newcomer in the copper mining industry, but he refused to sell his ore at their price. He set up his own smelting at Amlwch on Anglesey and by 1786 had thirty-one smelting furnaces there.[132] He also ran the smelting works associated with Mona Mine, Stanley Company, near Ravenhead, Lancashire.

---

129 P.G. Embrey and R.F. Symes (1987) *Minerals of Cornwall and Devon.*
130 J.R. Harris (1964) *The Copper King* pp14-15.
131 M.K. Komanecky (1999) *Copper as Canvas* p129.
132 www.parysmountain.co.uk (accessed 5.9.2008).

As many as 1,500 people were employed at Parys Mountain, and the population of its associated port of Amlwch had soared to 5,000. The county town of Beaumaris at that time had a population of just 2,500, and Holyhead 2,000.[133] Eventually Williams owned mines in Wales, copper warehouses in Birmingham, Liverpool and London, chemical works in Liverpool and a bank in North Wales. The Anglesey Company ran their own fleet of ships to transport coal and ores. He also purchased Temple Mills in South Wales and the Greenfield site at Holywell, with its copper rolling mills, wire mills and brass works.[134]

Thomas Williams made copper ingots for shipment overseas from Liverpool and London, and items for the slave trade. At Greenfield, he was also associated with William Collins and John Westwood of Birmingham, in making ships' sheathing from 1784. First tried in 1761, the hulls of wooden boats of the Royal Navy were sheathed with copper to prevent the damage caused by marine worms. This increased the number of voyages before refitting was required. Copper bolts were initially too soft to use, and iron bolts used with copper sheathing had caused considerable corrosion, but in 1783 Collins and Westwood had patented an improved method for making copper bolts by hot and cold rolling. This meant that that copper sheathing could be used more extensively.[135] Copper bottomed ships were able to maintain British domination of the seas, due to increased speed. From 1784, the Admiralty started to order copper sheathing from Williams; 82 ships, 115 frigates and 102 sloops and cutters were 'coppered'. Williams also supplied the French, Dutch and Spanish navies before outbreak of war.[136] This new demand, especially during wars with France, increased the price of copper, and at times made it difficult to obtain sufficient copper for the Soho Mint; hence later issues of the regal coinage had smaller size coins.

Boulton and Williams

The association of Thomas Williams and Matthew Boulton alternated from close friendship to active hatred. During the formative period of the Soho Mint there was considerable co-operation between the two. Both were self-made men and like-minded entrepreneurs, with extensive knowledge of the copper industry, but they were not part of the mine-owning landed gentry. Both considered copper manufacture as an integrated whole, from mining the ore and smelting it, to the production and sale of the final products. They first met in 1780, when Williams had ordered a steam-engine to work a 7-8 cwt hammer, and again in 1781, when

133 D. Vice (1989) *The Soho Mint and the Anglesey Tokens of the Parys Mine Company* Format 38 March 1989.
134 J. Morton (1983) *Thomas Bolton and Sons Limited* p16; J.R. Harris (1964) *The Copper King* p53.
135 J.H. Morris (2003) *The Battle of the Tokens, 1789-1799: The Hibernian Mining Company v. The Associated Irish Mine Company* Mining Heritage Trust of Ireland.
136 P. Watts-Russell (2003) *A copper-bottomed life*. The Cornish Banner, August 2003.

Williams wanted to sell his copper to the Birmingham Metal Company, set up by Boulton and others to produce brass for local consumers.[137]

Williams wrote to Boulton in June 1781 to confer about *'Copper Trade of this country in general & the Mineral Concerns of the counties of Cornwall & Anglesey in particular'*.[138] Both men tried to persuade the Cornish Mine Adventurers to collaborate in challenging the dominance of the smelting cartels. But failing to get any cooperation, Williams started to sell his Anglesey ore to the Associated Smelters in September 1782. Eventually, Williams suggested to the Cornish Adventurers, the setting up of three smelting works with 50 furnaces, to smelt 10,000 tons of copper ore per year. This would make Cornwall free of the smelting cartels and increase the prices paid for Cornish copper ore.[139] Boulton investigated all aspects of a proposed works, at Penclawdd near Swansea next to Burry coalfield, and calculated the costs, and potential profits of such a venture.[140] However due to inertia by the Cornish Mine Adventurers, nothing came of these plans and in 1788, these works were managed by Williams alone.

In co-operation with Boulton, another proposal resulted in the founding of the Cornish Metal Company (CMC) on 1st September 1785, with £65,500 subscribed in fifteen minutes, a contribution of £25,000 from John Wilkinson being decisive.[141] A list of shareholders included many of the important Cornish Mine Adventurers, and both Boulton and Williams with an initial 20 shares each. Sir Francis Basset was appointed Governor as he owned about one fifth of Cornish ore, with John Vivian as Deputy Governor.[142] The division of the copper markets was agreed; with the Anglesey Copper Company to have Liverpool, and Cornwall to supply Bristol. The extensive markets in Birmingham and the export trade, especially that dominated by the East India Company in London, were to be shared.[143] In January 1786, Williams, Wilkinson, John Vivian, plus Thomas Harrison (Lord Uxbridge's agent) were all at Soho with Boulton. The meeting fixed copper prices at £86 per ton for cake copper and £88 for shot.[144]

The smelting cartel was initially worried by this Cornish Metal Company, as it would affect their copper sales, so some of the major smelters raised the prices they offered for ore. The English Copper Company, Mackworth, Mowbray & Gnoll Company, Lockwood Morris Company, John Freeman Company, Bristol Brass and Wire Company and Michell, Edwards and Company all initially capitulated.[145] But some smelters, such as the Duke of Devonshire and the

---

137 MS 3782 12-73 Item 61, Thomas Williams (London) to MB (Soho) 15 May 1781.
138 MS 3782 12-73 Item 62, Thomas Williams (London) to MB (Soho) 20 June 1781.
139 MS 3782 12-73 Item 65, Thomas Williams (Llanidan) to John Martyn 18 April 1785.
140 AD1583/1/81, MB to Wilson 24 Jan 1786; AD1583/1/83/2; AD1583/2/29 7 February 1786.
141 MS 3782-12-90 Items 31-40, 22 July 1785.
142 MS 3782-12-90 Items 41-50, July 1785.
143 AD1583/1/66, Watt (Birmingham) to Wilson 30 June 1785.
144 AD1583/1/80/1, MB (Soho) to Wilson 22 Jan 1786.
145 MS 3782-12-108-27, Boulton's General Notebook 1780-1790.

Macclesfield Company, sold their copper at low prices, and other companies imported foreign copper, which did not help Cornish copper sales.[146] Boulton was horrified in April 1787 to find the English Copper Company had purchased *'150 Ton of Spanish Copper at £78 & have Contracted for more'*.[147]

The formation of the Cornish Metal Company did not solve the problem of the oversupply of copper, and large stocks built up in Cornwall, as no one there took effective action. Boulton calculated the annual consumption in Birmingham, a major user of copper, to be 1,500 tons, but estimated that:

> *'the quantity of copper ore which will be produced by the Cornish mines for the present year 1786 will be about 40,000 tons and that the produce of such ores in fine copper will be equivalent to 5,000 tons of copper'*.[148]

That was a lot of copper to sell and extra uses had to be found. From this point a regal coinage contract became important for the survival of the Cornish copper industry. In turn, this would mean that Boulton would be paid his steam-engine premiums, but could also provide sufficient copper coinage for the use of the growing industrial population.

No one in Cornwall took direct responsibility for copper sales as did Williams for Anglesey; he had much better marketing skills. Paradoxically, despite the overabundance of copper, in May 1787 Watt wrote:

> *'that there was neither Tile, cake, nor shot copper in the [CMC] warehouse, indeed nothing but sheet copper... Judge also how it must appear for Mr Boulton to be obliged to send to the Duke's or Macclesfield warehouse for copper'*.[149]

Watt also passed on a report from Wilkinson in July 1787 that: *'all the Anglesea Copper at Hanley works is sold & all at Ravenhead and that he had just learnt upwards of 900 Tons which were at Swansea are sold ...... & it is added that they cannot get it made fast enough'*.[150] The Macclesfield Company was also able to sell copper at £82 per ton but the price was dropping rapidly.[151]

Nor was the situation better in August 1787. Watt recounted a letter from John Wyatt in which he wrote:

> *'I cannot help telling you that a friend of mine applied to the CMCo office and also at the agents house in order to inquire the price of Copper & to treat for £1500s worth to*

---

146 MS 3782-12-90 Items 31-40, Case of the Cornish Metal Company.
147 AD1583/2/42/1, MB to Wilson 10 April 1787.
148 AD1583/2/21, MB to Wilson 2 November 1786.
149 AD1583/2/48, Watt to Wilson 8 May 1787.
150 AD1583/2/62, Watt to Wilson 16 July 1787.
151 AD1583/2/63, MB to Wilson 21 July 1787.

go to Ostend. When he found he had no notice taken of him, he called at the Anglesea Co's office & though he found nobody but a boy in, an hour afterwards he was waited upon & Contracted for the Copper'.[152]

By August 1787, Williams, who had tried to solve the problem of over-production of copper, was feeling rightly aggrieved at being let down by the Cornish Mine Adventurers. He wrote to John Wilkinson stating that Anglesey had given the CMC:

'the delivery of near 200 tons of Sheathing for the Navy on the 3rd Sep last which they were to have accomplished in 3 weeks or a Month, but they did not finish that delivery till Feb'. Their sheeting was so irregular that we, as the contractors, have been disgraced by them at the Navy Board in so much it will be difficult for us ever to retrieve our Character there'.

In addition, Cornish ore was being sold, contrary to the agreement, to some of the excluded Associated Smelters.[153] Williams had valid grounds for complaint, and he decided that: *'we Anglesey Miners consider ourselves at full liberty to pursue the Copper Trade unrestrained by any engagements with those of Cornwall ever since their contract with the Smelting Cos. in May'.*[154]

By the late 1780s both Boulton and Williams were unpopular in Cornwall. There were miners' riots in February 1787, as North Downs and Dolcoath mines stopped production.[155] By summer 1787, the Cornish Metal Company was in crisis with over 6,000 tons of copper on hand.[156] A worried Boulton wrote that this copper had cost an average of £76 to produce, *'without the expense of rolling it. If W[illia]ms declares War, the price will be £60 or perhaps £50'.* This meant a loss of £16 per ton to Cornwall, and hence a loss of the engine premiums.[157] At this point Boulton was also losing patience with the Cornish Mine Adventurers, but still maintained good relations with Williams. In November 1787, whilst dining with Boulton, Wilkinson and Wedgwood, Thomas Williams proposed a plan to buy 3,000 tons of Cornish copper.[158] These proposals were eventually accepted by the Cornish Mine Adventurers, so effectively for the next few years, Williams had a monopoly on copper sales, and gained his nickname the "Copper King".

---

152 AD1583/2/66, Watt to Wilson 1 August 1787.
153 AD1583/2/76, MB (Chacewater) to Wilson (at Mr Holbrooks, Morriston, Swansey) 13 October 1787.
154 MS 3782-12-73 Item 68 Thomas Williams (Ravenhead) to John Wilkinson 28 August 1787.
155 J.R. Harris (1964) *The Copper King* p73.
156 MS 3782-12-90 Items 41-50, Special committee held 20 September 1787.
157 AD1583/2/76, MB (Chacewater) to Wilson (at Mr Holbrooks, Morriston, Swansey) 13 October 1787; MS 3782-12-90 Items 31-40, Case of the Cornish Metal Company.
158 AD1583/2/77, MB (London) to Wilson (Chacewater) 6 November 1787.

Buying Copper for Soho Mint

Back in 1786, Boulton and others had thought that the surplus of copper could be used for a regal coinage, and had started planning for this. Jean-Pierre Droz was engaged to engrave pattern dies. Initially, Boulton had considered Thomas Williams a possible rival for this contract, but Samuel Garbett, who was also interested in coinage reform, suggested collaboration between the two men.[159] Wilkinson visited Anglesey in May 1787 and returned with the idea that Williams should roll the metal, and Boulton would do the coining.[160]

Ironically, as soon as Boulton had set up Soho Mint, the price of copper started to rise from a low of £67 per ton. The copper surpluses and low price had been a major stimulus to the idea in the first place! Supplies became increasingly difficult to obtain, especially in 1799. When Boulton first expected a regal coinage contract, copper prices were falling, at around £73 per ton.[161] For his first regal coinage contract in 1797, Boulton paid around £108 per ton for copper, but for the 1799 contract this had risen to £121, and in 1805 the price was £169.[162] However, by 1807, the price of copper had dropped to £143 per ton.

Part of the reason for this was that by 1788, Thomas Williams had effectively gained control of the copper trade and his excellent sales techniques had stimulated price rises. Also, the consumption of copper by the navy for ships sheathing increased due to war with the French, commencing in January 1793. In addition, by the late 1790s the Parys Mines were in serious decline, lessening the supply of copper ore.

The price of copper depended on how it was purchased; and reductions were given for larger orders. Copper came to Soho Mint from a variety of firms. By 1790, these firms included Thomas Williams's Anglesey Company, Brass Wire Company, Freeman and Company, Macclesfield Company, Birmingham Mining Company, Fenton's Yorkshire Copper Company and Morris, Lockwood and Company.[163] It was usual to arrange relatively long contracts for copper supplies. For example, in May 1791 Boulton agreed to receive monthly amounts of copper for two years from Hayle Copper House. The total received per year was to be:

'Twenty tons of brass and battery cake at eighty pound per ton, 70 tons of tough cake at £80 per ton and more than 70 tons at £81 per ton, 60 tons of shot if they can produce so much beyond their present engagements (as above for tough too) at £82 per ton'.[164]

---

159 MS 3782-12-62 Item 36, Samuel Garbett (London) to MB (Birmingham) 28 March 1787; Item 41 31 March 1787.

160 MS 3782-12-73 Item 152, John Wilkinson (Chester) to MB (Soho) 5 May 1787.

161 MS 3782-13-36 Item 9, MB (Soho) to MRB (Versailles) 30 Jul 1787.

162 MS 3782-17-4, License to coin 9 June 1797; MS 3782-17-5, License to coin 4 November 1799; MS 3782-17-6, License to coin 18 April 1805.

163 MS 3782-12-108 1789-1795, General Notebooks 1790 Item 55.

164 MS 3782-13-96, Copper trade Volume 1 Item 15. Michell, Trevenen and Edwards (Hayle) to MB 23 May 1791.

The price of copper was rising due to international conflicts and there were often problems with getting the correct sort of copper. Boulton was let down by his Cornish agent, Thomas Wilson and later also accused Williams of withholding copper from the Birmingham markets.[165] Consequently, he investigated the cost of copper, via correspondence with a network of agents, in twenty-two locations in Europe, and from countries such as Turkey and India. This price survey involved knowledge of the monetary values and conversion rates for the weights used: for example, one concerning copper from Bussorah (Basra, Iraq) required converting from the local currency of sicca rupees and the local weight of mamodies.[166]

As one of his correspondents, Westermark, from Stockholm, commented in January 1798, the costs *'have been here these late years extremely high and almost continually rising'*. He was hoping to export 20-30 tons of cake copper to Boulton in February 1799, but could not guarantee it as they were: *'in daily expectations of the Royal Statute'* which might limit exportation.[167] In January 1799 George Henry Busch reported from Hamburg that he *'cannot execute your commissions in copper as well as you expect'* as *'only a small quantity of copper is on market at present'*. By the end of the month, Busch wrote again to say he had *'some hope of contracting for monthly supply of Swedish copper'*.[168] Similarly, Gros from St Petersburg in Russia reported very small amounts available from the Siberian mines.[169] Boulton's agent Mr Schmidt from Drontheim in Norway reported that the price of copper *'keeps fluctuating and has rose considerably since last autumn'*.[170]

An interesting series of letters from Joseph Franel of Smyrna (Izmir), Turkey, describes how copper was transported from mines, first by donkeys, then log rafts along the river, and then by boat, and could be shipped on to Europe. Franel gave prices, and also sent samples by Captain Richard Stocker of the *Sally* but unfortunately the ship sank.[171] Boulton commented to his banker, Charlotte Matthews, that though the price was very cheap, there was import duty of ten guineas per ton plus sundry expenses which raised the cost.[172]

Andrew Collins was responsible for the various translations of letters to foreign agents and also travelled on behalf of the firm. He kept records of exchange rates.[173] It is amazing that the copper trade was able to continue despite international war, and also severe weather in the late eighteenth century.

165 MS 3782-13-96, Copper trade Volume 1 Item: 10. Extracts from the Correspondence between MB, Mr Edwards & Mr Hurd February 1791 to December 1793.
166 MS 3782-12-90 Items 71-80, Prices for Battery copper 1787-1797.
167 MS 3782-12-90 Items 81-90, J. Westermark and Co (Stockholm) to MB 30 January 1798; 8 February 1799.
168 MS 3782-12-90 Items 81-90, G.H. Busch (Hamburg) to MB (Soho) January 1799.
169 MS 3782-12-90 Items 81-90, E.L. Gros (St Petersburg) to MB (Soho) 25 February 1799.
170 MS 3782-12-90 Items 81-90, Connor and Company (Trieste) to MB (Soho) 15 February 1799.
171 MS 3782-12-90 Items 81-90, 17 July – 2 September 1799.
172 MS 3792-12-68 Item 46, MB (Soho) to Charlotte Matthews (London) 3 June 1793.
173 MS 3782-12-90 Items 81-90, Mr A. Collins on foreign copper 8 March 1799.

Compared to the 1797 and 1799 regal coinage contracts, there were no problems with copper supply for the 1805-1807 regal issues, though the price was high. By 1802 Thomas Williams had died, and copper was provided by Thomas Williams's son, and his partner, Pascoe Grenfell. Boulton also supplied copper via the Rose Copper Company in which he now had shares.[174]

An enquiry in 1799 into the price of copper was held by the Committee on the Copper Trade.[175] Boulton was interviewed as an expert witness in April.[176] There were complaints that the price of copper *deprives a great part of the inhabitants of Birmingham of full Employment and fluctuations in price are prejudicial to manufactures*.[177] By this time, Thomas Williams and Matthew Boulton were not on good terms as Boulton was a consumer rather than a producer of copper, and was trying to lower prices. Mine Adventurers and smelters wanted the highest price possible for copper, which was in short supply all over Europe. Lord Hawkesbury moved a bill in Parliament to prevent the export of copper by the East India Company (EIC) in an effort to stop price rises and various articles appeared in newspapers including the *Morning Chronicle, Gazette* and the *Morning Herald* on 19 June 1799.[178]

Boulton blamed Williams for the lack of copper for his Soho Mint in 1799, and commented: *'W^{ms} from a principle of revenge upon me chooses to gratify that spirit at the expense of a few thousands'.*[179] Williams was not really at fault for the high prices and thought that Boulton had treated him unfairly when obtaining copper for the 1797 regal coinage contract, which may or may not have been true. He argued that the high prices were caused by war and that 60,000 to 70,000 people were dependent on the copper mines, let alone the colliers, coasters and carriers who were also involved. He accused Boulton of trying to profit from the situation. He wrote indignantly:

'Is it to be credited that a Contractor who at once gains upwards of £20,000 by copper, who had before acquired a very considerable fortune by Cornish concerns, and who, since May last, has been paid by them £40,000 for the use of his engines; is it to be credited that he should stand forward in a Deputation, to lessen the prosperity of those by whose means he has obtained that fortune? Should the proprietor of a steam engine, the contractor of a national coinage, the makers of buttons or the founders of brass be similarly constrained?'[180]

---

174 P. Watts-Russell (unpublished manuscript) *Making Money: Pascoe Grenfell, Matthew Boulton & the copper coinage.*

175 MS 3782-13-97-25, Observations on evidence to committee to enquire into copper mines and copper trade 1799.

176 MS 3782-13-36 Item 139, MB (London) to MRB (Soho) 30 April 1799.

177 MS 3782-13-9-21, *Review of the Arguments on the Copper Trade and Miners. Printed by G Woodfall, 23 Paternoster Row, London.* Printed document on the export and import of copper 1799.

178 MS 3782-13-97-23, Extracts from newspapers relative to the copper trade and contest with the miners 1799.

179 MS 3782-12-56 Item 124, MB (Soho) to Sir Joseph Banks (London) 29 November 1799.

180 MS 3782-13-97 Item 21, Copper coinage and government 1799.

Figure 2:7 Thomas Williams (1737-1802).[181]

---

181 Thomas Williams, image from Wikipedia.

Chapter Three

Iron and Steel

BOTH iron and coal were easily obtained in Birmingham, especially after the canal system was established in the 1760s, which enabled Matthew Boulton to experiment with materials. His interest in scientific matters helped in his business activities; advances in iron manufacturing were used in Boulton and Watt steam-engines which powered blast furnaces and drained mines. Then experience with the reciprocating engine in Cornwall led to the development of the rotative engine in 1788, necessary to the steam-powered coining press at Soho Mint. Iron and steel were also essential to make parts of the coining apparatus and for die making.

The molecular structure of metals including steel, or the crystalline structure and chemical composition of metallic ores, were not fully appreciated by Boulton, due to the lack of scientific knowledge at the time, but he did have a deep practical understanding of the metallurgy involved.[182] He was eager to keep up with current developments and in January 1788, discussed the French chemist Antoine Lavoisier's theories, with Joseph Priestley and Lunar Society members, even before Lavoisier published *Traité élémentaire de chimie (Treatise on Chemical Elements)* in 1789.[183] He wrote to his son, Matt, about the old doctrine which was that *'all metals are composed of a Metalick Earth & phlogiston'* and compared it with the new theory that metals were one homogenous substance. He understood that metals would form a calx with the air, in other words become oxidised. Smelting the ore removed oxygen, reducing it to the metal, what we would now call an element. Boulton advised his son to: *'Hear all sides with candor, see all the Experiment, read all the modern Authors & then judge for yourself'.*[184]

Iron furnaces had been set up at Coalbrookdale in 1709 by Abraham Derby, who previously worked at the Bristol Brass Company. Before 1750, three other iron furnaces were started at Redbrook, Forest of Dean, where copper works were also

182 MS 3782-12-108-27, General notebook 1780-1790.
183 MS 3782-13-36 Item 17, MB (London) to MRB (Paris) 15 January 1788.
184 MS 3782-13-36 Item 19, MB (London) to MRB (Paris) 8 February 1788.

located, at Bersham and in Cumberland.[185] Many iron furnaces were linked to a network of entrepreneurs who were personally known to Boulton. One significant iron works was set up in 1759 at Carron, near Falkirk, Stirlingshire as a partnership between Matthew Boulton's friend, Samuel Garbett, and Dr John Roebuck. It was here that James Watt had his first steam-engine cylinder made in 1766.

Figure 3:1 Remnants of James Watt's first steam-engine cylinder at Carron.[186]

The Wilkinson family were key players in the iron industry, having partnerships in Cumbria, the Midlands and South Wales.[187] Isaac Wilkinson introduced innovative cast-iron blowing cylinders, patented in 1757, to coal-fired furnaces. These were further developed by his son, John Wilkinson (1728-1808), who was an exact contemporary of Matthew Boulton and a similar type of thrusting entrepreneur. Their friendship had started in December 1766 when Wilkinson had wanted to form an *'Acquaintance with a Genius, that might in future afford Me great Satisfaction on many Accounts'*.[188] Most importantly, John Wilkinson was responsible for inventing an accurate boring machine to make cannon, which enabled Boulton and Watt to develop successful steam-engine technology. His New Willey works at Broseley later made iron on a large scale, with bellows powered by the first Boulton and Watt (B&W) rotary steam-engine.[189] Wilkinson was also involved in copper mining and with regal coinage contract negotiations. He issued three different types of tokens from 1787, some of which were made at Soho Mint.

---

185 T.S. Ashton (1924) *Iron and Steel in the Industrial Revolution*, Manchester University Press.
186 Image taken by author, August 2008.
187 C. Evans and G. Rydén (eds.) (2005) *The Industrial Revolution in Iron: The Impact of British Coal Technology in Nineteenth Century Europe* Ashgate, Aldershot p21.
188 MS 3782-12-23 Item 81, John Florry (Birmingham) to MB (Birmingham) 7 December 1766.
189 D. Vice (1990) *The tokens of John Wilkinson* Format 40 March 1990.

Further important iron furnaces were set up by John Guest at Broseley, Shropshire in 1776; his son was in partnership with Thomas Lewis and Isaac Wilkinson at Dowlais, near Merthyr Tydfil, South Wales. The Homfray family joined Anthony Bacon at the nearby Cyfartha iron works in 1782 and also ran Pen-y-darran Iron works close by, for which Boulton later supplied tokens. This increased output of iron freed Britain from dependency on imported iron from Sweden and Russia, except for high grade iron needed for steel making.[190]

Smelting Iron

Iron is found as a variety of ores such as magnetite (Fe_3O_4), or haematite (Fe_2O_3) usually combined with silica. Iron was first produced from its ores in a batch process, using charcoal in a bloomery. By the end of the fourteenth century, the furnaces used in smelting were becoming larger, with bellows used to force air through the 'charge' of iron ore, limestone and charcoal. This produced carbon monoxide which removed the oxygen, converting the iron ore to a spongy mass of brittle pig-iron. The pig-iron was used to produce wrought iron by hammering it in a finery forge to consolidate it and to remove slag and carbon. Wrought iron was used to make items such as nails, horseshoes, wagon tyres, rails and so on, and could be welded into chains and rivets, but not cast. Cast-iron was produced by remelting pig iron and was tough but brittle.[191] Iron could also be further processed to make steel.

The great breakthrough in the metal industries was the use of coke from coal instead of charcoal, for smelting both iron and copper ore. Abraham Derby introduced this technique at Coalbrookdale, Shropshire in 1709. The firm continued till 1789 when Abraham Derby III died, and then by his son-in-law as Reynolds and Company, also known as the Coalbrook-Dale Iron Company. A stream was initially used to power the furnace blast but later B&W steam-engines were used.[192] Derby's techniques, learnt from his experiences in the copper industry, initially spread slowly. Boulton was still writing about the amount of charcoal needed to make a ton of iron in his 1780-1790 notebook.[193] Further developments by Henry Cort (1740-1800) were patented in 1783-4. It involved stirring molten iron to allow the separation of impurities. The bars of iron might be tied together or faggotted, then heated and rolled to give wrought iron of the desired quality.[194] Boulton was immediately aware of this process as Cort wrote in June from Stourbridge to show Boulton the tough iron he had made.[195] Boulton was well ahead of the field, as Cort's processes did not become fully established until the 1820s.

---

190 T.S. Ashton (1924) *Iron and Steel in the Industrial Revolution* pp95-100.
191 K.C. Barraclough (1984) *Steel Making before Bessemer Volume 1: Blister steel* Metal Society pp1-10.
192 T.S. Ashton (1924) *Iron and Steel in the Industrial Revolution* p95.
193 MS 3782-12-108-27, Boulton's General notebook 1780-1790.
194 C. Evans and G. Rydén (eds.) (2005) *The Industrial Revolution in Iron* p14.
195 MS 3782-12-29-32, Henry Cort (—) to MB (Soho) 3 June 1784; MS 3782-12-29-31, Joseph Black (Edinburgh) to Mr. Cort (Stourbridge, Worcestershire) 28 May 1784.

Steel

Steel was considered a semi-precious metal in the eighteenth century, made in small batches with methods of production more often associated with gold and silver. It was used for decorative objects such as buttons and buckles at Soho Manufactory. It was also important for making functional objects such as specialist tools and dies.[196] Steel was made at first by 'accident,' as a by-product in the bloomery. To a trained eye it was possible to select the bits of iron that had been 'steeled' due to carbon being added.[197]

Just as developments in the extraction of iron and copper were interlinked, through the work of Abraham Derby, innovations introduced in the brass industry by William Champion (1710-1789) and others may have inspired parallel improvements by Benjamin Huntsman (1704-1776) in forming steel.[198] The cementation process, where metallic copper was heated with charcoal plus calamine ($ZnCO_3$) in enclosed containers to produce brass, was brought to perfection at the Cheadle Brass Company, where large-scale manufacture was introduced in 1781.[199] Boulton had researched brass making in conjunction with setting up a Brass Company in Birmingham, and wrote in his notebook: *'Champion says he has a patent for making brass in spelter pots; that the same furnace serves either for spelter* [zinc] *or brass as you want'*. He suggested his own method, with a research program to find out at what temperature zinc, brass and copper melt.[200] The cementation process was also used to make blister or bar steel by heating iron bars with charcoal in chests.

Boulton possessed a copy of Réaumur's *L'art de convertir le fer forgé en acier* (1722), a major attempt to theorise the properties of steel. This had been produced by the French government in an effort to promote a domestic manufacture of steel. France was the largest single producer of bar iron in Europe, but despite state sponsorship, they had not mastered the cementation technique. Gabriel Jars (1732-1769), a star pupil of the École des Mines, was commissioned to investigate foreign steel making, and in 1765 he published his *Voyages Metallurgiques* which Boulton also read.[201]

In Britain it was practical knowledge in the workshop that counted, rather than state sponsored research as in France, and here Boulton excelled.[202] By 1750, there was a steel works in Birmingham making five tons per day. When James Watt first came to Soho in 1767, he wrote:

---

196 G. Rydén (2007) *Steel in Britain in the age of Enlightenment* Colloquium held in Cardiff 7-8 December 2007.

197 T.S. Ashton (1924) *Iron and Steel in the Industrial Revolution* p87.

198 K.C. Barraclough (1984) *Steel Making before Bessemer Volume 1: Blister steel* pp60-69.

199 J. Morton (1983) *Thomas Bolton and Sons Limited 1783-1983*

200 MS 3782-12-73 Item 20, Thomas Williams (London) to MB (Soho) June 1781; MS 3782-12-108-27 1780-1790 Boulton's General Notebook.

201 J. Belhoste (2007) *Steel in Britain in the age of Enlightenment* Colloquium 7-8 December 2007.

202 C. Evans and G. Rydén (eds.) (2005) *The Industrial Revolution in Iron* p14.

'Boulton had a steel house for converting iron into steel, which was frequently employed to convert the cuttings of chapes [buckle fittings] *and other small iron wares into steel which was afterwards melted & made into cast steel for various purposes'.*[203]

Boulton corresponded with George Laidler from 1762, who had three steel furnaces, and with William Allen in 1764 discussing sources of steel.[204] Allen said that he was able to supply iron imported from Philadelphia which *'will make excellent steel, is very ductile and malleable, and at the same time is of a very strong body'.*[205] By 1779, Boulton had a three-chest steel furnace with a capacity of about 8 tons at Snow Hill. He was still interested in methods of making iron and steel in 1790 when he went to Bradley with Wilkinson to *'see the result of a new mode of making good Bar Iron without the use of any forge, or any charcoal de bois, which experiment fully answered our expectations'.*[206]

Suitable iron to convert into steel, was obtained from Spooners of Birmingham, Wright and Jesson at Wren's Nest, Nicholas Ryder of Marston Forge, and Richard Dearman of Eagle Foundry in Birmingham.[207] But most good quality iron for use in steel-making was still imported from Swedish and Russian sources in 1793. Boulton owned a book of Swedish ore marks.[208] Sven Rinman, a Swedish chemist and mineralogist, linked British blister steel production in 1772 to the consumption of Öregrund iron, made from Dannemora ore at less than twenty forges in Sweden.[209]

Crucible Steel

Steel can have a wide variety of differing mechanical properties, due the different formation of its alloys with iron, but this was only understood in a very empirical way in the eighteenth century. It was the consumers of steel, not producers, who decided how steel was to be defined. Depending on the type of steel required, the iron was heated to the correct colour of flame. Different colours indicate different degrees of hardening: pale yellow gave a very hard but brittle steel used for razors and fine cutting tools; straw coloured flames for chisels. Blue heat was used for saws which needed to be flexible; red heat at 900-1000°C for sharp tool steel. The metal was hardened by plunging it into a cold bath, and then reheating to 150-650°C to temper the metal, reducing brittleness.[210]

---

203 J. Watt, *Memoir of Boulton by Watt* written 17 September 1809 in: H.W. Dickinson (1937) *Matthew Boulton* p203.

204 MS 3782-12-23 Item 26, George Laidler Jr. (London) to MB (Soho). 30 October 1762; Item 27 2 March 1763.

205 MS 3782-12-23 Item 33, William Allen (London) to MB (—) 2 April 1764.

206 MS 3782-13-36 Item 41, MB (Soho) to MRB 4 January 1790.

207 C. Evans (2007) *Steel in Britain in the age of Enlightenment* Colloquium 7-8 December 2007.

208 MS 3147-10-4 Swedish Iron and Steel Marks.

209 G. Rydén (2007) *Sven Rinman and Swedish knowledge about British steel* Colloquium 7-8 December 2007.

210 K.C. Barraclough (1984) *Steel Making before Bessemer Vol. 1: Blister steel; Vol. 2: Crucible Steel: the growth of technology.*

A refining technique was needed to make steel more predictable in its qualities. Benjamin Huntsman had experimented in steel manufacture since the 1740s. Eventually he was able to make satisfactory cast or crucible steel in 1756. His firm was continued and extended by his sons William (1733-1809) and Benjamin Junior (dates unknown). Blister steel from the cementation process was melted in a crucible to prevent the entry of air which would oxidize the iron. Clay pots or crucibles were manufactured for the purpose, capable of holding about 34 lbs each, and charged with bar steel broken into pieces of about a pound each. Ten or twelve of these crucibles were placed in a melting-furnace, similar to that used by brass founders, and heated by a coke fire to white heat. The liquid steel was poured to make ingots of the required shape and size, which could be forged into rods or bars suitable for die making. The result was that the steel became more homogeneous in structure.[211]

Correspondence with Huntsman began from at least January 1757, just one year after he had first made crucible steel.[212] Boulton also personally investigated steel making. One way to make steel involved:

'Coals twelve pounds; horns ten; shoes, vine soot, and pomegranate, of each equal quantities three pounds all well mixed together. To make one hundred pounds weight of steel, there is required one hundred and twenty pounds weight of good, soft Spanish iron, not streaky; to which if you give the aforementioned dose of the said powders, prepared as directed, and put to the fire, for the space of forty-eight hours, you will get the best steel which can be had'.[213]

The firm of Huntsman & Asline supplied not only cast steel, but 'german steel', 'blister steel', and a wide range of termed as 'best', 'super fine', or 'common sort'. Agreements on prices were made according to the qualities of steel required, and the shapes of the semi-manufactured products, similar to the copper industry. Huntsman's son asked Boulton to recommend his rolled steel to other manufacturers and said that it would not 'rust so soon as that made by other Steel makers' and that 'It hardens very well'.[214]

Steel for Die Making

A very important part of the coining process was making the dies which imprinted the image onto the metal blank. From early in his career, Boulton was fully aware of the importance of homogenous steel to make dies for the Soho Manufactory. Tool steel was usually bought in round, square, hexagonal or octagonal rods. Tapered cylinders of special steel were used for matrices, dies and punches. He

---

211 C. Evans (2007) *Steel in Britain in the age of Enlightenment* Colloquium 7-8 December 2007.
212 MS 3782-12-23 Item 132, Benjamin Huntsman (Sheffield) to MB (Soho) 7 July 1769.
213 MS 3782-12-108 Item 53, Mint Note Book 1788 p56 on.
214 MS 3782-12-26 Item 101, Benjamin Huntsman (Sheffield) to MB (Soho) 10 September 1781.

used a variety of suppliers, including Benjamin Huntsman, whose steel, when annealed, was relatively soft for engraving or hubbing (multiplying dies), and could be struck without excessive work-hardening.

With coining dies, most knowledge of their metallurgical characteristics was gained from practical experience. For thousands of years coins were made by using a hard material, an engraved die, to impress an image into a softer material. Because silver and gold are relatively soft, the first coining dies around 600 BC were probably made of bronze in an iron holder. Later coining dies were made with a wrought iron body and hammer welded steel tip.[215] The die had to hit the metal sufficiently hard to compress and expand it into all the hollows of the die. As early as 1535, Cellini realised the importance of selecting good iron and steel for dies as steel was better able to withstand the stresses of striking.[216] However, slag inclusions often caused breakage of engraving tools, and had a grinding action on blanks.

Even in the eighteenth century, steel suitable for a coining die was difficult to obtain. It had to be soft enough to be engraved, but then made hard enough to transfer the design. It also needed to be tough and elastic to withstand the shock of the coining blow without distortion. Several blows might be necessary, especially if blanks were struck cold, as high mechanical pressures were needed to move metal. In some mints, metal blanks were heated.[217] However, when a large-scale coining was undertaken at Soho Mint, for speed and economy, a single blow on cold metal blanks was used.

Specific orders for steel coining dies were made with Huntsman Junior once the Soho Mint was set up. Boulton wrote in April 1789:

> 'I am about to undertake the striking of some millions of copper pieces which will require a hard blow in hardened steel dies. I have tried various kinds of steel but am not yet satisfied with any of them. I am of opinion that the best cast steel you are capable of making will answer the best, and therefore I must request the favour of you to send me a few bars by way of tryal of such firm strong nerved steel as you know how to make out of the best bar. NB it must be the best you can possibly make without any regard to price or expense, that being a trifling object in comparison to the quality of the steel. I presume that 8 solid bars will be the best form as they are to be forged into round dies with a coat of iron like the drawing. The steel I have hitherto tried will crack in the hardening or breaks afterwards in the striking, or is so soft as to sink in the middle and become hollow, both which extreams I wish to avoid.* He also asked Huntsman's advice in: *the management of the said steel both as to the forging, annealing, hardening and tempering of it'.

---

215 D.R. Cooper (1988) *The Art and Craft of Coin Making* Spink, London p19; p25.

216 D.R. Cooper (1996) *The development of coinage dies from bronze to steel* Newcomen Society Transactions Volume 67 1995-1996 pp93; 99.

217 W. Breen (1970) *The Minting Process: How Coins are Made and Mismade* American Institute of Professional Numismatists p13.

Boulton knew from practical experience exactly what he required from Huntsman and drew diagrams to illustrate what he wanted.[218]

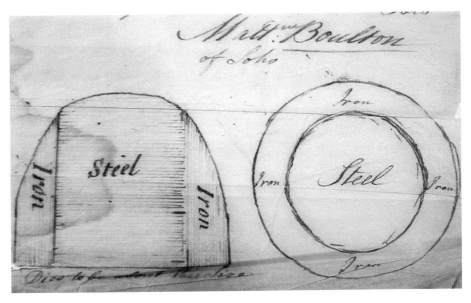

Figure 3:2 1789 Diagram of die drawn by Boulton.

Huntsman's reply, sent with ten pair of dies, recommended that they should be case hardened.[219] In January 1790, Boulton sent *'an exact sketch for the size of the dies and the manner in which the steel should be forged'* as none of the dies sent were fit for use at the Soho Mint. He wanted three to four cwt of best steel and intended to have the dies forged under his own supervision.[220] However not many moneying dies were able to do much work. Boulton therefore suggested making dies in a different way:

> *'I must beg of you to take the very best marks of the Swedish iron to make the steel … I recommend that the steel be as ductile as possible….I therefore wish to try to make them from bars of steel which are forged square or rather oblong square & then the engraving will be done on one of the forged sides whereas it is now done on the unforged end as we cut the round bars you sent me into short lengths'.[221]*

Samples of steel were also obtained via the Soho agent Richard Chippindall in London.[222] Another supplier was Rennie. Boulton wrote:

---

218 MS 3782-12-3 Item 114, MB (Birmingham) to Benjamin Huntsman (Junior) 24 April 1789 p112.
219 MS 3782-12-34 Item 83, Benjamin Huntsman (Junior) (Sheffield) to MB (Soho) 22 May 1789.
220 MS 3782-12-8 Item 36, MB to William Huntsman (Sheffield) 23 January 1790.
221 MS 3782-12-8 Item 31, MB to William Huntsman (Sheffield) 21 May 1790.
222 MS 3782-12-59 Item 17, Richard Chippindall (London) to MB (Soho) 9 May 1789.

'I receivᵈ some large size Cast Steel from you which proved good. I now beg of you to pick out one Ton of the best hoop L or double Bullett & Cast it, in your best manner into large Ingots & forge it down to size. This Steel is for fine Medal Dies & must be the best possible or it will be worth nothing to me I will not limit you in Price, charge it what you please so that it be as good as ever you made'.[223]

Without good steel it was impossible to make good dies, and without good dies, high quality coins were impossible to strike.

Huntsman was asked to make dies from bars of steel 2½ inch by 1½ inch in 1797. These were then forged into a conical shape: *'They are for striking penny pieces of the size I have sent with the Die but as they are struck in Collers they may require a very hard blow and if not steelᵈ through the dies would sink in the middle'.*[224] In 1802, Boulton wrote to request that the best type of Swedish iron should be used as *'my Mint is almost at a stand for want of better dies I must beg the favour of you to instantly prepare the 2 specimens aforementioned & send them by the most expeditious conveyance, even ten or 12 lb of each might be send by the coach'.*[225]

Dies

Workers at the Soho Manufactory would have used dies and stamps to make products such as buttons, candlesticks and other 'toys'. Boulton had also made medals ordered by Joseph Banks (1742-1820), later President of the Royal Society. The medal dies for Captain Cook's expedition in 1772 and for two other orders in 1774 and 1781 were engraved by the earliest recognised Birmingham medallist, John Westwood Senior.[226] They were struck at Soho by relatively primitive techniques, using a drop hammer, and not a coin or medal press.[227]

For coining, two dies were used at the same time, one for each side, the obverse with the main image, often the monarch's head, and reverse with a subsidiary image, and possibly a third die for the edge. The master dies were engraved with a mirror or reverse image from the best possible steel available. Punches, with a positive image, were cut from soft steel shaped at the tip and hardened before use, and used for adding textures and shapes to the die. Elaborate punches might be made for larger elements in a design such as a crown. Coining dies could be made using a series of punches, with fine details added later to each individual die by the engraver, which led to slight variations in the coins. In 1717, Newton at the Royal Mint estimated that it took six weeks to make the punches for a halfpenny, one punch featuring the bust, others for the inscription.[228]

223 MS 3782-13-49 Item 90, MB (Soho) to John Rennie 26 September 1791.
224 MS 3782-12-42 Item 165, MB (Soho) to Benjamin Huntsman (Sheffield) 6 July 1797.
225 MS 3782-12-47 Item 379, MB to Benjamin Huntsman (Sheffield) 19 November 1802.
226 D. Vice (1988) *The Resolution and Adventure Medal* Format 36 March 1988.
227 Banks papers in New South Wales Archives, Australia. Series 06.109 www2.sl.nsw.gov.au/banks/series 06.109 16 March 1772.
228 D.R. Cooper (1996) *The development of coinage dies from bronze to steel* p99.

For hammered coins, the lower die, known also as the anvil or pile die, could be hexagonal with bevelled edges to allow access of the moneyer's fingers and often had a spike to insert it into some form of holder. The upper die, the trussel or hammer die, was often shorter, so that the moneyer could place it accurately over the blank.[229]

When the screw press was introduced to mechanise coining, square shaped or cylindrical dies were more convenient and both dies could be made of equal size as forces were more evenly spread. In general, the practice was to engrave dies with a camber of 1mm in 25mm so that the centre was pressed first and the outside of the blank acted as a hoop to protect the design.[230] At Soho Mint a collar for the edge was used as a third die.

Once the correct steel had been selected for a die, it needed to be forged by the smiths at Soho Mint into the correct shape.[231] After experimentation, Boulton had concluded that a cylindrical shape was best as it was least likely to crack.[232] Most of the dies and punches seen from Soho Mint were in the form of a cylindrical steel block weighing between 500-1000g with a base diameter of between 58-64 mm, and a height of between 47-52mm.[233] On most coining dies there are slots, which may have helped with alignment in the coining press.

| 1798 Nile | 1805 Trafalgar | 1805 Trafalgar |
| reverse punch | obverse die | obverse die |

Figure 3:3 Dies and punches.

---

229 G.P. Dyer (1993) 'Punches and Dies in the Eighteenth Century' in: M.M. Archibald, M.R. Carrell (eds.) (1993) *Metallurgy in Numismatics 3*, Royal Numismatic Society Special Publication 24, London, pp160-168.

230 D.R. Cooper (1996) *The development of coinage dies from bronze to steel* pp96, 101, 102.

231 MS 3782-13-36 Item 60, MB (London) to MRB (Soho) 7 June 1791.

232 MS 3782-12-108 Item 53, Mint Note Book 1788 p87 21 April 1788.

233 Twenty-seven Soho Mint dies or punches made between 1792 and 1804 were examined by the author from the Assay Office, Avery Museum, Birmingham Museum and Art Gallery, Soho House and Think Tank in Birmingham.

Engraving the Die

Dies were engraved by a skilled engraver using tools such as gravers, punches and files to shape and move the metal.[234] The steel die was held on a sheepskin bag filled with sand, or by a chuck or clamp. To sharpen the tools, they were ground slowly on emery or corundum wheels, and the sharpening process was finished with fine sandpaper or a smooth oilstone.[235] The dies were cut on workbenches large enough to accommodate tools and accessories and which would provide a sturdy non-vibrating work surface.[236] Once hardened this first die, known as a 'matrix', could be used to make a series of working punches, sometimes known as puncheon dies or working hubs, which were in turn used to make working dies for a large coinage order.

Figure 3:4 Die engraver's bench from Paris Mint Museum.[237]

Boulton undertook his first coinage in 1786 for the EIC (East India Company) for Sumatra and these coins had a simple design. He used punches engraved by William Castleton in London and sent to Birmingham for the die sinker to make suitable dies.[238] Zaccheus Walker wrote:

---

234 MS 3782-3-13, Mint Day Book 1791-1795.

235 MS 3782-13-36 Item 60, MB (London) to MRB (Soho) June 1791 p8; MS 3782-3-13, Mint day Book 8 February 1791-16 May 1791.

236 MS 3782-13-120 Folder 6, Inventory of Property belonging to Coinage Account taken 31st December 1790.

237 Image courtesy Professor Peter Jones, taken at Paris Mint Museum, Hôtel de la Monnaie, Paris, France, 2008.

238 MS 3782-12-59 Item 2, William Chippindall (London) to MB (Truro) 12 September 1786; MS 3782-12-59 Item 3 William Gibbs (London) to MB (Truro) 22 September 1786.

'the punches with the Indian characters, which Mr Marsden says are well executed, came to hand on Tuesday last'.[239] Boulton wrote: *'there is no head upon it, or anything but letters or such things as are put in with punchions. I have therefore had no occasion to make any dies by means of an original'.*[240]

Therefore he needed a better engraver for portrait dies, before he could progress to making a regal coinage. Letter punches were often made for Boulton by the specialist engraver Richard Phillips of London, but he needed a better engraver for portrait dies. Before he could progress to making a regal coinage, he wanted to employ someone to work specifically at Soho Mint.[241] He had hoped that Jean-Pierre Droz from the Paris Mint would provide dies for a regal coinage contract. Though Droz produced numerous varieties of pattern halfpennies, very few of his dies or punches were used commercially. He would not make dies for token issues and left Soho in June 1790.

The first commercial coin made by Soho Mint was the 1789 Cronebane halfpenny. The dies were made by John Gregory Hancock, a Birmingham engraver, working independently. The legend and details such as the crosier, date, and windlass were added individually to working dies, as can be seen by the numerous varieties.[242] Hancock's punches were also re-used to make dies for the 1791 Leeds halfpenny tokens where St Patrick has turned into Bishop Blaise, with the crosier replaced by a woolcomb. He also provided dies for the Anglesey tokens and the Wilkinson token issues of 1787-1790.[243]

St Patrick   Bishop Blaise

Figure 3:5 St Patrick turns into Bishop Blaise.

---

239 MS 3782-12-74 Item 120 Zaccheus Walker (Birmingham) to MB (Chacewater) 21 September 1786.

240 MB to Droz 5 April 1787 quoted in: J.G. Pollard (1968) *Matthew Boulton and J.P. Droz* Numismatic Chronicle 1968 Volume 8 University Press Oxford pp241-265.

241 MS 3782-12-66 Item 9, James Lawson (Soho) to MB (London) 23 May 1791.

242 Around thirty varieties of the Cronebane halfpenny are listed. Dalton and Hamer *(1915) The Provincial Token Coinage of the Eighteenth Century Illustrated; Volume III Wales Scotland, Ireland and Addenda Part XI Anglesey and Wales.*

243 MS 3783-12-35 Item 73, John Gregory Hancock (Birmingham) to MB (Birmingham) 12 April 1790.

By August 1790, the engraver Rambert Dumarest had come to Soho to supply dies for the 1791 Southampton and 1791 Glasgow halfpenny tokens, and for many of the tokens and medals made for the Monneron brothers, and possibly for the 1791 Bombay issues. Dumarest also engraved a die for a proposed Anglesey token issue which was rejected by Williams and reused for the 1791 Cornish halfpenny token.

By spring 1791, Dumarest had left Soho and his place was taken by Noel-Alexandre Ponthon who worked for Boulton from June 1791 to September 1795. He had been recommended by both Augustin Dupré from the Paris Mint and Francis Swediaur, Boulton's agent in Paris.[244] The main engraver at Soho, from 1793 until his death in 1810, was Conrad Heinrich Küchler but Thomas Wyon, Augustin Dupré, John Phillp and G.F. Pidgeon were also employed to make both coin and medal dies.

Dies generally have a complete mirror image and inscription on their flat upper surface, such as seen in the Madras, Sierra Leone and Ceylon coinage dies, and for the Trafalgar and Marriage medal dies.

1791 Sierra Leone
50 cent obverse die

1795 Marriage die

Figure 3:6 Dies for Sierra Leone coinage and Marriage medal.

Punches, such as that for the Nile medal, have the image the correct way around.

---

244 MS 3782-12-91 Item 117, Francis Swediaur to 'Andrew Smith' (pseudonym for MB) 27 February 1791.

Nile punch   Nile trial strike

Figure 3:7 Punch and trial strike for Nile medal.

1791 Sierra Leone 50 cent   1804 Ceylon 1/192-rix
obverse die   dollar obverse die

1794 Madras 1/48-rupee obverse die   1803 Madras five cash obverse die

Figure 3:8 Coining Dies.

The punch shows the scene of the battle at Aboukir Bay with no inscriptions, whereas the trial strike has it included. It was probably added at a second striking.

Several of the coining dies have 'necks'; a cylinder on which the engraving was made, which could protrude into the collar. 'Necks' were only possible if homogenous crucible steel was used, as a welded tip would break off.[245] However, other coining dies are relatively flat.

Collar Die

One die, known as the Droz collar, was designed to strike an inscription ('Render to Caesar the things that are Caesar's') onto the edge of the pattern halfpennies.[246] This did not work well and was later modified into a one-part collar by James Lawson.

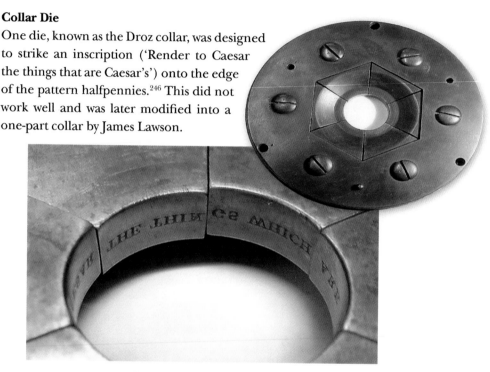

Figure 3:9 1788 Droz Collar Die.

Specialist engravers were needed to make the dies but, as Boulton wrote, any die sinker could engrave the 'nuts' to make the edge markings. *'Nichols or Bush or any Die sinker can put the letter puncheons into the nut particularly as Bush hath made a machine for that purpose'.*[247] Dies were also made to cut out blanks. The use of convex dies to make blanks, which aided in the prevention of fraud, may have been suggested by Busch.[248] He was also responsible for the production of the working dies for the regal coinage orders in 1797 and 1799.[249]

---

245 D.R. Cooper (1996) *The development of coinage dies from bronze to steel* p103.
246 P. Benedicz (1998) *The Droz Collar* The Anchor, Autumn 1998, The Assay Office, Birmingham.
247 MS 3782-13-36 Item 56, MB (London) to MRB (Soho) 27 May 1791.
248 MS 3782-12-66 Item 14, James Lawson (Soho) to MB (London) 5 June 1791.
249 MS 3782-12-59 Item 176 & 190, William Cheshire (Soho) to MB (London) 19 November 1798; 30 May 1799.

Heat Treatments: Annealing and Hardening

A variety of heat treatments were required during die making. Annealing and hardening change properties such as strength and hardness of a metal. In the cases of copper, steel and brass, annealing is performed by substantially heating the material, generally until glowing, then maintaining a suitable temperature for a specific time, allowing it to cool slowly or cooling it rapidly in a water or oil quench bath. The metal is 'frozen' into a particular state of crystallisation. Dies needed to be annealed so that they could be engraved with the appropriate image, and then were hardened to make the die durable, in order to be able to withstand the forces of the coining press. After hardening, the steel may be brittle and so may need further tempering by gradual heating.

To harden dies, they were often placed in a cast-iron pot, completely embedded in animal charcoal, chiefly made from leather. The pot was placed in an air furnace, in which coke was burned to give an even heat. Once the die had reached the correct heat, judged by the colour of the flame and metal, it was withdrawn and immersed in a large cistern of water, the temperature of which kept constant by continuous flow of cold water. At this point, the dies sometimes cracked and the whole work of the engraver was lost.[250]

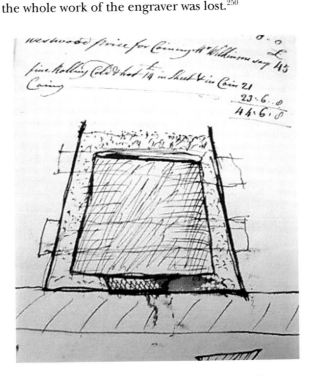

Figure 3:10 Notes on annealing dies.[251]

---

250 R.C. Bell (1964) *Commercial Copper Coins 1811-1819* Corbitt and Hunter, Newcastle.
251 MS 3782-12-108 Item 53, Mint Note Book 1788.

From the start of his career Boulton carried out experiments on die making. As early as 1766, he had contacted Benjamin Franklin describing his experiments on annealing dies.[252] Many pages of his 1788 Mint book are taken up with how to forge, anneal and harden dies. He employed various recipes, including using 'phlogistick' powder; he tested Wedgwood's thermometer to measure the degree of heat. Sometimes iron was case hardened, that is locally heated with additional carbon absorbed at the surface to make a steeled layer. Boulton used some interesting ingredients, including pounded garlic and juniper wood, which all add carbon to the iron. One recipe made charcoal from beech, willow, burnt ox horns and burnt shoes with various other ingredients to harden a die.[253] Amazingly, similar ingredients are incorporated in a commercial mixture made from burnt shoe leather or bones to harden modern dies used to stamp specialist items.[254]

By the time the 1797 regal coinage order was received, Boulton had a much better understanding of die making. Steel ingots were normally cast with the long axis vertical so that the slag and other impurities settle on the top. Boulton had found that if these ingots were turned at right angles, the impurities would be on the side of the bar and not on the top, where they would interfere with the engraving. He used his own observations, his quick intelligence and his practical experience to change die making practices. This important improvement in die technology, suggested by Boulton, forging the dies across the grain, was introduced at the new Royal Mint from 1811 and was used for the next 150 years.[255]

Multiplying Dies

Sufficient high-quality dies were absolutely essential to the functioning of the Soho Mint, so once the steam-powered coining presses were established, a more efficient method of multiplying dies was essential. The blow imparted was more uniform than that of the man-powered press so that dies did not wear so much, but, due to the faster speeds of working, the dies needed to be changed more regularly. Hundreds of working dies were needed for a large coinage issue.

At the Paris Mint in 1787, twelve engravers were employed to duplicate dies, but Soho Mint at that time had no experienced coin engravers. Boulton had employed Droz in the belief that he had mastered the multiplication of dies but in this he was greatly deceived.[256] But by at least June 1791, a screw press, known as the multiplying press, was used to provide the force needed to strike duplicate dies.[257] This is known as hubbing (or hobbing) and may be done several times,

---

252 MS 3782-12-1 Letter Book 1766-1768. Item 2, MB to Benjamin Franklin 22 February 1766.
253 MS 3782-12-108 Item 53, Mint Note Book 1788 p56-63.
254 Personal communication from Mark Andrew Powell, die engraver. www.eligius.co.uk.
255 D.R. Cooper (1996) *The development of coinage dies from bronze to steel* p103.
256 MS 3782-12-108 Item 54, Mint Note Book 1789 p27.
257 MS 3782-12-66 Item 16, James Lawson (Soho) to MB (London) 11 June 1791.

with annealing between each strike, and gradual cooling of the dies.[258] The process was carried out in the Multiplication shop at Soho and kept secret.[259] Dies were kept in a special locked mahogany cabinet.[260]

Boulton insisted that the dies were changed frequently, for example when Soho Mint was striking a large order for the East India Company in 1791: *'Pray request Mr Lawson to consult with Nichols about supplying the mint constantly with perfect neat sharp well-polished dies which I think should be changed after striking every 30 or 40 thousand pieces'.*[261] He suggested that:

> *'There must be always be 3 times the number of Dies that there are working presses viz one sett in work a 2d sett standing by the side of the Pres ready for changing the instant any one fails & a 3d sett in the hands of the Examinator & polisher & it would be better if there was a 4th Sett as I think they should be changed every 5 or 6 hours for I am not satisfied with the perfection of our money. I must have the metal of a better couler & freer from tarnish & finer polish befor tis cut out & No dies must be worked after losing their Sharpness & polish'.*[262]

This constant striving for perfection in coining was what made Soho Mint unique at the time.

Reducing Machine

A master die could be engraved with an image such as Britannia, which was then used for a series of coins of different sizes such as a penny, halfpenny and farthing. Modern methods of die reduction used a pantograph which enables a design to be transferred from a larger model to the die, though this has now been replaced by computer operated die-cutting methods.[263] The pantograph principle was used at Soho Mint but at what point is not certain. Boulton wrote in a letter dated 31st March 1788:

> *'I have sometimes though it possible to turn in a lathe one die from another, as I have a lathe in which I have turned medals in ivory and pearl from medals of hard metal, but this lathe is not strong enough for steel'.*[264]

---

258 P.P. Gaspar and G.P. Dyer (1980) *The Striking of Proof and Pattern Coins in the 18th Century* British Numismatics Journal Volume 50 1980 pp117-127.

259 MS 3782-13-120 Folder 6, Inventory of Property belonging to Coinage Account taken 31st December 1790.

260 MS 3782-13-36 Item 93, MB (London) to MRB (Soho) 15 January 1793.

261 MS 3782-13-36 Item 55, MB (London) to MRB (Soho) 17 May 1791.

262 MS 3782-13-36 Item 60, MB (London) to MRB (Soho) 7 June 1791.

263 Information from visit to the Royal Mint. 23 November 2009.

264 J.G. Pollard (1968) *Matthew Boulton and J.P. Droz* Numismatic Chronicle 1968 Volume 8 pp246-250.

In November 1789 Boulton's Paris agent, found a mechanic, Jean-Baptiste Dupeyrat (1759-1834) who could turn a steel die on a lathe from a model or a medal. This was known as a *tour à medailles* or portrait lathe, and Boulton ordered one in spring 1790 which was received in September of the same year.[265] Possibly this was the engraving lathe mentioned in 1792.[266] However, a reducing machine was certainly in use by 1799 when pattern coins were made for Denmark in five sizes. This enabled dies to be produced much more efficiently from the same design. Boulton's reducing machine was used by Pistrucci at the Royal Mint for the 1816-17 recoinage.[267]

265 J.G. Pollard (1971) *Matthew Boulton and the Reducing Machine in England* Numismatic Chronicle 1971 Vol. XI p314.
266 MS 3782-13-36 Item 87, MB (Truro) to MRB (Soho) 15 September 1792.
267 K. Clancy (1999) *The recoinage and exchange of 1816-17* PhD, University of Leeds, December 1999.

Chapter Four

The Technology
of Minting

MATTHEW Boulton's reputation as an entrepreneur has often over-shadowed his technical achievements. In his partnership with James Watt he has been credited with the business acumen and Watt with the mechanical skills. However, from an early age, he was interested in science or 'natural philosophy' as it was known, and before he met Watt, he had been making experiments with steam-engines from at least 1757. He wrote to Benjamin Franklin in 1766: '*My engagements since Christmas have not permitt*^d *me to make any further progress with my fire engine*'. The letter goes on to discuss different steam valves and whether it was better to introduce the jet of cold water in at the bottom or the top of the receiver.[268]

In fact, though thought by some to be merely the financial backer, Boulton also played an important part in making a practical reality of the reciprocating steam-engine in 1775-6. In addition, both he and William Murdock had contributed to ideas about sun and planet gears used to achieve circular motion in the rotary engine, competed in 1781.[269] This innovation enabled power to be applied to machines such as coining presses.

Having both an intellectual and a practical approach to life, Boulton recognised the importance of natural philosophy in relation to technological improvements and corresponded with others who were working in the fields of metallurgy, chemistry, and astronomy. For example: Boulton and his daughter Ann '*Called on Mr Hershall the astronomer at Windsor, and saw his great telescopes*' in

---

268 MS 3782-12-1 Letter Book 1766-1768 Item 2, MB to Benjamin Franklin 22 February 1766.
269 J. Andrew in: M. Dick (ed.) (2009) *Matthew Boulton: A Revolutionary Player* p112.

1787.[270] He was also a competent assayer of metal ores.[271] He wrote about a huge variety of scientific topics; investigating thermometers and electricity in 1761, and sending an electrometer to Joseph Priestley.[272] He ordered a microscope via Dr William Small in 1765, and was discussing a new orrery in 1771.[273] He had a naturally inquisitive mind; for example, he noted the time it took for a skip of coal to rise from a pit, and how iron was made from pig iron and pit coal, recipes for sealing joints, densities of materials and the temperature for blanking stoves.[274] He recorded methods for rolling platina, gilt and ormolu, and listed improvements. Boulton personally carried out investigations in gilding, and testing various recipes for *'Bradbury's yellow couler, Riddings yellow couler'* which were used to impart a more impressive finish to cheaper metals.[275]

Boulton's Soho Manufactory was well-known for advances in mass production, using superior tools and materials. New methods had always interested him both from a functional and intellectual point of view. He wanted to use machinery to make articles cheaply and with greater precision. He was using engines to operate battering hammers for silver-smiths, and a tilting hammer for forging button dies by 1773. He invested in a *'mill to work 50 lathes for scratching, burnishing & shaveing, and 2 shakeing boxes for polished stones & steel work'* and also considered how the processes of wire drawing, pressing, stamping, polishing, piercing and lapping could be improved in the manufacture of silverwares.[276]

Soho Mint was the first in the world to be powered by steam. Much of the information about the technological advances there comes directly from contemporary documents. Boulton himself wrote copious notes in his mint notebooks, including what had to be done to set up a mint, his reasons for doing it, and descriptions of various technical aspects of coining. In addition, memoirs about Matthew Boulton were written, including most notably by James Watt and James Keir.[277] There are also accounts of the development of the minting technology written by James Lawson, John Southern and Peter Ewart in 1810, plus numerous letters in the Archives of Soho. They acknowledge that

---

270 MS 3782-13-36 Item 9, MB (Soho) to MRB (Versailles) 30 July 1787.

271 E. Robinson (1963) *Eighteenth-Century Commerce and Fashion: Matthew Boulton's Marketing Techniques* Economic History Review Second Series, Volume XVI No.1 p56.

272 MS 3782-12-23 Item 12, Dr. J.L Petitt (Little Aston) to MB 25 February 1761; MS 3782-12-23 Item 13, MB (Birmingham) to Timothy Hollis (London) 4 March 1761; MS 3782-12-23 Item 14, E. Newton (Kings Bromley) to MB 26 June 1761.

273 MS 3782-12-23 Item 54, Peter Dolland (London) to Dr. Small (Birmingham) 5 September 1765; MS 3782-12-23 Item 209, James Ferguson (Kidderminster) to MB (Soho) 10 August 1771.

274 MS 3782-12-108 Item 11, Boulton's Notebook 1775-1776.

275 MS 3782-12-108 Item 5, Boulton's 1768-1775 Notebook.

276 K. Quickenden (1980) *Boulton & Fothergill Silver* Art History Volume 3 No 3 p278.

277 MS 3782-13-37, 'Memorandum concerning Mr Boulton commencing with my first acquaintance with him' by James Watt (Glasgow) quoted in: H.W. Dickinson (1937) *Matthew Boulton* p203-208; MS 3782-13-37, 'Memorandum for the Memoir of M Boulton'; with a letter from James Keir to MRB 3 Dec. 1809; quoted in E. Robinson *Eighteenth-Century Commerce and Fashion: Matthew Boulton's Marketing* pp39-60.

Boulton's direction of the team at Soho Mint to bring together a combination of new methods was vital. He was also willing to sell his new technology to the Royal Mint and others so that the *modus operandi* introduced at Soho Mint was widely distributed. Novel ideas in design were also tried there, including a bimetallic coin and a hexagonal coinage.[278] Boulton used innovative systems to control production, from the input of the raw materials to the distribution of the completed product.

A whole series of operations were required to make a coin; in 1788, Boulton wrote a list:

> 'Rough rolling, fine rolling, 1st anneal, pickle or boil, scour with sand, rolle to size; Anneal, scour, polish; Cut out, flatten in a screw machine mill, shake in sawdust & then shake in a riddle ye dust off; Coin'.[279]

Just to ensure that the coining blanks were up to Boulton's standard was a complicated process. They were:

> 'Sorted, weighed, Mill'd, Weighed below by Campbell, Boiled in Leas [dregs from brewing], Washed at fierce Cook, Rough shaked, Tubed, Annealed, Reshook, Weighed, Planished, Weighed, Milling again, Mill'd weighed, By Campbell to shakers & Annealing tubes, Boiled in vitriol. Washed clean, Shook Dry, Wiped on a Large table, Heated in Muffle, Weighed to Mint'. Then the blanks were: 'Struck, Weighed, Wrapp'd up, Packed in Casks'.[280]

Other aspects of coining were not neglected. As well as introducing the steam powered coining press, improvements in rolling copper, annealing metal, in the preparation of coining blanks, and in forging dies were made.[281]

The Technology of Coining
In order to appreciate the improvements introduced at the Soho Mint, it is important to understand how coins were made previously. Coins are one of the oldest forms of mass production, and for thousands of years they were made using relatively simple technology. Metal was cast into billets (log-shaped segments), and then flattened into strips using hammers. Round discs (blanks) were cut out with scissors, resulting in coins with irregular edges and surfaces. Later punches were used to make the blanks, like cutting biscuits from rolled out dough. Blanks were struck on a coining anvil using engraved dies and a hammer. This process

---

278 MS 3782-13-36 Item 73, MB (London) to MRB (Soho) 12 April 1792; MS 3782-12-66 Item 30, James Lawson (Soho) to MB (London) 14 April 1792.
279 MS 3782-12-108 Item 53, Mint Note Book 1788 p10-11.
280 MS 3782-13-120, Mint Inventions and Improvements, Vol. 1 Folder 7 (undated).
281 MS 3782-12-66 Item 59, John Southern (Birmingham) to MB (London) 6 July 1789.

was laborious. Hammered coins were issued from the Royal Mint at the Tower of London from 1279, but hammered silver coins were officially demonetised in 1697, though hammered gold coins remained in circulation until the 1770s.[282]

One technical improvement, first used in Augsburg in 1571, was to use a rolling mill both to flatten the metal, and to coin. Designs were engraved onto rolls which were turned manually, as strips of metal were passed through. The dies were oval to overcome distortions, but were very difficult to engrave. It was also difficult to cut out the coins from the imprinted strips. Charles I tried to introduce rotary coining to England by employing Nicholas Briot from the Paris Mint. But mechanical methods were greatly resisted by the moneyers at the Royal Mint, who thought that the series of operations required were too complex and time consuming.[283] Rotary coining presses were used until the eighteenth century in parts of Europe, but not in England, as they were superseded by the more efficient screw press as shown below.[284]

Figure 4:1 1772 Screw press for coining.[285]

---

282 P. Grierson (1975) *Numismatics* Oxford University Press p25.

283 D. Sellwood (1986) *The Trial of Nicholas Briot* British Numismatic Journal 1986 Volume 56 p108-123.

284 D.R. Cooper (1995) *The development of coinage dies from bronze to steel* p99.

285 Image from Denis Diderot's *Encyclopédie, ou dictionnaire raisonné des sciences, des arts et des métiers* (Encyclopedia, or a Systematic Dictionary of the Sciences, Arts, and Crafts) published in France between 1751 and 1772. www.valuable-coin-stories.com/screw-press.html.

The hand operated screw press, also known as a fly-press, was a machine for multiplying manual effort by use of a lever attached to a vertical threaded screw supported by an open framework. It was worked by a heavily loaded lever, a bar with metal spheres on the ends, which was pivoted centrally to increase the force of the blow. The force was provided by men pulling on the bar which was tiring, and meant each coin was struck with a different amount of force.[286] The upper die was attached to the end of the screw and could be brought down onto the lower die with sufficient force to strike a coining blank. A counterweight system returned the die up. The lower die was fixed to a bench and guides were added to move the screw and dies up and down accurately. Later, the screw press was also used for the mechanical reproduction of punches and dies.[287] The coining blank was put between the dies and the completed coin was removed by hand, a laborious and dangerous process.

The screw press was first used in England in around 1561 by Eloye Mestrelle but without success.[288] However it was successfully introduced by Peter Blondeau to the Commonwealth Mint in 1651, and later improved in 1662 at the Royal Mint, to be used along with a rolling mill, and cutting and stamping presses. By 1676 the screw press could strike a blow every two seconds.[289] Blondeau also introduced milled edges by rolling the coin between thin strips of engraved steel.[290] By the time Isaac Newton was in charge of the Royal Mint between 1699-1727, it had eight rolling mills, eleven coining presses and twenty-two blank cutting presses, all hand-operated.[291] However, no further improvements were made there as new technology was resisted due to fears of loss of employment and privileges. By the late eighteenth century some of the machinery in use had been installed over one hundred years earlier.[292]

Boulton and Coinage

Matthew Boulton had thoughts about improving the coinage from the 1770s. He wrote to Lord Dartmouth on 10th November 1772 to propose that Parliament should consider the poor condition of coined and paper currency.[293] He had also suggested adding a steel rim to guinea coins to prevent them being filed down to obtain gold.[294] In his memoir about Boulton, Watt recalled a conversation with him in 1774 regarding applying steam power to coining and also wrote:

---

286 D.R. Cooper (1988) *The Art and Craft of Coin-making* p51.
287 P. Gaspar (1994) *Coining and Die Making Techniques in the seventeenth century* Metallurgy in Numismatics 4, Royal Numismatic Society Special Publication, London pp130-143.
288 A. Avery and P. Gaspar (1989) *Mestrell's Minting Methods* Numismatic Circular July/August 1989 Volume XCVII Number 6 pp187-188.
289 J. Craig (1953) *The Mint* p164.
290 D.R. Cooper (1988) *The Art and Craft of Coin-making* pp48-49.
291 J. Craig (1953) *The Mint* pp198-222.
292 MS 3782-13-112 Item 85, John Rennie's report to the Committee of Coin 8 January 1805.
293 H.W. Dickinson (1936; reprinted 1999) *Matthew Boulton* p135.
294 MS 3782-12-23 Item 282, Sambrook Freeman (Fawley) to MB (Soho) 1 August 1773.

'When the new coinage of gold took place in 1773 Mr. B was employed to receive &
exchange the old coins which served to revive his ideas on the subject of coinage, which
he had considered as capable of great improvement'.[295]

In a letter to Samuel Garbett in 1790 Boulton wrote an account of the
'arts of coining' mentioning Briot and Blondeau.[296] He thought that the prices
charged by the Royal Mint were too high, as various mint officials who did little
received too much money, and that they produced coins of inferior quality so
that counterfeiting was easy. Boulton considered that his team had sufficient
technical expertise to improve the coining process so that coins of the same
denomination would have the same size and weight, and he could make a regal
coinage more cheaply if he used a steam-powered press.[297]

Methods for coining gold were also being considered. Boulton wrote:

'It should be coined in a coller so as to be perfectly round ..., perfectly of the same
diameter, perfectly concentral in ye work of it & consequently of the same thickness ...
The letters, arms etc. should be indented instead of relief and the head should not rise
above, so that 20 guineas when put together should be close on ye edge and look like a
solid gold cylinder'.[298]

These were important improvements which may not seem much to a modern
audience, but prior to the Soho Mint, coins were not all perfectly round,
they were struck with designs that could vary, and they were difficult to stack.
Boulton introduced standardization for the first time in coinage. This has had
far reaching effects, introducing standard methods of production in other areas
of industry.

Boulton's first experience of coining had been during the 1786 and 1787
contracts for the East India Company (EIC)'s Sumatra issues. The EIC had
employed Boulton because inefficient and expensive methods of coining were
still being used in India; hammered coins were being made in 1792 in Calcutta,
and as late as 1895 by coiners of the Nizam of Hyderabad's Mint.[299] Thomas
Williams was instrumental in obtaining these contracts, when nearly 50 tons of
copper were made into over 8 million coins of three values.[300] Boulton had just
'built a new [rolling] *mill and had then no customer for it'.* The price, he wrote later
to Williams, was *'much against my judgment'* and he had lost money by coining
the small, low value coins, which were mainly issued at 140 to the lb.[301] But he

---

295 J. Watt, *Memoir of Boulton* in: H.W. Dickinson (1936) *Matthew Boulton* p203.
296 MS 3782-12-62 Item 82, MB (Soho) to Samuel Garbett (—) 14 Jan 1790.
297 MS 3782-12-108 Item 53, Mint Book 1788 p5, pp10-11.
298 MS 3782-12-108 Item 53, Mint Note Book 1788 p84.
299 D.R. Cooper (1995) *The development of coinage dies from bronze to steel* p96; p101.
300 MS 3782-12-73 Item 66, Thomas Williams (London) to MB (Soho) 12 July 1786.
301 MS 3782-12-3 Item 64, p70 MB to Thomas Williams 3 July 1788.

had learnt a lot from the experience. He had used hand operated screw coining presses and coining blanks made at Soho, but made the Sumatra issues at a temporary mint in London.

In February 1788 it was thought that a contract had been obtained from the government to make regal coinage and Boulton started to set up the Soho Mint.[302] In his 1788 notebooks, he detailed what needed to be done.[303] He also listed all the things he had to pay for:

> 'Finding at my own expense: 1. New Building 2. Tools, Machines & Repairs 3. New invention 4. Wast of copper 5. Loss by thieving 6. Carriage from the canal to the Manufacture 7. Unloading & Weighing 8. Carriage of the casks when packed to the canal or wagon 9. Clarks & assistants 10. Guarenteeing all things & running all risks. 11. Papering in 2/6 parcels'.[304]

The necessary staff were listed along with their prospective wages, and additional items needed:

> '5 presses will require 5 persons at 18s; Milling 4 persons, one each for tools, press and harden dyes, engrave, polish, assistant engraver, superintendent, repair presses, weigher, packer, fire and furnaces, annealing pans, boil, dye forger & steel book keeper total £45 12s'.[305]

From early on, Boulton intended to make Soho Mint steam-powered. He had written to Jean-Pierre Droz in April 1787 to say: 'Je suis d'Intention de faire marcher les grandes presses par un Machine a feu'.[306] The first steam-powered mint in the world was built as a single storey building about 110 metres from the principal buildings of Soho Manufactory, below Boulton's garden.[307] The Soho Mint did not need water power, as did the Soho Manufactory, and therefore the location could be chosen for reasons of security against industrial espionage. The mint was rebuilt several times, as Boulton and his team improved the equipment used for coining. A drawing by John Phillp shows the Soho Manufactory to left of centre, with Soho Mint in the trees to the right. Soho House is seen on the top of the hill.

---

302 MS 3782-13-36-19, MB (London) to MRB (Paris) 8 February 1788.

303 MS 3782-12-108 Item 53, Mint Book 1788.

304 MS 3792-13-120 Folder 7.

305 MS 3782-12-108 Item 53, Mint Note Book 1788 p14.

306 'I have the intention of making the large presses work by a steam engine'. MS 3782-12-6 Item 67, 23 April 1787.

307 R. McLean (1993) *Restoration of Matthew Boulton's House* Numismatic Circular September 1993 Volume CI Number 7.

Figure 4:2 Phillp's drawing of Soho c1795.

All the coining operations at Soho Mint were concentrated on one site. This gave Boulton the opportunity to control all aspects, from the rolling of the metal, to the final packing of the coins. John Rennie was involved in providing drawings and estimates for the new building and it was under construction by January 1788. The building work was supervised by Peter Ewart with records kept by John Roberts.[308] The detailed plans show a curved site with a coal vault at one side, the Mint engine, and a diagram showing eight presses in two rows slightly off set with a complex mechanism to rotate a rod. The engine house was constructed at the end of the yard and held an eight-horse power double acting sun & planet engine. Later plans dated 22nd July 1788 show the presses powered by an overhead wheel. There are also views of the exterior of the building.[309]

Letters detail progress of the early Soho Mint and show the contributions of various members of the team. By January 1788, Roberts wrote that one of the large presses was ready and an additional press would soon be completed.[310] By February, Boulton's nephew, Zaccheus Walker Junior was drawing plans of the mint apparatus, William Harrison was involved in coppering the roof, Anthony Robinson was adjusting the screw for the large press and Bullock the smaller ones, to designs sent by Droz. The large screw was cast at Wilkinson's works at Bradley.

Matt in Paris had been kept up to date with progress. In April 1788, Boulton wrote:

'Let Mr Droz come as soon as he will; he will find one of the New large Presses completed agreeable to his last Model & I believe we shall be able to compleat one per week after

---

308 MS 3782-12-66 Item 106, John Roberts (Soho) to MB (London) 27 January 1788.
309 MS 3147-5-714a, Soho Mint Plans 1788-1789.
310 MS 3782-12-66 Item 105, John Roberts (Soho) to MB (London) 22 January 1788.

the first is finished. … I now wait for his opinion respecting the best mode of casing the female screw in Brass'.[311]

By June 1788, Roberts was able to report that:

'the Boiler for little engine is set, the chimneys built. The cistern is nearly fixed in its place, the Nozzles are fitted, the working gear forged, and other work forging. The cylinder is ready. John Smith is making the pattern of the rotative wheels which will be ready tomorrow; The pattern for the frame of the Shears is gone to Bradley; Four cutting out presses are fitted, & fixed in the gallery; One fly is come home, the fifth press will soon be finished; Three large presses, according to model are come home; Four screws for presses are brought home. I expect Anthony [Robinson] will finish two more in a few days; Each screw will cost about £22'.[312]

James Lawson, originally employed as an engineer in Cornwall, was reporting from January 1789 almost daily to Boulton, who was in London campaigning for the regal coinage contract. Several individuals were involved, and their progress was listed:

'Monday: Fixing the pin wheel to the proper height & Mr Southern marked out the place for the press Mill. Mr Harrison & J Webb turning the large piece of Wood for fixing the rolls. John Smith fixed the cistern in its place. Tuesday: John Smith in the Mint fixing the large press Mill. Mr Harrison & Webb turning for the Rolling Mill. Wednesday: Mint J Smith finished fixing the press. Millwrights put on the arms for the great cogwheel. Mr Harrison & Webb about Turning for the Mill. Thursday: Mint Millwrights fixing the Cog Wheel. Harrison & Webb finished the piece of wood for fixing the rolls. Peploe on Tuesday in chipping the Bottom of Cutting Out press hurt his eye & has not been able to do much bifor this day but is now able to work'.[313]

By November 1789, Boulton had a functional mint and claimed that he had perfected:

'at very great expense, such an apparatus of machinery as he is persuaded will enable him to make coin, not only superior in beauty and workmanship to that of any nation in Europe, … but also so manufactured that the counterfeiting will be effectually prevented. My metal is rolled, cut out and coined and the whole operation done by a new Fire Engine'.

---

311 MS 3782-13-36 Item 24, MB (Soho) to MRB (Paris) 24 April 1788.
312 MS 3782-12-66 Item 110, John Roberts (Soho) to MB (London) 18 June 1788.
313 MS 3782-12-66 Item 1, James Lawson (Soho) to MB (London) 22 January 1789.

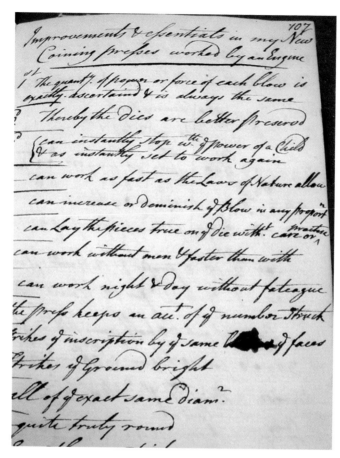

Figure 4:3 Boulton's notebook 1788. List of improvements at Soho Mint.[314]

He told his son that he was expecting to 'receive orders for 1500 Ton of my new Copper half pence for which I have prepared superior Dies' but was ready to furnish anyone with minting equipment or to coin one hundred million pieces per year 'whereas the officers of the English Mint are very much hurried to make 3½ million per Year'.[315] This was a huge amount of coin to produce unless the new equipment worked well.

The new steam-powered press was tested out during 1789 and 1790 on a variety of token orders rather than a regal coinage contract, to the relief of most of the engineers at Soho who realized that a lot of work still needed to be done to make the Mint more effective. At this point, Soho Mint made tokens for Roe and Company for their Cronebane mine in Ireland, for John Wilkinson, and Anglesey tokens for Thomas Williams. Boulton was also starting a large order for the EIC for the Bombay Presidency. Further small orders for tokens were received

314 MS 3782-12-108 Item 53, Boulton's Mint Notebook 1788 p10.
315 MS 3782-13-36 Item 37, MB (Soho) to MRB (Germany) 12 November 1789.

in 1791 for Cornwall, Southampton and for Glasgow. Modifications were made to the mint in 1791 when it was rebuilt in anticipation of a large coinage order for the French government which did not materialise, and then again in 1798 after Boulton's first regal coinage contract.

The Soho Mint made coining more efficient, economical and faster, and was also intended to prevent counterfeiting. Boulton wrote many versions of the advantages of the new steam-powered mint in his Mint Notebook, in letters to his son and in various papers sent to correspondents who might promote a regal or other coinage contract.[316] The improvements included the fact that the coins were perfectly round, equal in diameter and brightly polished. The force of the blow was more uniform compared to coining presses powered by men. The blanks were mechanically loaded onto the die, and the completed coin removed. An account of the number struck was also kept automatically. This enabled Boulton to assess the efficiency of its operation.

An inventory of Soho Mint, taken in December 1790, specifically mentions the Great room with four presses for coining and one old press for experiments, the Fire [steam] Engine in the adjoining building, Busch and Harrison working in Busch's shop, a Smith's shop with room adjoining and room above, the Multiplication Shop known as 'la Bastille' where multiple dies were made for large coining orders, and the Cutting out shop on the rolling mill premises, Peploe's shop adjoining cutting out shop, the Mill Gallery, the Shaking shop, the Annealing shop and a Melting shop.[317]

Rolling metal

Rolling metal was a very important part of making coins at the Soho Mint and in the processes used at the Soho Manufactory. Boulton had originally moved to the Soho site in the 1760s due to the availability of water power to run the rolling mill and laps for grinding and polishing. Interestingly, it was the lack of water power that had first interested Boulton in James Watt's steam-engines, and the first functional B&W steam-engine, set up in 1774, was used to pump water back up to the mill pool.[318] The success of this engine led to Boulton's involvement in the Cornish copper industry as previously discussed.

The rolling mill made silver plate for various decorative wares at the Soho Manufactory. In May 1780, John Hodges, the manager of the Plated Works, had pointed out that a new rolling mill was needed.[319] A new mill, run by John Kellet, was erected in 1785 to roll metal and power laps; it could also be used to

---

316 MS 3782-13-36 Item 37, MB (Soho) to MRB (Germany) 12 November 1789; MS 3782-12-108 Item 53, Boulton's Mint Note Book 1788 p107.

317 MS 3782-13-120 Folder 6, Inventory of Property belonging to Coinage Account taken 31st December 1790.

318 G. Demidowicz in M. Dick (ed.) (2009) *Matthew Boulton: A Revolutionary Player* pp120-121.

319 MS 3792-12-63 Item 15, John Hodges (Soho) to MB (London) May 1780.

roll copper for coins.[320] Due to its increased capacity, Boulton took on the EIC coinage contract of 1786 which was his first attempt at coining.

When the Soho Mint was built in 1788, a new steam-engine was installed in the Manufactory, to power the laps and eight cutting out presses for blanks, leaving the water wheel free to roll metal. This 18-inch rotary steam-engine, the lap engine, was the first to use the centrifugal governor, and was at work until 1840. It is now in the Science Museum.[321] Boulton calculated that the water wheel's rolling capacity could easily be increased to 900 tons per year.[322] When the mint was not busy, the rolling mill at Soho could be used to roll metal for other businesses.[323] But when increased rolling capacity was required for large coinage orders, such as in 1797, other local mills were used.[324] This meant that Boulton was able to be flexible in his working practices.

Copper was ordered from suppliers in a variety of forms and was sometimes hot-rolled elsewhere, such as at Wilkinson's Bradley mill, then fine rolled at Soho. In April 1788, Boulton visited Bradley with Joseph Harrison and William Murdock to inspect the rolling mill, which took the 80lb copper cake from 2 inches to 1/5th inch thick. *'Each cake ... was heated in a furnace full of coals & took about 10 minutes to get red hot, and then each cake took about 4 minutes to roll. It still needed four more rollings at Soho'.*[325]

To make coins, the metal needed to be rolled to the exact thickness required, using steel rollers and then the coining blanks could be cut to the correct weight and diameter. Previous experience of making coin weights, sold at the Assay Office in Birmingham from 1773, had given Boulton's workmen experience in accurate rolling and weighing metal.[326] In the mass production of coins, the methods were improved, with the introduction of a calliper to measure the thickness of the metal. Boulton wrote:

> *'Copper, when hot, rolls very soft & easy, in comparison to what it doth when cold. It is sufficiently hot roll'd when it becomes equal to twice the thickness of the coin intended to be made. ... I shall rolle it twice in fine polished rollers, ... rolle it again twice in finer rolls, ... but previous to the last rolling, I guage it by my new invented calliper & in the last time passing the rolls bring it very exact to the proper thickness'.*

The rolling would normally cost *'£11 13s 11d Per Ton of Sheet Copper for Hot & Cold rolling'*, quite a considerable expense in a coining contract.[327] Boulton emphasised

320 MS 3782-12-3 Item 64, MB to Thomas Williams 3 July 1788 p70.
321 G. Demidowicz in: M. Dick (ed.) (2009) *Matthew Boulton: A Revolutionary Player* pp122-123.
322 MS 3782-12-108 Item 53, Mint Book 1788 p28.
323 MS 3782-13-36 Item 84, MB (Truro) to MRB (Soho) 3 September 1792.
324 MS 3782-12-42 Item 44, J. Kellet (Soho) to MB (London) 9 March 1797.
325 MS 3782-12-108 Item 53, Mint Book 1788 p87.
326 N. Biggs (2004) *Provincial Coin Weights in the Eighteenth Century* British Numismatic Journal Volume 74 pp102-120.
327 MS 3782-12-77 Item 100, MB (Soho) to Thomas Williams (—) 24 January 1791.

that cold rolling was necessary to obtain the exact thickness and a fine finish.[328] This accuracy was vital to the success of the Soho coining enterprise, as it enabled uniform coins to be made.

In the presence of air and other substances, copper is slowly attacked and forms various compounds, and Boulton wanted to maintain its lustre, so as rolling was carried out, the copper was also cleaned and annealed. The copper 'cakes' were 'pickled' or 'scoured' in urine or aqua regia (concentrated hydrochloric and nitric acid) to remove 'scale' (copper oxide). A scraper fixed to the rolls also helped. Boulton described the laborious process in his 1788 Mint Notebook:

> *'The strips cast by Ryley are about 7lb each and are before rolling about ¾ inch thick. Rolled 1st time from 17 inches to 24 inches long, and 2nd time to 30 inches long, then annealed, … then rolled third time to 39 inches, annealed 2nd time, rolled 4th time to 50 inches, 4th time to 58 inches. Annealed 3rd time, rolled 6th time to 72 inches and 7th time to 82 inches, then annealed 4th time, scoured'.*

He also noted that the workers should be careful when handling the metal, as *'dirty greasy fingers rolls in that dirt & tarnishes the metal'.*[329] Gloves were ordered for the workers by the dozens from Robert Blood.[330] The metal was brushed before rolling and washed, polished and then the blanks were cut out to fall into tubes, pickled and were automatically loaded into the mint.[331] This kept the metal in excellent condition.

Thomas Williams agreed to supply copper for the Bombay coinage issue of 1791 but said:

> *'I will not undertake the polished Rolling or the adjusting to exact weight, on any account. To finish all to that is far more troublesome than other work … At this rate I would furnish you with 100 to 150 Tons in the course of the next 8 or 9 months'.*[332]

This careful preparation of the copper blanks ensured that the completed coins from Soho Mint were of excellent quality.

Size of Coins, Medals and Tokens

Coins were generally prepared to a specified weight in grains, or at so many per pound (lb). The Soho Mint produced items that varied in size; the smallest made

---

328 MS 3782-13-120, Mint Inventions and Improvements Volume 1 Folder 7.
329 MS 3782-12-108 Item 53, Mint Book 1788 p32.
330 MS 3782-3-13, Mint Day Book 1791-1795 For example, a dozen pairs of gloves were ordered from Robert Blood on 24th December 1793 for the cutters out; 2½ dozen more on 22nd March 1794; MS 3782-3-14, Mint Day Book 1795-1798 6 dozen gloves were ordered on 18th February 1797 price £2 8s and more on 6th January 1798 and 20th June 1798.
331 MS 3782-12-108 Item 53, Mint Book 1788 p100.
332 MS 3782-12-73 Item 100, Thomas Williams (Anglesey) to MB (Soho) January 1791.

was the 10mm diameter, 5 grain (0.35g) Bengal pattern coin, but this design proved too problematic to make in large numbers. The smallest coin in mass production was the 1803 Madras one cash, at 11mm diameter and 0.65g weight and the largest, the 1797 two pences, were 42mm in diameter, each weighing 2 ounces (56g). Generally, halfpennies were 29mm, and pennies 33mm in diameter.

Medals, around 48mm diameter, made in low numbers, could be struck from heated blanks, which gave a good finish. One of the largest was the 56mm diameter, 87g medal produced for Gustav III of Sweden in 1792. However, most coin blanks were struck cold for speed and economy.

Boulton recorded the sizes and weights of various coin issues in his Mint Notebook of 1789. The halfpennies produced by the Royal Mint at the Tower of London were made at 46 per lb or 152 grains, but the 1787 Anglesey Druid halfpenny tokens were much heavier at 32 per lb or 218 grains, and the penny tokens at 16 per lb (437 grains or 28g). The largest coin produced at Soho Mint was the 1797 two pence weighing in at a heavy 8 per lb. The 1791-2 Monneron issues for France were also substantial pieces, made at 15-16 per lb for the 5-sol tokens and 24-26 per lb for the 2-sol. These heavy tokens were technically difficult to make, and led the team to make improvements to the coining process. For the East India Company 200, 150, 100 and 50 grains weight were the standard size for coin issues made at Soho Mint; later issues were lighter, as the price of copper rose.

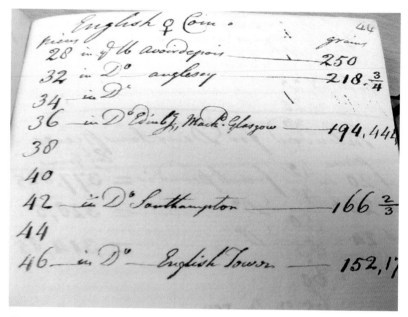

Figure 4:4 Boulton's research into sizes of coins and tokens struck.[333]

333 MS 3782-12-108 Item 54, Mint Book 1789 p44.

Soho Mint was able to maintain a very uniform standard of production for large coinage issues, which had not been possible at other mints. Boulton planned to make coins and tokens with *'the intrinsic value of all money equal to its nominal value, deducting the expenses of coining'.*[334] This, he believed, would take away the temptation of counterfeiting light-weight money. From 1787, it became especially important to ensure that good quality pieces were made, as the tokens made for industrialists such as Williams and Wilkinson, could be redeemed for gold. The issuers did not want to give good money for lighter counterfeits. This was not an important consideration for the Royal Mint which did not exchange copper coins for gold ones.

Blank Cutting

Once the dimensions of a coin, token or medal had been specified, the metal strips were rolled to the correct thickness and inspected, and blanks were cut out to a predetermined diameter on the cutting presses. If the proper size-to-weight ratio was not exactly correct, the coins made would either be too light and the order refused, or too heavy, when Boulton would be charged for the extra metal used, so it was important to get this process correct.[335]

Boulton had installed powered blank-cutting presses as one of his first improvements when the lap engine was installed in 1788. Those at Soho Mint had steel bedplates with holes corresponding to banks of rams which punched out blanks from a sheet of metal on each downward cycle, leaving scissell which could be re-used. Because of the shearing action of the punches, the blanks had rough edges or burrs which were removed by abrasion in shaking bags, powered by the steam-engine. The blanks were then cleaned, sometimes with vitriol (sulphuric acid) or whiteing (lime) and dried with sawdust.[336] Defective pieces were eliminated over a gauge and re-melted along with the scrap metal, the scissell, in the two reverberatory furnaces at Soho.[337] The scrupulously cleaned, dried and polished blanks were then loaded into tubes, ready to be struck on the mint's steam powered coining presses.

Usually blanks were of copper for currency issues, but could also be made from gold, silver, lead, tin, brass or white metal for medals. Some gilt and bronzed blanks, prepared with a variety of special finishes before striking, were also used for proof coins and medals for collectors. John Middlehurst from the Plated Works at Soho was asked to produce bronzed blanks for a large order of Monneron tokens in March 1792. He used copper blanks, baked in bronzing powder, freely available in London, to produce tones varying from yellow to dark chocolate. It was left to the specialist worker how the task was carried out, thus

334 MS 3782-13-36 Item 37, MB (Soho) to MRB (Langensalz, Germany) 12 November 1789.

335 (anon) (1913) *Boulton's Copper Coinage* Numismatic Chronicle 1913 pp379-80.

336 MS 3782-12-108 Item 53, Mint Day Book Reference is made for example on 29th September 1791 *'For Richard Skeldon for shaking bags £ 4 2s'*; and 30th June 1792 *'20 bags of sawdust from T Lucas £2 10'.* Boulton's friend, Samuel Garbett, provided both *'Silver and Vitriol £41 15 8d'* on 16th Feb 1792.

337 AD1583/4/44, MB (Soho) to T Wilson (Cornwall) 19 Jan 1791.

encouraging initiative, but Boulton provided the facilities: *'It would be well to have such a hearth as he might approve built up in the room over the Shakeing shop'.*[338]

On another occasion, Boulton suggested that: *'Medals may be given to Nelson to Gild as he may fill up his Gilders time … Perhaps 2 or 3 Doz of Medals may be done at once by laying then on a Copper Riddle'.*[339] The gilding hearth was set up in a dedicated room, as Boulton was fully aware of the dangers of mercury poisoning. As an employer, Boulton took care of his skilled employees, and wrote:

> *'When the Gilders are Slovenly & do not wash their hands clean, particularly about the finger Nails, before they eat their Dinners, or if the Gilding Chimney doth not properly draw off the Mercurial Vapour, the party will very soon grow paralitick. To use the Gilders language they will very soon get the Shakes & I have seen Women equally as bad as the Men'.*[340]

He personally designed a gilding hearth which would draw off mercury vapours. Not only did this prevent danger to the workers, but also the improved technology saved expensive mercury for reuse.

Edge Marking

Milling, or edge marking on the third side of the coin, medal or token, was often done in a separate operation before coining. This could protect against clipping. Edges could be milled with vertical or diagonal stripes known as graining, or with ornamental patterns. Many of Boulton's earlier tokens have lettered edges, such as an inscription saying where the token could be redeemed. Medals usually have plain edges but some were individually engraved on the edge for each recipient. A special dedication is found on the edge of the Trafalgar medal: TO THE HEROES OF TRAFALGAR FROM M:BOULTON.

The edge was marked by rolling the blanks in a milling machine. This had two steel bars, one stationary and the other moved by a rack and pinion. The blank was squeezed and force to roll in the grooves between the parallel bars. As the blank rotates its edge is thickened and impressed with a design.[341] A milling machine was used during Boulton's first coinage for Sumatra in 1786,[342] and John Peploe had made a new version by May 1791.[343] This was modified in 1792 to be fed with blanks from both sides, as the cutting-out presses were working so efficiently. This was a practical improvement made by engineers working directly on the job.[344]

---

338 MS 3782-13-36 Item 64, MB (London) to MRB (Soho) 21 March 1792.
339 MS 3782-13-36 Item 64 & 71, MB (London) to MRB (Soho) 21 March 1792; 9 April 1792.
340 MS 3782-12-46 Item 109, MB (Soho) to Charles Hatchett (Hammersmith) 26 March 1801.
341 P.P. Gaspar (1976) *Simon's Cromwell Crown: Dies in the Royal Mint Museum and Blondeau's Method for the Production of Lettered Edges* British Numismatics Journal Volume 46 1976 p55-63.
342 MS 3782-12-74 Item 121, Zaccheus Walker (Birmingham) to MB (Chacewater) 28 September 1786.
343 MS 3782-12-66 Item 11, James Lawson (Soho) to MB (London) 27 May 1791.
344 MS 3782-12-66 Item 22, James Lawson (Soho) to MB (London) 21 January 1792.

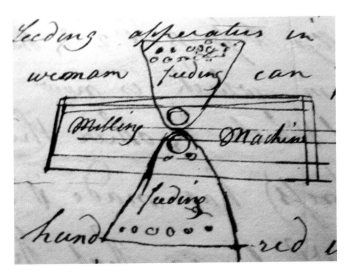

Figure 4:5 Diagram of suggested improvement made to milling machine.

Soho Mint Steam Powered Coining Press

Once the blanks had been prepared and the dies made, the coins or tokens could finally be struck by the steam-powered press. These presses are shown on the 1790 patent diagram, and details of their functioning are given in the accompanying description (A moves B and so on).[345]

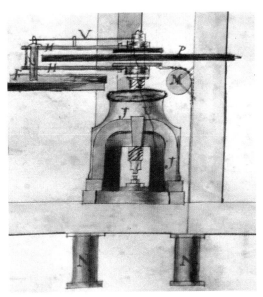

Figure 4:6 Coining press from 1790 patent diagram.

---

345 MS 3782-17-2, Coining press from 1790 patent diagram.

An automatic feed system to Boulton's own specifications was introduced at an early stage to the steam-powered press. The blanks, loaded in tubes, were placed between the dies by a laying-in tool fed by gravity. The lowest blank was pushed forward by a metal fork to drop into a circular steel collar. This collar had been modified by James Lawson, who used a steel ring and a triple spring fitted around the bottom die. Levers kept the ring level with the surface of the die until the screw descended with the upper die. Then the spring allowed the ring to rise, so that as the blank was struck, it was surrounded by the collar. Once the upper die rose, the collar could be made to fall so that the struck coin could be automatically removed by the layer-in to a suitable container, and a fresh blank placed on the die. This enabled Boulton to develop the increased speeds of striking which were impossible if the blanks were fed in by hand. A modern coining press uses a similar method but is now powered by electricity.[346]

New drawings were made of modifications from 1797 which show the position of the dies and the levers with a different method of working.[347] Further scale diagrams of the coining presses installed in 1799 were made at one inch to the foot.[348]

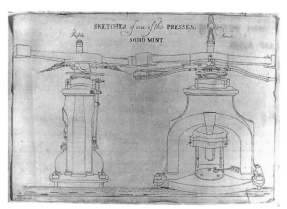

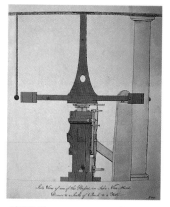

1797 Steam-powered press   1799 Steam-powered press

Figure 4:7 Drawings by Phillp of steam powered coining presses.

A large team at the Soho Mint was involved in the huge technological advances made there. Various engineers including Peter Ewart, William Murdock, John Southern, James Watt, James Lawson and Boulton himself set up the equipment, along with workers such as John Peploe and Joseph and William Harrison. Joseph

---

346 Information from visit to the Royal Mint. 23 Nov 2009.
347 MS 3782-12-66 Item 80, J. Southern (Soho) to MB (London) 22 May 1797; Phillp album 1797 BMAG 2003-0031-184a.
348 Side view of coining press for New Mint, drawn by John Phillp in 1799. Phillp album BMAG 2003-0031-149.

Harrison had been in charge of the mint set up in London to make the Sumatran coinage in 1786. Specialist blacksmith Anthony Robinson, under the direction of John Busch, modified the screws for the presses.[349]

Full descriptions of the various incarnations of the Soho Mint were written by Ewart, Lawson and Southern in 1810 at Matthew Robinson Boulton's request.[350] The equipment was modified many times and various experiments were carried out to impart motion from the steam-engine to the flywheel of the coining press and thus power the blow on the die.

Peter Ewart recollected that when he first came to Soho in August 1788 there was a horizontal rod connecting the presses in rows, with *'the strokes of the presses produced by the alternate opening & shutting of the communications of the air pump with the engine & with the atmosphere'*. He thought the idea was Murdoch's. He himself claimed only the idea of varying the force of the blow and designing a catch to prevent the press from going into reverse at the wrong time.[351] Ingenious planning by Boulton made the engine also turn the scouring barrels, and sawdust could be dried on top of the hollowed-out boiler.[352]

James Lawson, who later installed Boulton's new steam-powered coining apparatus at the Royal Mint in 1810, began to assist at Soho Mint in September 1788. He recollected being shown samples of pattern halfpennies when he was in Cornwall, and that the sliding rod connected to the condenser had already been abandoned before he came to work on the project.[353]

By November 1788 there were major changes: the steam-engine drove a horizontal and then a vertical shaft, via a 'sun-and-planet' crank, which moved a flywheel above eight coining presses arranged in a circle.[354] The horizontal flywheel eventually worked when modified by Watt's suggestion to reverse the action of curves.[355] The blow on the screw press was made by a weight falling when a curved arm reached a certain point. The weights were replaced by air pumps from at least April 1789. In writing to Watt Boulton explained:

'I find from experience that I must work my coining press with air pumps & apply the great wheel to wind them up by which means I can reduce my blow to a certainty whether the engine goes fast or slow & I have reversed the curve on the fly bringing the stroke nearer the centre & ending it at the extremity of the fly with a contrivance to make the balls approach or recede from the centre of the press & thereby adjusting the time of the vibration of the fly so exactly that the Cam will catch the Curve in the right place &

---

349 MS 3782-13-36 Item 58, MB (London) to MRB (Soho) 4 June 1791.
350 MS 3782-13-120, Mint Inventions and Improvements 7 January 1810.
351 MS 3782-13-120 Folder 4, Peter Ewart to John Southern 12 December 1809.
352 MS 3147-5-714, Plan of Soho Mint 1788-1789.
353 MS 3782-13-120 Folder 5, Mint Inventions: Memorandum by James Lawson 27 November 1809.
354 G. Demidowicz in: M. Dick (ed.) (2009) *Matthew Boulton: A Revolutionary Player* pp122-123.
355 MS 3782-13-120 Folder 4, Peter Ewart to John Southern 12 December 1809.

the right time & thus the fly will work as fast as gravity & nature will allow & that without bringing it to stop and to catch at each stroke'.[356]

Modern authors do not often credit Boulton with such engineering and technical skills himself.

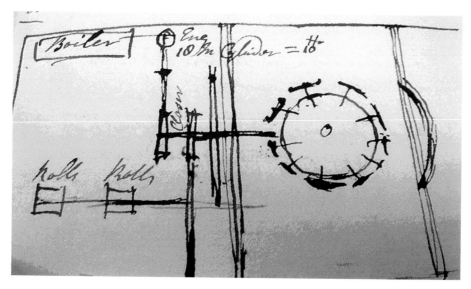

Figure 4:8 Sketch of coining press and engine plan from Boulton's 1789 notebook.[357]

Lawson wrote that the first press was:

'got to work sometime in the year 1789 & the others followed as fast as they could be made. At this time we were all schemers & one press was made with contrivances by Joseph Harrison, another by Mr Busch, and also by Mr Droz and myself. That by Mr Droz never worked, and that by Mr Harrison did not work well and was altered but those called Busch's & mine were long worked together as rivals'.[358]

Like Ewart, he remembered the series of experiments to make the presses work:

'I further know that the wooden arm was my suggestion – and many iron ones were broke before it was adopted. This plan was after many expts adopted – and continued to be improved by making a <u>loose Arm</u> & <u>air pumps</u> instead of Weights – this was chiefly in the year 1789 & 90'.[359]

---

356 MS 3147-3-13 Item 5, MB (Soho) to James Watt (London) 1 April 1789.
357 MS 3782-12-108 Item 54, Mint Book 1789 p22.
358 MS 3782-13-120 Folder 5, Mint Inventions: Memorandum by James Lawson 27 November 1809.
359 MS 3782-13-120 Folder 5, Mint Inventions: Memorandum by James Lawson 27 November 1809.

A patent was granted in August 1790, and describes with the aid of a detailed diagram how the coining press works. The diagram shows the circular arrangement of the eight coining presses.[360]

Figure 4:9 Diagram of coining press arrangement from 1790 patent application.

By spring 1791, as there seemed to be plenty of orders, it was decided that the Mint should be modified and a new building erected. Eighteen detailed resolutions were sent to Boulton's moneying committee consisting of Zaccheus Walker, James Lawson and Matthew Robinson Boulton, who was now twenty-one and fully involved in the business.[361] Boulton described how the rooms should be arranged, how the metal should be rolled, cleaned and dried by two shaking frames and double brushes, how the dies should be forged, engraved and so on.[362] Glover was to *'drive on with the building 2 stories high from as near the end of the Mint yard'.*[363] Boulton was convinced that expansion was essential as *'I have blanks ordered, as well as Coined pieces & I must Coin 4 Ton per Day'.* Contracts may possibly have been expected from the French government or from America, which did not materialise, but a contract for the Monneron brothers of Paris was received.

---

360 MS 3782-17-2, Coining apparatus patent specification for *The Application of Motive Power to Stamping and Coining (Patent Number 1757)* 5 August 1790.
361 MS 3782-13-36 Item 60, MB (London) to MRB (Soho) 7 June 1791.
362 MS 3782-13-36 Item 54, Resolutions on the Mint sent from MB to MRB 26 May 1791.
363 MS 3782-13-36 Item 58, MB (London) to MRB (Soho) 4 June 1791.

Further details and plans were sent in June 1791. Boulton wanted a carpenter's shop, counting house, store room and '*2 Necessary Houses & Coal Vaults*' plus a smith's shop and a room for four coining presses and room for shaking machines. It was also suggested that the Lap Engine was removed to the Mint. He specified that spring water should be used in the pickling shop to clean blanks, rather than canal water, '*which will not tarnish the bits so bad as the canal water in which AF*. [Aqua fortis; i.e. nitric acid], *& all sorts of nastyness hath been mixed in it*'. He also included details of obtaining staff:

> '*I must have 16 persons for the 8 Coining presses & therefore I must beg of Mr Tyson if he is return^d to spend a few days at Handsworth, Bromwich, Smethwick, Litchfield, Yoxall or where ever he thinks some uncorrupted boys from 14 to 20 years of age can be found. Make my Comp^{lts} to him & to Mr Scale & beg their assistance & advice in respecting the aforesaid & likewise an addition of 8 or 10 Cutters out for I had rather have too many than too few*'.[364]

Once this was all done, the processes of coining could be done in one building, except for rolling the metal.

By September, Boulton was already thinking of further changes, so that he could make small coins more easily. He wrote:

> '*I wish I had one of Williams presses mounted with such a Fly as to be able to make 100 Blows per minute. The screws of the Large presses are too large in diameter to admit of that speed but if they were ¼ smaller in diameter and worked with a short light fly without collars I think 100 or 105 blows per minute might be accomplished & then I could undertake to make the very small India or very small French money*'.[365]

Boulton was looking ahead to future orders and had an appreciation of what would be marketable.

A further series of letters detail the progress made in January 1792. This new mint was being used for the Monneron coinage but the large five sol pieces were giving problems as they were '*too wide for the other Machines*'. The chief delay was caused by '*adjustments of the layer-in spring collers which Bu[s]ch has now got in good order and they go at present very well*'. A third press was installed by 23rd January 1792.[366] Many accidents and failures of equipment were reported but each incident led to improvements in the coining process; the use of recoil air pumps lessened damage caused by the blow of the coining press, but also saved power.[367] However, the new press was not really required as the Monneron coinage came to an end

---

364 MS 3782-13-36 Item 60, MB (London) to MRB (Soho) 7 June 1791.
365 MS 3782-13-36 Item 87, MB (Truro) to MRB (Soho) 15 September 1792.
366 MS 3782-12-66 Item 21 to 23, James Lawson (Soho) to MB (London) 20-23 January 1792.
367 MS 3782-12-66 Item 65, John Southern (Soho) to MB (London) 30 January 1792.

by January 1793 when war with France broke out. Apart from 1794, when over 22 million coins were made for the EIC, Boulton had no large coinage contracts until 1797. He did make several token issues, plus medals and items for collectors, and a small issue for the 'Gold Coast'. A final snapshot of this incarnation of the Soho Mint is seen in an inventory taken in August 1795 which showed a cutters shop, polishing shop, soldering shop, mounting shop, leather room, warehouse, counting room, reading room and dye [die] room on the premises.[368]

After the national coinage contract was completed in 1797-8, Boulton decided to build yet another version of the Soho Mint. The new broad curving building stood lower than the original. He realised that he could not rely on equipment set up ten years earlier, as it did not incorporate the latest coining technology. Mint apparatus bought between October 1798 and October 1799 came to over £300, and more expenses were involved in the actual building.[369] John Southern, back at Soho after a tour promoting the 1797 coinage, was in charge.

The 1798 Soho Mint had an entirely new method of working installed, as the coining presses were worked in line by pistons and cylinders attached to a vacuum tube, known as a 'spirit pipe'. Levers connected with a hollow elongated cast-iron 'trumpet', broad side down, attached to the top of the screw and fly of the press. The motion of the pistons downwards was due to the expansion of air let into a partial vacuum, which imparted motion to each coining press screw. A heavy balance beam returned the screw to the upper position and reduced the violence of the recoil, as it was connected to another small piston and cylinder.[370] Southern claimed that he had suggested the idea of vacuum pumps in 1789, and produced a letter from Boulton in support of this.[371] Lawson agreed that the idea had been mentioned then but said too much had been invested in the original plan so no changes were made until the new mint was built in 1797-8. However, he could not remember who suggested the matter:

> 'Mr Southern, Mr Ewart or myself at the time never thought of whose scheme it was – We were however all convinced it would have been the best and I should think some sketches may be found among the old Mint schemes in the end of 1789 or 1790'.[372]

The original 1798 Mint plan did not allow enough room for the coining presses and so was modified.[373] Cheshire reported on progress in April: *'the cutting-out machinery will be compleated this afternoon … Mr. Busch has just set two presses to work on*

---

368 MS 3782-3-14 Mint Day Book 1795-1798 August 1795.
369 MS 3792-13-120 Folder 6.
370 G. Demidowicz in: M. Dick (ed.) (2009) *Matthew Boulton: A Revolutionary Player* p127.
371 MS 3782-13-120 Folder 3, MB to John Southern 17 Jan 1798, included in Southern's statement. 4 June 1810.
372 MS 3782-13-120 Folder 4, Mint Inventions 1809 Lawson (London) to MRB (Soho) 12 December 1809.
373 MS 3782-12-66 Item 90, John Southern (Soho) to MB (London) 25 April 1798.

2d pieces, and is ready to begin the penny pieces as soon as they can be brought forward'.[374]
Building continued slowly during the summer but was not complete in November
1798 when Boulton requested a new doorway and windows.[375] Southern, worried
about industrial espionage, reminded him that the vacuum pipes were intended
to be put in that position but suggested alternative routes.[376] A fortnight later he
sought reassurance: *'My wish is to put down the spirit pipes and the pumps before the
erection of the engine is completed but that will in some degree expose the latter (the pumps)
to the people concerned in the erection of the engine'.*[377] The new presses could strike
faster than the old ones but were also quieter and more efficient.[378] By February
1799, Boulton, who had been busy with court actions over steam-engine patent
infringements, was able to tell his old friend Sir Joseph Banks of his victory in the
case and at the same time report that:

> *'I have now finished & set to work the Leviathan which turns out to be equal in
> perfection to all my hopes, wants & wishes. You will probably remember that my first
> Coining machine struck about 42 pence per minute with each press & made an
> unmusical noise. The present works 60 pence p[er] minute p[er] press & is perfectly
> silent. … I declare it to be a beautyfull harmonious simple & perfect Machine'.*[379]

Boulton was exaggerating a little about the silence of the machine, but it was
certainly an improvement on anything that had gone before. Four new presses
were operating successfully by April and all eight presses on 1st May 1799.[380]

Banks had been a great help with the regal coinage contract, being a member of
the Privy Council Committee on Coin. Boulton was able to write with pride to his
son, who was in Cornwall collecting the steam-engine premiums owed:

> *'I expect Lord Hawkesbury (the present master of the mint) at Soho tomorrow with some
> others of the P[rivy] Council to dinner. They come down expressly to see my new mint
> which is singularly beautiful and in high order; eight presses have struck 40,000 pieces
> of money of 1 inch diameter (which is rather larger than a guinea) per hour and in
> other respects is the ne plus ultra of coining'.*[381]

The Soho Mint new steam-powered presses were ready for the 1799 issue of
halfpennies and farthings, which came in November 1799. Further contracts

---

374 MS 3782-12-59 Item 166, William Cheshire (Soho) to MB (London) 18 April 1798.
375 MS 3782-12-59-172, William Cheshire (Soho) to MB (London) 6 August 1798.
376 MS 3782-12-66 Item 91, John Southern (Soho) to MB (London) 8 November 1798.
377 MS 3782-12-66 Item 92, John Southern (Soho) to MB (London) 21 November 1798.
378 MS 3782-12-59 Item 182, William Cheshire (Soho) to MB (London) 22 February 1799.
379 MS 3782-12-56 Item 96, MB (Soho) to Sir Joseph Banks (—) 1 February 1799.
380 MS 3782-12-66 Item 101, John Southern (Soho) to MB (London) 1 May 1799.
381 MS 3782-13-36 Item 140, MB (Soho) to MRB (at Mr Thos Wilson, Truro) 7 July 1799.

were made for the government in 1805 to 1807, and Soho Mint was to provide the machinery to re-equip the Royal Mint with new technology. This included a rotative engine, eight coining presses and twenty-four layers-in, twelve cutting out presses, six double milling machines, iron work for four furnaces for annealing blanks, press and apparatus for multiplying dies, iron work for six furnaces for annealing and hardening dies, two lathes for turning dies, and a steam apparatus for warming the coining room.[382]

Espionage

Britain was more advanced technically than the rest of Europe, or indeed the rest of the world, in the late eighteenth century. This was due to a variety of circumstances, including free trade opportunities, increased technical knowledge and an enlightened society. The country benefited from an open market economy where collaborative acts for the public good, such as setting up turnpike roads or canals, were carried out by private groups.[383] Peace and stability could be maintained more easily than on the continent. In France, industry, including the thirteen French mints, was highly controlled by the government.[384] By contrast in Britain, inventors and entrepreneurs were able to benefit from their improvements due to restraints on the elite which prevented over-taxation. Boulton positively encouraged creativity in his employees; when the Soho Mint equipment was being installed in 1789, the whole team was involved in sorting out technical problems.

The sharing of knowledge was encouraged by enlightenment thinking in the eighteenth century, through visits, encyclopaedias and technical books, though social conventions expected that individuals would respect information given and not use it for their own benefit.[385] Some individuals such as Abraham Derby, John Rennie and John Smeaton did not patent their ideas. Others had their methods stolen, despite a patent; for example, Huntsman had his method of preparing steel spied upon and disseminated. Many visitors from Europe took back accounts of British industry.[386]

Loss of technology abroad could be a serious worry. Laws were passed banning the export of certain classes of workers, as the French government was actively encouraging the emigration of British workers to sponsored new industries. One refugee from the Jacobite revolution of 1745, John Holker, was appointed Inspector General of Manufactures in France in 1755. He set up metal manufactories, and tried to import the process of making sulphuric acid in 1769,

---

382 MS 3792-13-120, Details of the Materials, Machinery to be furnished by Matthew Boulton for the Establishment of a Mint. Mint Inventions and Improvements Volume 1.

383 J. Mokyr (2009) *The Enlightened Economy: An Economic History of Britain 1700-1850* Yale University Press.

384 MS 3219-4 Item 124, MB (Soho) to James Watt (Frankfurt) 10 October 1802.

385 J. Mokyr (2009) *The Enlightened Economy* Yale University Press pp368-375.

386 R.R. Angerstein (2001) *R.R. Angerstein's Illustrated Travel Diary, 1753-1755 Industry in England and Wales from a Swedish Perspective* translated by T. & P. Berg, Science Museum, London.

but found it difficult to scale up production to a level comparable to that in Britain. Further legislation, for example the 1785 Tools Act, was another attempt to prevent technological transfer.[387]

Initially, Boulton was willing to show foreign visitors around the Soho Manufactory, especially when requested so to do by the government, as it helped his sales.[388] However, this could be abused; he wanted to maintain his position as a gentleman of the Enlightenment, but also did not want his original ideas stolen. For example, in 1787, Count Wilhelm Friedrich von Reden, head of the Prussian mining administration, visited Boulton while touring Britain, intending to take information back to his own country, as did Baron Stein. Wilson at Chacewater was warned not to allow them access to steam-engines.[389] Another visitor to Soho assumed a false title which, with a letter of recommendation, made it difficult for him to be refused entry. Watt:

'then shew them one of the New Steam Engines at Work upon the Birmingham Navigation, & such other Particulars as were necessary to gratify the Curiosity of Gentlemen travelling for pleasure'. In fact, the sightseer was spying.[390]

Boulton was ambivalent about the export of technology except when it affected his own affairs. He had initially recommended that William Wilkinson work at Le Creusot, France, but by 1787 was unhappy, as they were making steam-engines.[391] There had already been problems with infringements of the steam-engine patent, and Boulton and Watt had taken a series of legal actions against engineers in Cornwall.[392] Once the Soho Mint was fully operational, he was eager to maintain the secrets of his coining processes as he did not want the Royal Mint to benefit, rather than himself. However, he was willing to sell his coining equipment abroad, when no orders were received from the British government.[393]

Several foreign spies tried to view the coining processes. In 1803, Boulton wrote:

'I have been visited by 5 different Mechanical Spies in the course of the last Year for the express purpose of Stealing my Mint, & 'though I have shewn it to most of them, I have reason to believe they are not much the Wiser, & without it, they will never be able to recoin all the Money of France in Bonapartie's Life time not even with their 13 Mints'.[394]

---

387 J.R. Harris (1998) *Industrial Espionage and Technology Transfer: Britain and France in the Eighteenth Century* Ashgate, Aldershot pp67-68, 276, 460-461.
388 AD1583/10/26, Boulton to Wilson 28 March 1798.
389 AD1583/2/33, Boulton to Wilson 27 January 1787.
390 MS 3782-12-56 Item 86, MB (Soho) to Sir Joseph Banks (London) 13 February 1787.
391 AD1583/2/33, Boulton to Wilson 27 January 1787.
392 AD1583/1/40, MB (Gloucester) to T. Wilson (Chacewater) 20 November 1784.
393 MS 3782-13-36 Item 36, MB (Soho) to MRB (Germany) 26 October 1789.
394 MS 3782-12-81 Item 131, MB (Soho) to Ambrose Weston (London) 8 September 1803.

The diagram of the rolling press illustrates the problems that Boulton and others had with industrial espionage. The drawing was by Jon-Matthias Ljunberg, a Swede working for the Danish government, who had made a series of observations of the technology in use by Wedgwood, Boulton, Crawshay and others, over a period of fourteen years. In a letter to Watt in 1789 Boulton described how John Wilkinson had personally shown Ljunberg over his works.[395] Josiah Wedgwood tried hard to prevent the export of this technical information but without success.[396]

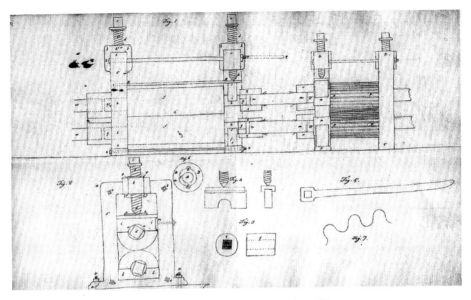

Figure 4:10 Rolling press drawn by Ljungberg in 1788.[397]

Industrial espionage continued to be a problem. James Morrison, the deputy Master of the Royal Mint, had accompanied Boulton to Soho in November 1799 and for ten days appeared to be poking his nose into everything.[398] Boulton commented to Banks: *'though 3 different officers of the Tower Mint have examined mine as well as their Inspector of the Money presses, yet I do not believe they are quite Master of the subject'.*[399] He was worried that Royal Mint officials would try to steal the secrets of his new coining apparatus and that they were preparing for another copper coinage without him.

---

395 MS 3147-3-13 Item 14, MB (Soho) to James Watt (6 Green Lettice Lane, London) 6 October 1789.
396 MS 3782-12-74 Item 178, Zaccheus Walker (Birmingham) to MB (Manchester) 26 August 1789. This included a transcript of a letter from Joshua Wedgwood (Etruria) to MB dated 24 August 1789.
397 J.M. Ljungberg drawing from Mynt Arkivet, State Archives, Stockholm, Sweden. Thanks to Professor Peter Jones for this.
398 MS 3782-12-59 Item 197, William Cheshire (Soho) to MB (Soho) November 1799.
399 MS 3782-12-56 Item 124, MB (Soho) to Sir Joseph Banks (London) 29 November 1799.

A subtle form of espionage was undertaken by Jean-Pierre Droz from the Paris Mint. He had been engaged in December 1786 to engrave dies, and had also promised an improved design for a screw press and a better method of multiplying dies. He arrived at Soho in October 1788 and returned to France in June 1790, taking Soho's new technological ideas with him.[400] Boulton complained that: *'He [Droz] is a quack and hath been only learning at Soho and not teaching; his only value is as engraver'.*[401]

Security was not only important to prevent industrial espionage, but also to prevent theft of the valuable goods and materials used at Soho. Walker wrote in 1788, worried about 20 tons of copper coming from Mr Vivian in Cornwall.[402] He also reported accounts of an attempted robbery in 1792.[403] Orders in the Soho Mint records show payments for items such as bars for cellar windows, bolts for doors, and plates for window shutters, bought from William Whitmore in 1789. There were also monthly expenses for guard dogs.[404] Thomas Jordan was paid for making an alarm machine in 1797.[405] Boulton was concerned that only trusted workers should be used in specific areas to prevent theft and some workers were dismissed for pilfering.[406]

---

400 MS 3782-12-66 Item 7, James Lawson (Soho) to MB (London) 8 June 1790.
401 MS 3782-13-36 Item 47, MB (London) to MRB (Amsterdam) 13 July 1790.
402 MS 3782-12-74 Item 159, Zaccheus Walker (Birmingham) to MB (London) 24 January 1788.
403 MS 3782-12-75 Item 25, Zaccheus Walker (Birmingham) to MB (London) 20 March 1792.
404 MS 3782-13-96, Copper trade Volume 1 Item 1-2.
405 MS 3782-6-195-22, Bills from September 1797 to November 1797.
406 MS 3782-13-36 Item 84, MB (Truro) to MRB (Soho) 3 September 1792.

Chapter Five

Customers, Design and Transport

Customers

MATTHEW Boulton is well known for being a consummate salesman. There were many strands to his marketing including the development of Soho Manufactory and showroom as a destination for industrial tourists. Images of the Soho Manufactory and Boulton's own name and personality formed part of the marketing strategy of Soho's products.[407] He held London auctions, and sold through agents, both at home and abroad. By 1772 *'every country in Europe was doing some business with Boulton'.*[408] Goodison lists the patrons that Boulton cultivated by 1778, including ambassadors and visitors from America, Austria, Denmark, France, Germany, Italy, Netherlands, Poland, Portugal, Russia, Sardinia, Spain, Sweden and Switzerland.[409]

The Soho Mint needed to be a profitable business so it was vital to gain sufficient customers. Boulton had spent considerable sums setting it up, only to find that his original plan to produce a regal coinage was no longer viable. He emphasised the cheap price he could charge in order to gain coining contracts, and sometimes underestimated the costs. On occasion he did not get paid. He continued to use influential friends such as Sir Joseph Banks to lobby for a contract from the government, producing pattern coins for presentation to important individuals.[410]

407 V. Loggie (2009) 'Picturing Soho: Images of Matthew Boulton's Manufactory' in: S. Mason (ed.) (2009) *Matthew Boulton: Selling What All The World Desires* Yale University Press, London pp22-30.

408 E. Robinson (1963) *Eighteenth-Century Commerce and Fashion: Matthew Boulton's Marketing Techniques* p42.

409 N. Goodison (1974 amended 2002) *Matthew Boulton Ormolu* pp404-406.

410 MS 3728-12-56; MS 3782-21 and www2.sl.nsw.gov.au/banks/series 84

There were a huge range of customers for Soho Mint products, ranging from private individuals who wanted a few medals, to commissioners of large issues consisting of millions of coins. They came from many walks of life and included merchants, shopkeepers and industrialists, kings and governments. Items were made in tin as cheap medals, or in gold, as exclusive pieces, and ranged from truck tokens for use at Pen-y-darran Iron works, to coins and medals for reigning monarchs.

Business connections were important in gaining orders for the first tokens made on the steam-powered press; the 1789 Cronebane, Anglesey and Wilkinson tokens. William Roe, Thomas Williams and John Wilkinson were all involved in the copper industry, all well known to Boulton, as was the Cornish Metal Company, for whom the 1791 Cornish halfpenny token was made. Williams had also been instrumental in Boulton's first coinage contract for the East India Company (EIC), and further contracts for Sumatra, India and Ceylon were obtained because of trust in Boulton as an individual.

The Soho Mint was advertised both at home and abroad. By June 1790, accounts of his new steam-powered press were translated into French and German by Henry Stieglitz.[411] Letters were also translated into other languages as Boulton had an acquaintance *'who writes and speaks every language in Europe gramaticaly, being born in Sweden, and have lived for some time in Spain, Italy, and Russia'.* This un-named paragon also had beautiful neat handwriting.[412] Boulton's agents in various parts of the world also sought work for the mint. This resulted eventually in orders for pattern coins from Canada, Denmark, Russia, and Würtemberg in present Germany, and currency orders from the Gold Coast, Sierra Leone, Bermuda, and the Bahamas, plus millions of tokens for the United Kingdom and France. Boulton also made blanks for the United States Mint at Philadelphia, and for Portugal.

An important part of his sales pitch was the cost. In writing to John Motteux in January 1791, he said that the EIC could: *'obtain any quantity of fine copper coin they may please to order at the above rates which I am persuaded is cheaper than it has ever been made at Paris'.* He continued:

> *'As I am concerned in many of the copper mines of this country & in copper smelting works as well as in rolling mills & as I have now invented & completed a steam mill for coining which is worked by the power of our steam engine, with many late improvements, working upon a new principle ...with more regularity & precision than can be done by human hands, I am enabled to offer to supply copper coin in almost any quantity of the quality of the 2 pieces inclosed which you'll observe are lettered upon the edges with letters in relief or indented & from them being struck in collers are round & of equal diameter'.*[413]

---

411 MS 3782-12-75 Item 3, Zaccheus Walker (Birmingham) to MB (London) 7 June 1790.
412 MS 3782-12-8 Item 64, MB to Henry Stieglitz 2 May 1790.
413 MS 3782-12-91 Item 1, MB Sketch to John Motteux 3 January 1791.

Similar letters were sent to other prospective customers. The resultant order for Bombay in February 1791, for 17 million coins, was a vital contract; the steam-powered Soho Mint would have a pedigree in making a large coinage issue. This could then be used to promote further deals, including the all-important regal coinage contract. This EIC contract was later hindered by a lack of copper and failure of the mint apparatus. An anxious Boulton wrote to his son:

'I have lost an immense sum by the coinage and now an opportunity offers by which I may in a great degree refund myself. Your interest and happiness depend much upon this opportunity not being lost'. He urged that *'Everyone concerned in the Management of the coinage should study morning noon and night how to vanquish difficulties rather than raise them'.*[414]

He was worried that if this order failed, he would lose not only his reputation and the chance to make a profit, but also be pursued for breach of contract. The team at Soho were able to respond to this call, and their reputation for quality then led to further commissions. Boulton's next coinage order for the EIC was not until 1794, but they proved one of his most loyal and long-lasting customers. A total 220 million copper coins were made for the EIC between 1786 and 1809.

Another important early order was from the Monneron brothers in Paris, gained via his contact with Balthazar-Georges Sage, the chemist, mineralogist and assayer who held a post at the Paris Mint. Initially Boulton had hoped to coin for the new French government, and had sought the Monnerons' support in the French assembly; but in fact he received a series of orders for tokens from the brothers instead, culminating in a total of over 11 million heavy copper pieces being produced between 1791 and early 1793, using over 197 tons of copper.[415]

It was not always possible to complete a contract for a variety of reasons, and some customers had to be disappointed. A lack of engravers meant that no tokens were made for Sir Richard Arkwright, as Dumarest, who arrived in August 1790, had too much work.[416] Sometimes bigger orders took preference. In January 1794 Lawson wrote:

'Mr Marshall (who has the Engine here) was asking me some days ago if you now coined halfpence as he thought of having some made, but I suppose the quantity would only be small. If you are in the way of coining I can let him know otherwise if will not be worth your attention'.[417]

---

414 MS 3782-13-36 Item 58, MB (London) to MRB (Soho) 4 June 1791.

415 P. Jones (2009) 'Commercial Tokens and Medal Coinage for the Monneron Frères' in: R. Clay and S. Tungate (eds.) (2009) *Matthew Boulton and the Art of Making Money* pp24-38.

416 D. Vice (forthcoming).

417 MS 3782-12-66 Item 44, James Lawson (Leeds) to MB (Soho) 28 January 1794.

At the time a large commission for the EIC for Madras was under production, and it was not cost-effective to make this small token issue.

At times the Soho Mint was very busy. In 1791 Boulton wrote: *'I want the East India order done by Oct next; 2nd the 16 ton of Anglesey done in one month; 3rd one two or three tons of Southampton directly'.*[418] There were Monneron tokens, EIC coins, pattern coins for Barbados and Bengal, and a complex order for Sierra Leone, plus tokens for Britain being made in 1791-1792. At other times the Mint lacked orders and workers had to be laid off, as only small token orders for Leeds and Inverness, and Bermuda halfpennies followed in 1793. These commissions plus medal making, kept the mint ticking over but were not big enough to warrant the steam-powered press. There were plenty of other coin manufacturers in Birmingham who could make small orders on hand-powered presses. The steam-powered press had been designed for large coinage issues, which came again in 1794 with more EIC orders. Then there was another lull, with only small token orders for John Wilkinson, and the towns of Bishop Stortford, Penryn, Dundee and Hornchurch.

Much correspondence was required when contemplating a contract in a foreign market. Exchange rates and restrictions on trade had to be considered, as well as the credit worthiness of foreign agents. Boulton was unwilling to enter markets where he was unsure of payment. He had problems in obtaining money owed from Russia for example.[419] He also had several opportunities to supply America, but a request in 1788 was not followed up.[420] He wrote later to his son in 1793:

> *'I must observe that although I wish to serve them with goods of Soho Manufactory, yet as I am not in the way of supplying American markets, I think I had better decline a general dealing with them as the Cred[t] is long'.*[421]

By 1797, however, he was supplying blanks for the Philadelphia Mint and continued to do so in considerable amounts; 22 million were sent from Soho Mint until 1809.

Outside events, over which Boulton had no control, could have serious effects on Soho Mint production. The Monneron contract was fraught with problems caused by the unfolding French revolution, and by August 1792, Boulton was worried that *'the times are now so horrable in France that I fear I can't get drafts negotiated'.*[422] It was eventually abandoned by January 1793 when Britain declared war against France. The idea of coining for the French government reoccurred in 1802 when the Peace of Amiens was declared. This would have been a great

---

418 MS 3782-13-36 Item 58, MB (London) to MRB (Soho) 4 June 1791.
419 MS 3782-12-42 Item 272, Andrew Collins (Birmingham) to MB (London) 28 November 1797.
420 MS 3782-12-108 Item 53, Mint Book 1788 p68.
421 MS 3782-13-36 Item 101, MB (London) to MRB (Soho) 14 June 1793.
422 MS 3792-12-68 Item 9, MB (Soho) to Charlotte Matthews (London) 15 August 1792.

coup for the Soho Mint as a correspondent had told Boulton that a *'Thousand Million of pieces'* would be required. Several parties were interested but none had authority from the French Government, so Boulton did not proceed further.[423] When war recommenced in 1803, the opportunity was lost. A prospective contract for Denmark was also lost due to hostilities with the League of Armed Neutrality in 1801. Nelson's bombardment of Copenhagen didn't help! Though eventually, Soho did provide the mint equipment for the Danish Mint.

The most productive period at the Soho Mint was reached from 1797 when Boulton was finally commissioned to make a regal coinage issue. The mint was fully employed making blanks for the United States Mint in Philadelphia, and minting and distributing 500 tons of copper coins for the British Government, plus over 16 million coins for Madras.

This was continued in 1799 with contracts for over 46 million British halfpennies and farthings, and further blanks for the Philadelphia Mint. In the period from 1805-7 at least 175 million regal coins were made. Eventually Soho Mint made over 320 million copper coins for the British Government in ten years using over 4,200 tons of copper.[424] Previously, it had taken the Royal Mint around seventy years to make a quarter of that amount.[425] The steam-powered press finally was used for its intended purpose.

Items for Collectors

Medals from the Soho Mint provide a valuable historical record of the eighteenth century and are still popular with collectors today.[426] Medals have no monetary value in terms of legal tender, but are an art form, obverse and reverse images struck onto metal, often accompanied by short inscriptions. Medal production enhanced Boulton's status, as collecting medals and coins was a royal pursuit, but it also kept Soho Mint in the attention of those who might order a more substantial coinage.

Royal coin collections were reassembled from the reign of Charles II, after their dispersal during puritan purges. George III's father, Frederick, started a personal collection which was passed on to him. Queen Charlotte and Augusta, Princess of Wales were also keen collectors. Other eminent eighteenth-century coin and medal collectors included the Earl of Pembroke, and the 2nd Marquis of Rockingham, who bought the collection of the 4th Earl of Sandwich in 1771. Horace Walpole, James 'Athenian' Stuart and John Murray, 3rd Duke of Atholl, were also collectors. William Marsden had started the EIC collection by 1782.[427]

423 MS 3219-4 Item 124, MB (Soho) to James Watt (Frankfurt) 10 October 1802.
424 D. Symons (2009) in: S. Mason (ed.) (2009) *Matthew Boulton: Selling What All The World Desires.*
425 C.E. Challis (ed.) (1992) *A New History of the Royal Mint* p436.
426 Sales of Soho Mint coins are detailed by Bill McKivor, thecopperman@thecoppercorner.com
427 K. Sloan (ed.) (2003) *Enlightenment: Discovering the World in the Eighteenth Century* British Museum Press p171.

Medals were exhibited at a variety of eminent societies in London and sold by several retailers.[428] One was Thomas Snelling (1712-1773) who had the largest numismatic shop in London. Another was Christopher Pinchbeck, a licensed dealer in precious metals, and John Kentish who had a shop opposite the Royal Exchange. Henry Young, with a shop on Ludgate Hill, was dealing with Boulton by 1793.[429]

A few medals had been made at Soho Manufactory, as part of Boulton's toy trade, and then from 1789 by Soho Mint. Though sold in small numbers, they proved good advertising. They were produced in a variety of metals, such as silver, gold, brass, bronzed copper, or gilt, but cheap versions in tin and white metal were also sold; Boulton was catering for a wide market.

Marketing of medals needed to be focused directly on the intended audience, and initially at Soho Mint this was not achieved successfully. In 1789 Chippindall, one of Boulton's agents in London, had been approached by three retail firms, who wanted items to sell during the procession to celebrate the restoration of the health of George III. A medal had been commissioned. He wrote to tell Boulton that *'I have got copys of the advertisements out to three papers, the* World, Herald *and* Diary, *some of which I hope will appear on Monday, Tuesday & Wednesday'.*[430] However, dies produced by Droz cracked, and so the medals were not completed in time. Chippindall wrote that he was:

> *'almost mad with vexation at the misfortune in the dyes. I fully thought all was hardend & ready or I would not have scuffled so to get its advertisement in two papers today ... The grand consumption would have been <u>on Wednesday next</u> – as after Thursday it will be a flat piece of business'.*[431]

Time was of the essence in selling such a fashionable consumer item.

To promote a regal coinage contract, pattern coins had been sent from Soho Mint to those holding influence. These became eagerly sought after. Boulton decided to produce proof coins as well as medals for collectors. Proofs are struck in a special press with meticulously polished dies and blanks, and should be virtually flawless in appearance, with a brilliant mirror like finish and sharply defined designs.[432] It took time and effort to strike proof pieces as the dies needed be polished between each strike.[433] In addition to Boulton having a potential

---

428 C. Eimer (1995) *The Pingos and the development of Engraving Techniques in the second half of the Eighteenth Century* University of Leeds M Phil.

429 MS 3782-12-108, Item 69 Medal ledger *Ledger of Medals, coins etc. furnished to Sundry Persons from the Soho Mint within the above dates* 1793-1816.

430 MS 3782-12-59 Item 13, Richard Chippindall (London) to MB (Soho) 19 April 1789.

431 MS 3782-12-59 Item 14, Richard Chippindall (London) to MB (Soho) 20 April 1789.

432 P.P. Gaspar and G.P. Dyer (1980) *The Striking of Proof and Pattern Coins in the Eighteenth Century* British Numismatic Society Journal Volume 50 1980 pp117-127.

433 MS 3782-13-36 Item 116, MB (London) to MRB (Soho) 2 February 1795.

market to exploit, this meant that key workers could be retained in employment at the Soho Mint. In 1792, James Lawson wrote:

'Herewith you will receive—100 Medals of J. J. Rousseau, 100 La Fayette, 36 Serment du Roi, 100 Deux Sols, 50 Cinq Sols, 25 Cinq Sols Federation, 100 Glasgow Halfpence, 100 Southampton Halfpence, all bronzed'.[434]

The copper blanks had been treated with a special coating to make the items more attractive.

Sets of proof coins and tokens were sold from 1793.[435] Early sets included twenty-one items: two types of British halfpenny, the 1789 Kings Recovery medal and tokens for Cronebane, the 1791 Anglesey Halfpenny, Cornish Halfpenny, Wilkinson Halfpenny, four sizes of coins for Bombay and the Sierra Leone penny plus others. By the end of 1793, they also included Ibberson and Inverness halfpennies. The coin collector, Samuel Birchall, the commissioner of over 2 tons of tokens for Leeds in 1792, ordered coins on five different occasions between July 1793 and 1st November 1794.[436] Charles Pye, who wrote a book for collectors, had several sets of Soho Mint products in 1795. Further items were added to Soho Mint's output: pattern Kentucky silver coins were sold by 1796, although they did not go into general production. A total of 346 sets of Soho Mint coins were sold between 1793-1803 with most sold up to 1797.[437]

Boulton wrote to Chippindall that it was more profitable than coining small orders of tokens:

'Nothing can be got by coining unless a very great number of Tons are coined of the same die & even then, more may be got than is possible, by specimens, although they are charged at 12 times the price of current money. So soon as I have wrote a short paper and printed it, I will send you a hundred setts or as many as you can find the means of selling, they being already made – as fast as I can get other dies engraved I shall send you specimens of them to add to the collection'.[438]

His client list included a range of collectors, and a special record book of medal sales was kept, with requests being recorded till 1816. The notebook lists sales to dealers and individuals, plus presents to various people including Lord Aylesford, the British Museum, Samuel Garbett, Lord Hawksbury, the Empress of Russia, Dr Withering and Mrs Watt.[439] From 1793 Conrad Heinrich Küchler was employed

---

434 MS 3782-12-66 Item 38, James Lawson (Soho) to MB (London) 24 August 1792.
435 MS 3782-12-59 Item 46, MB (Soho) to Richard Chippindall (London) 16 February 1793.
436 MS 3782-13-36 Item 94, MB (London) to MRB (Soho) 18 January 1793.
437 MS 3782-12-108 Item 69, Medal ledger pp74-75.
438 MS 3782-12-59 Item 48, MB (Soho) to Richard Chippindall (London) 12 March 1793.
439 MS 3782-12-108 Item 69, Medal ledger *Ledger of Medals, coins etc. furnished to Sundry Persons from the Soho Mint within the above dates* 1793-1816.

to engrave medals on a speculative basis, and between 1793 and 1799 he was responsible for around fifteen different medals. This ensured that he was also available to make dies for the regal coinage contract in 1797.

The collection of Soho Mint items became increasingly fashionable. Sarah Sophia Banks, sister to Sir Joseph Banks, was an enthusiastic collector. Two years later in 1791, Banks wrote jocularly to Boulton:

> *'My sister is a great pusher; she has seen your 5 sous piece & has not got one of them. If you fear a lady's resentment or wish to Court her favor, I would advise you to furnish her with one as speedily as convenient and if you add to it any other new tokens, it may be well, as the sight of them will certainly work favourably in her eyes'.*[440]

By 1804, Sarah Sophia thought that she had most examples of Soho Mint's coinages but asked to be sent any new coins struck, and enclosed a catalogue of her collection for Boulton.[441] He was particularly proud of his regenerated Spanish dollars and wrote:

> *'If Miss Banks deposits the dollar in her cabinet, she should also deposit a copy of my letter or explanation to Lord H* [Hawkesbury] *otherwise the merit of the piece will be overlooked'.*[442]

She continued to receive samples throughout her life. The British Museum, opened in 1759, acquired the Sarah Sophia Banks collection on her death in 1818.[443]

Boulton was eager to impress Banks, who was influential both within government and at Court, and was also responsible for passing many of Soho Mint's proof coins to George III. In July 1797, Banks wrote to report that:

> *'The King did me the honor yesterday to accept from me one* [penny] *for each of the Royal Family & more than that, he took another which in my Presence, he gave to the Keeper of his Medals saying "Take Care of this. I like one struck for Common use better than a Fine one"'.*[444]

Banks also passed on a request from the Duke of Portland for a two-pence and a penny bronzed proof, along with his own request for a guineas worth of the new farthings in November 1799.[445] In 1803, Chippindall wrote: *'Mr Wilkins of the EIC wanted a set of the EIC coinage and Seringapatam for the Library at India House and one*

---

440 MS 3782-12-56 Item 22, Sir Joseph Banks (London) to MB (Soho) 19 December 1791.
441 MS 3782-12-56 Item 69, Sir Joseph Banks (London) to MB (Soho) 28 March 1804.
442 MS 3782-12-56 Item 105, MB (Soho) to Joseph Banks (London) 23 January 1804.
443 K. Sloan (ed.) (2003) *Enlightenment: Discovering the World in the Eighteenth Century* British Museum Press p171.
444 MS 3782-12-56 Item 34, Sir Joseph Banks (London) to MB (Soho) 26 July 1797.
445 MS 3782-12-56 Item 53, Sir Joseph Banks (London) to MB (Soho) 23 November 1799.

of MB's likeness for their own museum'.[446] These were all important individuals to impress and a potential source of new contracts for Soho Mint.

A total of around fifty-five different medals were eventually made at Soho Mint. Usually not more than three to five hundred copies of any given medal were struck, an exception being the 14,000 Trafalgar medals made in 1805. With small numbers, time and care could be taken in their production. Some commissioned medals were even made in single figures over a period of years, for example, Agriculture Society prize medals, which were individually engraved with the recipient's name.[447]

While in London dealing with steam-engine patent infringements in 1795, Boulton wrote for medals to be sent for sale or as gifts.

'Pray send me all the silver medals of the K[ing] and 2 of France, Lord Cornwallis & the King of Denmark that are already struck and Bush must go on with more in Silver and in Tin when the Frogmore medals are done.... I want a Silver Medal of Lord How for the King'.[448]

Even when the regal coinage contracts were undertaken, items for collectors were still produced, to impress future customers. In February 1799, Boulton was sent:

'6 dozen copper farthings—struck from the new dies; plus a further 4½ dozen gilt; 6 dozen each of gilt, copper halfpennies and 5 dozen bronzed; plus 6 dozen bronzed farthings, plus three pieces from Raikes's dies, [Claude Martin pieces] *viz. 1 each silver, bronzed, and copper'.*[449]

Boulton's box was also replenished with an assortment of penny and two penny specimens to use as advertisements. In May 1799, Cheshire wrote:

'Herewith you will receive five sets of bronzed medals, which I believe exceeds your order, but as I am not quite clear how many sets you wished, I have thought it best to err on the safe side. You have also herewith six bronzed Nelsonian medals and a packet of coins and medals'.[450]

Thirty sets of specimen coins *'each set consisting of 6 pieces, viz. a gilt, bronzed, and ♀ [copper] halfpenny; a gilt, bronzed, and ♀ [copper] farthing'* and twelve boxes of halfpence and farthings were sent in October, and a further one hundred and ten

446 MS 3782-12-59 Item 135, Richard Chippindall (London) to MB (Soho) 3 February 1803.
447 MS 3782-12-108 Item 69, Medal ledger *Ledger of Medals, coins etc. furnished to Sundry Persons from the Soho Mint within the above dates* 1793-1816.
448 MS 3782-13-36 Item 130, MB (London) to MRB (Soho) 16 May 1795.
449 MS 3782-12-59 Item 182, William Cheshire (Soho) to MB (London) 22 February 1799.
450 MS 3782-12-59 Item 189, William Cheshire (Soho) to MB (London) 27 May 1799.

sets in November 1799.[451] This enabled Boulton to satisfy important individuals who could use their influence on behalf of further orders for the Soho Mint.

The importance of Matthew Boulton's work as objects of art with excellent designs can be seen in several contemporary catalogues. Thomas Spence, who sold tokens as well as books, published a catalogue *'The Coin Collectors Companion'* in 1795.[452] This described a *'universal rage of collecting coins'*.[453] Several other publications were important, including Charles Pye's 1801 *'Provincial Coins and Tokens'* and James Conder's 1798 *'Arrangement of Provincial Coins, Tokens and Medalets'*.[454] Conder's book remained the standard work on the subject for nearly a century. To this day, many American collectors refer to 'Conder' tokens. The preface, written by James Wright who contacted Boulton in 1797, emphasised the importance of coins as:

> *'the most faithful of all recorders, the cheapest, most minute, and portable of all pictures; … if well designed and well executed during the present age in Britain, they will form a true mirror of the existing features of the times, and hand down to posterity the well-earned reputation of our islanders for industry, commerce and arts'.*[455]

Wright also described Küchler's designs as being comparable to the best antique coins and the 'cartwheel' as being *'by far the most elegant coinage that was ever actually brought into circulation by government at any period of British History'*.[456]

The interest in tokens by numismatists was not generally sustained in the nineteenth century. However recently there has been increased awareness in the contemporary social and industrial developments portrayed on coins, medals and tokens, and in particular in Soho Mint.[457]

Design at Soho

The driving force of Enlightenment culture was improvement in all things. In addition to his metallurgical and technological skills, Matthew Boulton was also interested in the design of items made at Soho. Thus, perfecting the artistic aspects of Soho Mint was very important; he even embellished the mint

---

451 MS 3782-12-59 Item 194, William Cheshire (Soho) to MB (London) 31 Oct 1799; MS 3782-12-59 Item 195 and 196 William Cheshire (Soho) to MB (London) 7 and 10 November 1799.

452 R.H. Thompson (1969) *The Dies of Thomas Spence 1750-1814* British Numismatic Journal Volume 38 1969.

453 T. Spence (1795) *The Coin Collector's Companion: Being a descriptive alphabetical list of the modern and provincial, political and other copper coins*, London.

454 R. Clay and S. Tungate (eds.) (2009) *Matthew Boulton and the Art of Making Money* p41; pp50-53. Books included Thomas Prattents *The Virtuoso's Companion and Coin Collector's Guide* of 1795-7. D.W. Dykes (2003) *The Eighteenth and early Nineteenth century Token* British Numismatic Journal Volume 73 (2003) pp169-174.

455 J. Conder (1799) *An Arrangement of Provincial Coins, Tokens and Medalets*, Jermyn, London.

456 MS 3782-12-42 Item 215, James Wright Jr. (Dundee) to MB (Soho) 1 September 1797.

457 Soho Mint website (www.sohomint.info) was set up in 2008. R. Clay (2009) in: R. Clay and S. Tungate (eds.) (2009) *Matthew Boulton and the Art of Making Money.*

apparatus beautifully.[458] He needed to produce items that would could be sold in their millions as coins, but also satisfy his customers' tastes. When medals were made, time and care could be spent in striking them, but for a large coinage issue, such as the third regal coinage, when over 165 million coins were made in fifteen months, speed and efficiency were essential. Designs had not only to be aesthetically pleasing but also incorporate the practical needs of coining on his steam-powered press. This important distinction must be kept in mind.

Lots of factors, political, social and economic, played a part in the design of coins, medals and tokens made at Soho Mint. Many of them featured portraits, including those of reigning monarchs of various countries; George III, Queen Charlotte, Gustav of Sweden, Catherine the Great of Russia, Ferdinand of Naples and Alexander I of Russia. There were also individuals ranging from industrialists and merchants to revolutionaries, John Wilkinson, Daniel Eccleston, Lafayette and Jean-Jacques Rousseau. Medals celebrated naval and military victories, such of those of Lord Howe in June 1794 and Admiral Nelson in 1798 and 1805, General Suvorov and Seringapatam in 1799. A variety of other representations on coins and tokens included allegorical figures, cornucopiae, ships, shields, coats of arms, saints, buildings, and national emblems, the Irish harp, Scottish thistle and Britannia.

Boulton was able to provide suitable designs, which commemorated current events, as well as those images used in the past, for customers who would perhaps buy his medals or commission a coinage issue. The discoveries of Herculaneum in 1709 and Pompeii in 1748 had stimulated interest in Roman and Greek antiquities, such as coins, which were collected by connoisseurs.[459] The appreciation of medals and coins was a sophisticated activity linked to social status, since a classical education was seen as essential for a cultured gentleman. But the Royal Society actively encouraged the practical applications of science, and society valued technological advances as well as art and literature.[460] Artists and poets treated industry as part of their environment, and celebrated engineers such as John Rennie, Thomas Telford and others were *accepted not only as great engineers but as great artists*.[461] Thus there was a new and growing audience for pictures, etchings and medals, both modern and 'antique'.[462] Also, increasing interest in other cultures was shown by many in the late eighteenth century. Charlotte Matthews wrote to Boulton in 1780 to let him know that: *I am learning Arabic of the Turks*.[463]

---

458 Phillp album BMAG 2003-0031-68.
459 K. Sloan (ed.) (2003) *Enlightenment: Discovering the World in the Eighteenth Century* British Museum Press p171; J. Brewer (1997) *The Pleasures of the Imagination; English Culture in the Eighteenth Century* Harper Collins, London p256.
460 A. Boime (1987) *Art in an Age of Revolution 1750-1800* University of Chicago Press, Chicago and London p203.
461 *Art and the Industrial Revolution* (1968) Manchester City Art Gallery, Manchester p1.
462 J. Brewer (1997) *The Pleasures of the Imagination; English Culture in the Eighteenth Century* Harper Collins, London pp222-256.
463 MS 3782-12-67 Item 46, William Matthews (London) to MB (Redruth) 16 November 1780.

The intended audience for a particular product was important. As early as 1772, Boulton wrote to his friend and social promoter, Elizabeth Montagu, that fashion had a lot to do with sales, and he was content to copy styles: '*makeing new combinations of old ornaments without presumeing to invent new ones*'. But one country's tastes did not suit another. He complained that he had £600 of goods for St Petersburg in his warehouse but '*the taste of goods ordered ... is not suitable for others*'. Due to an edict '*lately published by the Empress of Russia*' which prohibited the import of various goods, Boulton had problems in selling these items in 1793.[464]

For articles made in the Soho Manufactory, Boulton had incorporated ideas from a variety of sources; for example, he was influenced by James Wyatt, James (Athenian) Stuart and William Chambers, architect to King George III. He had also made visits to collections and had borrowed items from the Earl of Shelburne, Lord Dartmouth, Mrs. Montagu and others as design sources. By the 1780s the styles reflected in the design of Soho products showed a move from rococo, the 'French style' to 'antique taste'.[465]

For design ideas for the Soho Mint, Boulton made a collection of medals, and purchased illustrations of Hedlinger's medal collection from his bookseller Peter Elmsley.[466] He also bought prints via an agent in Rome, who asked if he wanted antique medals as well. Boulton was also well acquainted with Russian medallic art. John Phillp, one of Boulton's engravers, visiting London in June 1802, wrote in his diary:

> '*Went with Mr Chippendall to Mr Young the medal seller in Ludgate Hill. He has a fine and well chosen collection of medals of all descriptions. ... I saw a collection of Russian medals, the same, as Mr Boulton had presented to him from the Emperor of Russia. He asks 50 [guineas] for the set*'.[467]

These were used as sources for portraits of Russian personalities such as Suvorov, or Catherine the Great.

A group of eight figures, including a small statue of 'Prudence' and 'Mars' for use in the engravers' room was paid for in January 1799.[468] A bill in 1804 from John Flaxman Junior lists sixteen different models.[469] Flaxman also assisted the drawing master G.F. Pidgeon in designing medals for Soho Mint.[470] In May 1803, Boulton requested that:

---

464 MS 3782-12-75 Item 59, Zaccheus Walker (Birmingham) to MB (London) 4 July 1793.
465 K. Quickenden (1980) *Boulton and Fothergill silver* Art History Volume 3 no 3 p278.
466 Johann Karl von Hedlinger (1691-1771) was a Swiss engraver. *Complete de toutes Les Medailles de Chevalier Jean Charles Hedlinger* E. Robinson (1953) *Matthew Boulton: Patron of the Arts* Annals of Science 9 pp368-373.
467 Phillp's Diary 1802. Personal communication; Olga Baird, Curator, Wolverhampton Art Gallery.
468 MS 3782-3-267 Item 39, List of figures purchased for the use of the Engravers room.
469 MS 3782-6-195 Item 57, 4 February 1804.
470 D. Bindman (1979) *John Flaxman (1755-1826)* Thomas and Hudson, London p25.

'some proper person to purchase at reasonable Prices all the octavo, quarto & folio Books upon the Subjects of Coins & Medals which are in the first Days Sale, part of the late Mr. Barker's collection'.[471]

Boulton himself thought that *'Medalick art is less cultivated & Encouraged in England than in any other Europian Nation; although the most durable record of Facts, & of the taste of the times'*. He wanted his lawyer Ambrose Weston to suggest some ideas for *'Patriotick Medals with apropriate inscriptions'* and thought that *'in general the divise should not consist of more than 2 figures'*.[472]

Boulton expected his images would be understood and appreciated by his customers, though allegorical figures have lost much of their meaning for a modern audience. The image might be very complex, such as the Penryn token, with details of coats of arms and piles of weapons. Alternatively, the image might be a simple inscription, giving information such as the value of the coin or token, or where they could be exchanged, or an advertisement of services available such as on the Ibberson, Tullamore, Pen-y-darran, Hafod and Dundee tokens and on the medals for Frogmore, Washington and Manchester Volunteers. More details of these images will be given in Chapter Six.

For medals, it was necessary to get suitable texts that were historically and linguistically accurate, so that they would appeal to connoisseurs. This was an important market as it kept Soho Mint in mind with important and influential collectors, such as George III, while Boulton was awaiting large coinage orders. Inscriptions were often in Latin, nowadays only translated by a few individuals, whereas most eighteenth-century gentlemen would be expected to be able to quote the classics and therefore could understand them easily. Boulton's engraver, Noel-Alexandre Ponthon, did however suggest that Latin should not be used on designs intended for revolutionary France, and most of the inscriptions on Monneron tokens were in French.[473] The initial EIC issues had inscriptions in the local language, but later Latin inscriptions appeared on one side.

Letters from various correspondents discussed the design on Boulton's coins. For example, in 1789, one wrote concerning the specifics of the lettering:

'I observe that you make use of the round U upon the halfpenny and the sharp V on the medal. All Roman Coins and Latin Inscriptions have the sharp V but at this time o'Day & upon English money the round U may be equally as proper, & also to reduce the dipthong A/E in Cesar to plain E is more concise and elegant'.[474]

---

471 NADM Charles Roberts Autograph Letters Haverford College Library, Pennsylvania, USA MB (Soho) 4 May 1803.

472 MS 3972-12-48 Item 131, MB (Soho) to Ambrose Weston (London) 8 September 1803.

473 MS 3782-12-58 Item 16, William D. Brown (Soho) to MB (London) 10 January 1793.

474 MS 3782-12-34 Item 185, John Scott Hylton (Halesowen) to MB (Soho) 9 October 1789.

These details would have been very important to Boulton's customers. How lettering can be used as an image continues to be debated in modern times.[475]

Revolutionary symbols were not frequently used in Soho designs, except on the Monneron issues. The only other apparent use was on tokens made for Arnold Works, a wool spinning mill near Nottingham, in 1802, where the obverse shows a golden fleece (*toison d'or*) suspended from an apple tree, and the reverse shows the Roman fasces with the axe, spear and cap of liberty. These tokens were issued by Robert Davison and John Hawksley, the owners of Arnold Works. The mill employed about 1,000 male hands, 400 adults and 600 apprentices; it had a high mortality of 6-7 apprentices per week.[476]

1802 Arnold Works
one shilling

1802 Arnold Works
crown trial strike

Figure 5:1 Arnold Works token.

Many of Boulton's friends such as Priestley and Keir supported the French Revolution initially, as it was thought to be similar to the Glorious Revolution of 1688 in Britain.[477] Events were quickly reproduced in visual form, as low-quality engravings, within weeks, and the Revolution brought about changes in attitudes towards design. After the start of the Revolution, in 1791 and 1792, Boulton produced a series of tokens and medals for the Monneron brothers in Paris, which featured revolutionary emblems such as 'Liberty' and 'Louis XVI accepting the Constitution'. The female figure of 'Liberty' was seen as an active proponent of the principle she embodied, and Hercules ceased to indicate the power of kings,

475 Talk by Stephen Raw, lettering artist. 'The Visual Language of Coins' at *Art In Coinage* The British Numismatic Society and The Royal Numismatic Society Conference, Caius College, Cambridge, 5 July 2008.

476 F.E. Burton (1923-24) *Arnold Village Tokens* British Numismatics Journal Volume 17 pp177-178.

477 P. Leather 'A Sorry End: the Priestley Riots of 1791' in M. Dick (ed.) (2005) *Joseph Priestly and Birmingham*, Brewin, Studley p82.

becoming a symbol of the strength and unity of the French people. In his design of the Monneron pieces Boulton tried to respond to the rapidly changing events in France. But the visual culture of radicalism started to disappear around 1793 as the French revolution progressed and became less popular in Britain. Boulton then wanted to repair the damage done to authority, by rehabilitating the figures of Louis XVI and Marie Antoinette. In three medals produced between 1793-1794 at Soho Mint, Louis was portrayed as father figure, and Marie Antoinette as a mother torn away from her children, before their brutal executions.[478]

The wearing of short cropped hair instead of wigs became a sign of radicalism during the last years of the century, but interestingly even George III's image had short hair on the 1806 coinage issue.[479] Boulton was keeping up-to-date with fashionable trends in order to increase sales from the Soho Mint. More details of the design for the regal coinage are discussed later.

A new concept in design was the raised rim and incused lettering. It was used on the Lancaster halfpenny for Daniel Eccleston but also on the EIC issues for the 1794 and 1797 Madras coinage. It was later removed due to the difficulty in striking large quantities of coins with wide borders.

Figure 5:2
Louis XVI Farewell Medal.

Figure 5:3 1806 proof
halfpenny obverse.

478 D. Bindman (1989) *The Shadow of the Guillotine* pp12-28; p54.
479 D. Bindman (1989) *The Shadow of the Guillotine* p66.

1794 Madras 1/48-rupee   1797 Madras 1/48-rupee

Figure 5:4 Cartwheel rim on 1794 and 1797 Madras coinage.

How Soho Mint items were designed

Boulton believed that: *'whether it be French, Roman, Athenian, Egyptian, Arabask, Etruscan or any other, simplicity of device is the greatest beauty of Money or medals'.*[480] He wrote down the principles of design at the Soho Mint as follows:

'The first thing to be done is to express a good design in Words; *the 2d is to make a good* drawing *of the Idea; the 3d is to make a correct Model in* Wax *wth may be alterd to y^e taste of the Committee; & the 4th is to Engrave it in a* Steel Die *at Soho & lastly to strike y^e medal in Gold, Silver, or Copper in my improvd Press'.*[481]

Often though, design ideas came from his customers, some of whom preferred ornate images.

In many letters, ideas for designs are described, though few drawings of Soho Mint products survive. One example is Droz's design for a

Figure 5:5 Design for a pattern halfpenny by J.P. Droz, c1787.

---

480 MS 3782-12-39 Item 140, MB (Soho) to Captain Charles Stevenson (London) 29 May 1794.
481 MS 3972-12-48 Item 131, MB (Soho) to Ambrose Weston (London) 8 September 1803.

pattern halfpenny coin from 1787. This shows an image of Britannia that Boulton thought suitable for a new regal coinage issue, but does not resemble the version on the pattern coins made. More details of the design of the regal coinage will be given in Chapter Six.

Some ideas for medals came from published prints, such as the proposed Bridgewater medal, based on a drawing of 1788.[482] Francis Egerton, 3rd Duke of Bridgewater (1736-1803) was responsible for commissioning the Bridgewater canal completed in 1764. Boulton had visited Bridgewater's developments around 1762.[483] The only mention of the medal in the archives is a note to Küchler in November 1802 when Boulton wrote to say that he wanted various busts engraved including *'The Duke of Bridgewater with his aqueduct for the reverse'*.[484] However the original design, probably by John Phillp, and trial strikes exist.[485] This medal was not completed, possibly due to the Duke's death in March 1803.

Figure 5:6 Design for Duke of Bridgewater medal and trial strike.

Once a drawing was prepared, corrections to the design could be made. On the 1793 Board of Agriculture medal Boulton commented on the inscription. Küchler was told to delete *'FR ET HIB'* which was usually used for George III, *'as it is only in the capacity of King of Great Britain that he is founder of the Board of Agriculture'*, not France and Ireland.[486]

The reverse showed a female figure standing facing right holding a spade with a snake twined round the handle, Boulton asked: *'*What is this ball intended for?'* The final design still has the ball shaped item, possibly some sort of tool, as there is a scythe beneath it.

482 Duke of Bridgewater Archive www.library.salford.ac.uk DBA/1/8d.

483 H.W. Dickinson (1936; republished 1999) *Matthew Boulton* p50.

484 MS 3782-12-59 Item 130 MB (Soho) to Richard Chippindall (London) 28 November 1802; MS 3782-12-59 Item 132 Richard Chippindall (London) to MB (Soho) 2 December 1802.

485 MS 49 Reference 82934 Timmins Volume 1 Item 33, BMAG: 1976N221803 Duke of Bridgewater trial strike obverse.

486 MS 49 Reference 82934 Timmins Volume 1 Item 34, Board of Agriculture designs.

Figure 5:7 Drawings made for the Board of Agriculture medal in 1797.

Figure 5:8 1793 Board of Agriculture Prize medal.

Corrections were also made to the Welsh inscription on the Hafod medal. BRAWDGARWCH, meaning brotherhood, had been mis-spelt.[487]

---

487 MS 49 Reference 82934 Timmins Volume 1 Item 35, Hafod design.

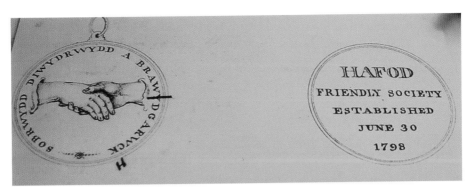

Figure 5:9 Drawing made for 1798 Hafod medal by John Phillp showing corrections.

More designs were made than could be engraved, but each was carefully discussed in detail. For example, Boulton suggested changes to the 1804 Irish regenerated 'dollar' token:

> 'it is <u>unusual to place the date at the top</u> neither will it read so well in the dollar because it will read (according to the Sketch sent to me) BANK of 1804 TOKEN nor do I think the word TOKEN should be conspicuously larger than the rest (as in the sketch). I have sent sketches of sundry different ways of placing the words'.

His modifications would: *'not impede the progress of Madame Hibernia'* as the inscription could be added after the figure was engraved.[488] The final design had the date under the exergual line.

Figure 5:10 1804 Bank of Ireland Six shillings reverse.

---

488 MS 3782-12-56 Item 118 MB (Soho) to Joseph Banks (London) 23 April 1804.

Three-dimensional wax models or plaster impressions could be prepared to allow judgments about the composition of the design. When in 1790 Dumarest engraved a new die for the Druid's head on the Anglesey token, Boulton approved of the style. Williams, asked for his opinion, wrote:

> *'I am sorry to tell you we sh^d be abused for offering a large quantity from this die. It is universally condemned as not in Character & out of proper time; the face being much too large for the rest of the Head which some critics say is in so stuck a compress it admits no Form for Brains. In Short the Old Druid by Hancock is so far beyond everything since produced, nothing else is allowed and unless we can adhere to that style & character I would rather give up the Coinage entirely than continue it otherwise'.*[489]

Further questions followed. Boulton wrote in December 1790 that he had received two models of the Druid in clay and one in wax, but: *'would you have the long beard or ye short beard or ye Wax one follow^d?'*[490] Williams wrote back: *'I like not either the very short matted beard or the long one combed out …. That between both seems to me the best & I wish your Engraver would go on with that die'.*[491] Finally a suitable die was used from June 1791 made by Hancock, and Dumarest's version was used for a Cornish halfpenny instead.[492]

1791 Anglesey halfpenny   1791 Cornish halfpenny

Figure 5:11 Anglesey and Cornish Druids (obverses).

489 MS 3782-12-77 Item 96, Thomas Williams (Temple House, Marlow) to MB (Soho) 31 October 1790.
490 MS 3782-12-73 Item 97, MB (Soho) to Thomas Williams (—) 7 December 1790.
491 MS 3782-12-73 Item 98, Thomas Williams (London) to MB (Birmingham) 14 December 1790.
492 MS 3782-12-73 Item 103, Thomas Williams (London) to MB (London) 9 June 1791.

Trial Strikes

The dies were engraved, but before hardening, trial impressions or strikes were taken in a soft material such as lead to check for mistakes. Sometimes an initial trial strike can show circular or vertical lines to enable the positions of inscriptions to be planned. The design and trial strike for the Bombay coinage is seen below. Once the final design was agreed with the customer, the die could be hardened and used to produce millions of images.

Design for Bombay   1804 Bombay double pice trial strike

Figure 5:12 Bombay design and trial strike.

A trial strike for the Tullamore token shows the inscription around the rim, but not elsewhere, and two figures are roughly sketched out on either side of a shield without detail. At this stage it was often possible to alter minor details such as a date. The completed token can be seen on the right.

Figure 5:13 Tullamore trial strike and token.

Boulton also made trial strikes for coins for Würtemberg but the trial strikes were taken no further. Frederick II was Duke of Würtemberg for only two years. When he died in 1797 his son, Frederick III (1754-1816), took part in the war against France in defiance of the wishes of his people but retired when the French again invaded the country in 1803. He also accepted the title of Elector of Würtemberg from Napoleon and in 1805 took up arms on the side of French.

Figure 5:14 1798 Würtemberg trial strikes.

Training Engravers

Boulton was constantly in search of skilled engravers and designers for the Soho Mint. He had set up a school of industrial design at Soho for apprentices who showed any talent, and they were trained to draw; John Phillp studied there.[493] They copied allegorical figures such as Hymen, the god of marriage, and Victory, which appear on Soho issues. But Boulton's designers also produced positive images of industry and commerce, and scenes from contemporary life. The image of a plough, drawn by Phillp, was engraved on the Lancaster token die.

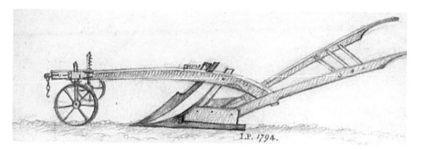

Figure 5:15 Pencil drawing of plough dated 1794 by John Phillp.

---

493 MS 3782-6-195 Item 7, To instructing J. Phillp in Architectural Drawing 4 Quarters at 15s per quarter £3 W. Hollins Bills 1795.

Figure 5:16 Section of 1794 Eccleston token.

Many well-known die engravers were first employed or trained at Soho Mint, which had a widespread influence. These included John Gregory Hancock, who was apprenticed to Boulton in 1763 along with his brother,[494] and members of the Wyon family, including George and at least two of his sons, Peter and Thomas. The Wyon family went on to supply several engravers to the Royal Mint in the nineteenth century.[495] Sir Edward Thomason was apprenticed at Soho in 1786. In his memoirs he recollected: *'I was initiated in this scientific school at Soho which induced in me a versatility of taste for mechanics and to cultivate the arts and sciences'.* He was also impressed by the extent and variety of the machinery used there, saying that it excelled *'all others of the like in Europe'.* In explaining its influence on his future work, he wrote:

> *'Having been accustomed ... at Soho to witness continuous new inventions in mechanisms and metallurgy, the mind becomes restless to produce some novelty of invention worthy of being patented'.*[496]

Thomason later produced a series of medals and inventions which were greatly admired.

Another former pupil, Thomas Halliday, manufactured tokens at his own works in Newhall Street from 1810 on, and engraved dies for firms such as Edward Thomason, and Young and Deakin of Sheffield. Halliday in turn had William Joseph Taylor as an apprentice in 1818, who made restrikes of Soho Mint material.[497] Thus the Soho Mint spread its influence into future generations of engravers.

---

494 MS 3782-12-95 Item 3, 25 August 1794.
495 George Wyon (? -1796) came to work at Soho about 1775. George had four sons, Thomas (1767-1830), his twin Peter (1767-1822), George and James. K. Quickenden (2009) *Boulton Silver and Sheffield Plate* Silver Society, London p356; N. Carlisle (1837) *A Memoir of the Life and Works of William Wyon* Nicol, London.
496 E. Thomason (1845) *Memoirs* Longman Brown, Green and Longman's, London p3.
497 D. Vice (1995) *A Fresh Insight into Soho Mint restrikes and those responsible for their manufacture* Format 52 1995.

Klingender writes that a visually educated audience was ready to receive Soho Mint products, which demonstrate a *'combination of intellectual vigour, social consciousness and imaginative design'*, a *'blend of classical symbolism and contemporary reportage'* and are *'masterly in their clear and harmonious presentation'*.[498]

Many of his mint products can still be appreciated as works of art today.[499]

Transport

Transport was an important consideration in the overall running of the Soho Mint. The efficient supply of raw materials to Birmingham, and the distribution of completed products to the customer illustrates Boulton's managerial abilities. In the case of the regal coinage contracts, the coins were delivered round the country, and for foreign orders, shipped to countries all over the world. The cost of transport included port fees, customs, wharfage, and clerical work, such as writing letters, dealing with invoices and bank drafts. The whole affair needed an organised approach to administration, especially considering the Soho Mint operated mainly during wartime.

In the mid-eighteenth century it had been cheaper to ship merchandise to Lisbon by sea than to transport goods from London to Norwich by land, due to the state of the roads.[500] Communications gradually improved due to increasing prosperity, with more investment in roads, shipping and canals; by 1777 there were 52 coaches from Birmingham to London per week, with 16 to Bristol, and 4 to Sheffield.[501] Boulton was interested in all aspects of transport and had campaigned with others for improved turnpike roads, but despite progress, the cost of land transport remained high.[502] One of the reasons that Boulton had wanted to establish the Birmingham Assay Office in 1773, was so that valuable goods from his Soho Manufactory would not be damaged or stolen, in transit to and from the assay office at Chester, and to eliminate the extra cost of transport.[503]

Transport was also vital to maintaining the networks by which Boulton obtained his orders, and exerted his influence. From the 1760s, Boulton had cultivated good relationships with local aristocracy, members of parliament and royalty. He had many contacts with British ambassadors, such as Lord Cathcart who went to Russia, and William Hamilton, ambassador to Naples from

---

498 F.D. Klingender (1948; 1968) *Art and the Industrial Revolution* Kelley, New York pp41-43; p46.

499 Richard Clay has argued that Boulton and the Soho Mint made important contributions to the 'massification of art'. R. Clay (2009) in: R. Clay and S. Tungate (eds.) *Matthew Boulton and the Art of Making Money* pp39-55.

500 E. Hopkins (1989) *Birmingham: The First Manufacturing Town in the World 1760-1840* Weidenfeld and Nicholson.

501 M.J. Wise (1967) *The Influence of the Lunar Society in the Development of Birmingham* University of Birmingham Historical Journal Volume 9; pp79-93.

502 MS 3782-12-107-15, 1787 Notebook 25 February 1787.

503 S. Baggott (2009) 'Real Knowledge and Occult Mysteries: Matthew Boulton and the Birmingham Assay Office' in: M. Dick (ed.) (2009) *Matthew Boulton: A Revolutionary Player* pp201-216.

1764-1800, plus foreign ambassadors to Britain such as Moussin Pushkin and Count Woronzow.[504] Boulton's ability to maintain his connections was helped enormously by improvements in the postal system. Until 1784 the mail was robbed regularly, and it would take at least three days for a letter to reach London from Birmingham. John Palmer of Bath organised a faster and more reliable system, with armed guards, and by the 1790s it was possible to receive post daily from London, taking around sixteen hours per trip.[505] In 1794, Soho Mint actually provided tokens for Christopher Ibberson which advertised 'MAIL AND POST COACHES TO ALL PARTS OF ENGLAND'.

Boulton was able to respond quickly to information received; a daily box was sent by the mail-coach to Soho's London agents, taking letters, drafts and small orders such as medals. He kept up a correspondence with individuals such as Wilkinson, Williams and Banks, and was able to arrange meetings with them in Birmingham, Cornwall, London and elsewhere. Boulton details many journeys in his diaries and letters.[506] Similarly, he maintained contact with members of the Lunar Society.[507] Regular letters were sent to and from his agent, Thomas Wilson, in Cornwall. In 1787 Zaccheus Walker, Boulton's warehouse manager, informed him that 'an Express from Birmingham will be in Truro in 48 hours'.[508] This was a great improvement in postal delivery, but it still took Boulton personally at least five days to get to Cornwall.

Post could also be received from the Continent, as Boulton noted in his 1786 diary 'the pack[et]s with mail sets out from Calais every Wednesday and Saturday to England'.[509] Surprisingly, even during the Napoleonic wars, the links with continental Europe were maintained. Through a network of agents Boulton was able to communicate with places as far apart as India, Sumatra, Russia, France, the United States and Canada despite the problems caused by war.

Boulton himself travelled extensively in the 1780s while simultaneously trying to sort out the problems of the Cornish copper industry and attempting to gain a regal coinage contract. Between February and May 1786, he was in London and then travelled to Cornwall, London again on several occasions, and to Paris.[510] In September 1787, a particularly energetic trip for the fifty-nine year old Boulton involved travelling, in one week, from Birmingham to visit John Wilkinson's iron empire in Shropshire, and Thomas Williams's copper mine, rolling mills and copper works in Anglesey, plus conferring with Lord Uxbridge at Bangor en

504 N. Goodison (1974; 2002) *Matthew Boulton Ormolu* pp404-426.
505 A.F. Amann (1985) *John Palmer and His Mail Coach* Seaby Coin and Medal Bulletin April 1985 no 799 p113.
506 MS 3782-12-107-14-16, Boulton's diaries 1786-1788.
507 J. Uglow (2002) *The Lunar Men: Friends who Made the Future.*
508 MS 3782-12-74 Item 132, Zaccheus Walker (Birmingham) to MB (Soho) 5 May 1787.
509 MS 3782-12-107-14, Boulton's 1786 Diary.
510 MS 3782-12-107-14, Boulton's 1786 Diary.

route.[511] This journey, cementing the relationship between Williams, Wilkinson and Boulton, was to establish who was to bid for a regal coinage contract, vital to the survival of the Cornish copper industry.[512]

Immediately after this trip, Boulton spent three days with Droz in Birmingham and returned with him to London on 17th September and was off to Cornwall again by 23rd October 1787.[513] This travelling was to have a long-lasting effect on Boulton's health. The kidney problems, which were to trouble him for the rest of his life, appear to have started while travelling from London to Cornwall by the new patent mail coach.

> *'The Coach was the most uneasy I ever rode in. I got no sleep & my back hurt. The pain increased in my back and at Charmouth I became very ill and vomited & could go no further than Axminster where I was obliged to abandon the coach & go to bed'.*[514]

He was also unfit for a meeting with Wilkinson and Williams at Soho House in December 1787 and unable to attend a Privy Council meeting with them to decide on the regal coinage contract, as he had: *'Voided 12 stones about ye size of vetches. 11th Dec voided 19 stones like ye last. 12th Dec voided several stones, some larger'.*[515]

Transport by water

A lot of goods in the eighteenth century were transported by water by coastal vessels and along navigable rivers as it was much cheaper. By 1758, there were regular trips by 'trows' carrying 50 tons from Bristol to Bewdley and Bridgnorth along the River Severn. However, Birmingham had no river transport, and was many miles away from the sea.[516] This was remedied by the canal system. The Bridgewater canal was opened in 1761, and canals in the Midlands swiftly followed. The Staffordshire and Worcester canal from the River Severn was navigable to Newhall Wharf in Birmingham by 1772, and the Trent and Mersey canal, connecting Birmingham via the rivers to the North Sea and Irish Sea, was opened by 1777.[517] But when the Soho Mint was first set up, it was not possible to go directly to London from Birmingham by canal.

---

511 MS 3782-12-107-15, 1787 Boulton's Notebook.
512 MS 3147-3-11 Item 7, MB (Truro) to James Watt (Harper's Hill) September to October 1787.
513 MS 3782-12-107-15, 1787 Boulton's Notebook.
514 MS 3782-12-107-15, Boulton's 1787 Notebook, 25 October 1787.
515 MS 3782-12-107-15, 1787 Notebook, December.
516 M.B. Rowland (1975) *Masters and Men in the West Midlands Metal-ware Trades before the Industrial Revolution* Manchester University Press, Manchester p99.
517 S. Holland (1992) *Canal Coins* Baldwin, Cleobury Mortimer.

Figure 5:17 1803 Duke of Bridgewater trial strike reverse,
showing the canal crossing the river Irwell.

Boulton had been heavily involved in the extension of the canal system to Birmingham, and remained interested in its progress.[518] It was essential to the development of the Soho Mint. Without the canals it would have been very difficult to transport the heavy loads of copper from Cornwall and Anglesey to Soho Mint and distribute the coin. Canal narrow boats, due to limitations in the size of locks, were restricted to loads of around 25 tons, pulled by one horse, but to move the same amount by land would need two hundred horses. Before Birmingham was linked to the canal system, it had cost 2s per ton per mile to move coal by mule from the south Staffordshire coalfield, three miles away, but once the canal opened the cost of transport dropped by two-thirds.

Many engineers, including James Watt, gained experience working on canal construction, and the B&W reciprocating steam-engine was used to pump water back up the canal system, as well as to pump water in mines; the Smethwick engine on the Birmingham canal was in operation from 1779. John Smeaton and John Rennie, who both worked with Boulton, were also involved in canal building.[519] Hugh Henshall, who had taken over as an engineer on the Trent and Mersey canal, after James Brindley's death in 1772, later became an important haulage contractor for Boulton's Soho Mint products.

Boulton was able to organise the transport of shipments to and from Soho by certain trusted carriers. A variety of routes were used, depending on how quickly

518 MS 3782-12-23 Item 113, Peter Bottom (Cornhill) to MB (Birmingham) 8 March 1768.
519 G. Demidowicz in: M. Dick (2009) *Matthew Boulton; A Revolutionary Player* p122; p180.

an order was required. For fast small deliveries Boulton used Thomas Sherratt, who operated 'Sherratt's Flying Waggon', which delivered items to London in less than a day.[520] Bulky shipments went by water and regular payments for haulage were made to Thomas Toye, Hugh Henshall, Charles Broadley and Edward Doughty.[521] Toye took consignments the short distance from Soho Mint to and from the Birmingham Wharfs. Doughty shipped items south along the canal to Stourport and the River Severn, where copper arriving from Swansea or Bristol could be exchanged for orders to the south-west. Henshall's firm moved orders north, along the Staffordshire and Worcester canal and the Trent and Mersey canal north-west to Liverpool, or north-east via Gainsborough and the River Trent, to Hull, where Broadley would take goods for passage on to London or to France by sea. This method was used for 183 tons of tokens, consisting of 8 million coins in 1,100 casks, sent between 1791-3 for the Monneron Brothers in Paris and for early EIC coinage issues.[522] The more south-easterly canal route to London via Oxford and the Thames was finally available by the time of the 1797 regal coinage orders.[523]

For America or Ireland, items could be sent to Bristol, or to Liverpool, depending on port charges and sailing times.[524] In 1799 an order of 103 casks, each containing 130-150 kg of copper blanks, consigned to the Philadelphia Mint, was forwarded to Liverpool to be shipped on board the *Swanwick*.[525] For other foreign orders Boulton was dependent on vessels such as those belonging to the East India Company. Orders for Sumatra, India or Ceylon had to reach St Botolph's Wharf, London, in time for their regular spring or autumn sailings to South East Asia. Other ships went to Africa with Soho coins as part of their cargo. Eventually coins from Soho Mint were distributed around the world, though orders for South America were mainly after Boulton's death. His products even reached China with the 1793 Lord Macartney expedition.[526]

Because of the difficult terrain and ample coastal provision of shipping, improvements in road transport had not reached the Cornish mining district. Mine roads and track-ways were often unsuitable for wheeled vehicles, so copper ore was transported by mules to the ports at Hayle, Copperhouse, Portreath and Devoran, because there was no suitable local coal for smelting. Ore was sent to smelting works near Swansea, and coal, needed for pumping steam-engines, was transported back to the mines in a similar way. Boulton estimated that there were 1,000 mules at a time in Hayle in 1780, and 2,500 in 1800. Each mule could

---

520 MS 3782-12-59 Item 169, William Cheshire to MB 26 April 1798.

521 MS 3782-3-13, Mint Day Book 1791-1795.

522 MS 3782-3-13, Mint Day Book 1791-1795 26 December 1792.

523 R.A. Pelham (1955) *The Worcester and Birmingham Canal* Birmingham Historical Journal Volume 1 (1955) pp60-82.

524 MS 3782-12-59 Item 186, William Cheshire to MB 4 March 1799.

525 MS 3782-3-15, Mint Book 30th June 1798 to 24th December 1799 p206.

526 MS 3782-12-75 Item 49, Zaccheus Walker (Birmingham) to MB (London) 18 October 1792.

carry up to 90kg on average, and travel 30 km or more per day in summer, but in winter or rainy periods, the tracks became virtually impassable.[527]

It was the expense involved in transporting coal to the mines to power Newcomen engines, which led to the use of the more efficient B&W steam-engine, and hence to Boulton's interest in the Cornish copper industry. Cheaper transport was one reason why Anglesey copper could be produced at a lower price than in Cornwall. Parys Mine is only two miles from a natural harbour at Amlwch. Ore could be shipped to smelting works at Swansea, and Ravenhead on Merseyside where there was coal available, and coal could also be easily imported to treat ore at the port. Ships were also loaded at low tide on local beaches and re-floated when the tide was high. There was a huge amount of traffic. Records for 1792 show 327 ships with a gross tonnage of 13,287 tons visiting Anglesey. This compares with Swansea which received 96 ships and 5,521 tons in the same year.[528]

Figure 5:18 Amlwch harbour, Anglesey, August 2009. (The sailing ship in Amlwch harbour is a modern replica of the HMS *Pickle* which brought the news of the battle of Trafalgar to Britain).

Problems of Transport

Between 1789 and his death in 1809, Boulton had to organise the delivery of an average of six tons of copper per week, and the distribution of coins to countries as far apart as Canada and Ceylon, although there were times when orders

527 J. Griffiths (1992) *The Third Man: The Life and Times of William Murdoch (1754-1829)* Deutsch, London p105.
528 www.amlwchhistory.co.uk.

were plentiful and others when they were sparse. This was an impressive feat of administration, given the transport and financial structures in place at the time.

When international transport was involved, completion of orders at Soho Mint had to be in line with shipping dates.[529] When conditions were favourable, Boulton was able to complete orders on time. But transport could be affected by the weather; by frosts, snow, rain and floods. In February 1795, Boulton was very worried about 120 tons of coin for Madras. He wrote from London to his son to say that:

> 'the time now grows very short for the delivery of the remainder of the East India Coin.... What is already Coined; What quantity of Copper is yet wanted at Soho to compleat the 120 tons of Coin; What steps are taken to obtain the remainder; When it is probable the last Cask of ye 120 Ton will be sent off?'[530]

Matt wrote back:

> 'the floods having put a stop to Land as well as Water Carriage, the copper coming in the wagons have been detained upon the Road & this disappointment in the supply of Metal will much retard the coinage. I am sensible this delay will cause you some vexation & yet I do not see any way of preventing it'.[531]

In addition, Sherratt was sending casks of coins by the slower canal route rather than by road. Boulton requested that 'Wallis the carrier' could take some 'as every ton that is not shipped will be a loss of more than 40 Guineas to me'.[532] Boulton could not do anything about the weather, but he could change his haulage contractors.

Copper and coin were valuable cargoes, and needed secure storage both during and after transport. Boulton preferred to have items shipped in casks so that there was less risk of pilfering, and consignments could be traced. However, this was expensive; casks alone could be one twentieth of the cost of coining.[533] That was without the charges for transport which added considerable expense. Though several attempts at robbery were made at the Soho site, only one theft during transport of coin was reported.[534] Boulton was concerned enough to suggest that cargoes were shipped in locked barges.[535] When valuable silver tokens were sent to Ireland in 1804, they had an escort of twelve armed soldiers.[536]

---

529 MS 3147-3-12 Item 9, MB (London) to James Watt (Harper's Hill) 20 February 1788.
530 MS 3782-13-36 Item 116, MB (London) to MRB (Soho) 2 February 1795.
531 MS 3782-13-36 Item 174, MRB (Soho) to MB (London) February 1795.
532 MS 3782-13-36 Item 121, MB (London) to MRB (Soho) 26 February 1795.
533 MS 3782-3-13, Mint Day Book 1791-1795.
534 R. Margolis (2005) *Those Pests of Canals: A theft of Monneron Tokens intended for France* British Numismatic Journal Volume 75 pp121-131.
535 F. Tait (2009) in: S. Mason (2009) *Matthew Boulton: A Revolutionary Player* p89.
536 D. Vice (1994) *The 1804 Bank of Ireland Six Shilling Token* Format 50 1994.

Apart from the obvious dangers of travel during a time of war, ships were often destroyed by shipwreck. A letter of 1798 details the *'loss of the "Rose", Captain Cooper, a vessel on board of which Messrs. Doughty & Co. had shipp'd 23 casks of coin for sundry correspondents at Plymouth'*. It was reported initially that *'13 whole casks, and about a cask and a half of loose pieces, had been dug out of the sand'* at Bigbury Bay. But another report said that only a small proportion of the coins sent would be saved.[537] Another loss was reported from the wreck of the Fife packet in January 1798. Boulton did carry insurance for some of these losses but it meant disruption and trouble at the Soho Mint.[538] Some Madras coins were lost with the wreck of the *Hindostan* in 1803, and more in early 1809 when the *Admiral Gardner* sank on the Goodwin Sands.[539]

The Sierra Leone coinage seemed particularly prone to problems of transport. Many of the 10 cent pieces sent to Sierra Leone in 1793 were destroyed in a fire on board the *York* shortly after arriving in Africa. Most of the remaining silver coinage was taken when the colony was ransacked by the French in 1794. Between 1798 and 1799 only six ships were sent to Sierra Leone; four of these were taken by the French and a fifth wrecked.[540]

Regal Coinage Distribution

Previously, new regal coins were only available at the Royal Mint located at the Tower of London, issued in 5s or 10s packets (or rouleau) collected personally.[541] By the time Boulton gained the regal coinage contract in 1797, he insisted that distribution was included as part of the deal:

> *'I conceive this coin should be deliverd in every great Town in the Kingdom from whence it will spread into the small towns & Villages ...I proposed to send to each Town a quantity in the proportion of 1 Ton to every ten thousand inhabitants'.*

He thought it would be:

> *'bad Policy as well as bad oeconomy to deposit the <u>whole of the Coinage</u> in any place previous to putting any of it into circulation. Moreover it would be laying a Burthen of £70,000 upon my shoulders which is more that I can bear. Whereas if it is distributed & paid for as fast as it is made (say 20 Tons per Week) it will support itself & be a burthen to no party'.*[542]

---

537 MS 3782-12-59 Item 180, William Cheshire (Soho) to MB (London) 5 December 1798.
538 MS 3782-3-14, Mint Day Book 23 May 1795-16 June 1798 p183.
539 R. Doty (1998) *Soho Mint* p332.
540 D. Vice (1983) *The Coinage of British West Africa & St Helena 1684-1958* Format, Birmingham p21.
541 D. Symons (2009) in: M. Dick (ed.) (2009) *Matthew Boulton: A Revolutionary Player* p171.
542 MS 3782-12-42 Item 171, MB (Soho) to Stephen Cottrell (London) 14 July 1797.

In this way Boulton could afford to pay for the transport of coin to all parts of Britain before he was reimbursed for his efforts by the Government.

Initially he was to be allowed 17s for delivery no matter how near or far.[543] This was increased to £4 for the 1799 contract.[544] He planned to deliver coins to bankers or other individuals in each town, who would pay for £25 worth of coins at a time. Some of these customers were known to Boulton from prior orders at Soho. He also suggested that coins could be distributed through government run organisations such as dockyards, where large numbers of workers were employed.[545] This meant that Soho Mint's regal coinage spread easily across the country unlike coins from the Royal Mint.

Before the first issue of the 1797 coins agents, such as James Lawson and John Southern, travelled around England promoting sales of the coins. From Leeds, Southern told Boulton: *'I have been to 3 banks as being most likely to promote the circulation. ... they will each take £500 worth as soon as you please to send it'.*[546] As the customer was not paying for delivery, Southern advised that: *'The carriage to different parts of England is a very serious matter & I think your attention should be directed to those parts of the kingdom only where water carriage can be employed'.* It cost, for example, more than £10 per ton to get coin by road to Newcastle but less than £2 by water. Three out of the four banks there were willing to take £200 each, and Southern also saw *'some of the principle shopkeepers who are extremely glad to hear of the new coinage & will give it every support'.*[547] This prior 'advertising' made it easier to introduce the new regal coinage issue.

In the Mint Record books, lists of customers all over the country can be seen for the 1797 coinage issue. Penny pieces were wrapped in paper packets of 2s each, and packed into casks, each weighing 375lb, and containing 6,000 coins worth £25. Customers were charged the face value for the order. 17,500 casks of coins were distributed, including 2,654 casks to Lancashire, 1,141 to Yorkshire, 1,212 to Staffordshire, 1,204 to Warwickshire and 1,452 casks to Somerset House and to Charlotte Matthews, Boulton's banker, in London.[548]

It was an enormous task to keep track of the orders coming in, and the dispatch of coins all over the country. These records were kept by a variety of individuals including Boulton himself, his son, Matt, James Lawson, John Southern, and Zaccheus Walker. Most of the important industrial and financial associations in Britain in the 1790s are seen in the lists. For example, Benjamin Huntsman Junior from Sheffield ordered £50-worth of cartwheel pennies in August 1797, as did Richard Crawshay of Cyfartha Ironworks. The Birmingham bankers, Taylor and

---

543 MS 3782-17-4, License to coin 9 June 1797.
544 MS 3782-17-5, License to coin 4 November 1799.
545 MS 3782-12-42 Item 171, MB (Soho) to Stephen Cottrell (London) 14 July 1797.
546 MS 3782-12-66 Item 84, John Southern (Leeds) to MB (Soho) 5 July 1797.
547 MS 3782-12-66 Item 86, John Southern (Newcastle upon Tyne) to MB (Soho) 16 July 1797.
548 MS 3782-3-15, Mint Book 1798-1799 p75 on.

Lloyd had £25-worth of pennies by Soho Cart on 4th September as did Spooner and Attwood, and Gotwaltz at the Post Office. By 14th September 1797 orders totalling £1,875 were sent to places as varied as Nottingham, Darlington, the Bank of Scotland, Edinburgh, Glasgow, Bedford, Perth, Sunderland and Market Drayton.[549]

Boulton wrote that:

'I have not principle assistance in my Coinage, which has open'd a new field of trouble & correspondence. I have the pleasure to say it is going on rapidly yet nevertheless the demand is more rapid at present, and the reflux of money after so great an outlay is very agreeable, but I am sorry to say that no addition has been made to my order which does not exceed 500 tons although I wish it did'.[550]

Further regal coinage orders were received at Soho Mint in 1799 which irritated the Royal Mint. They hindered the operations as inspectors would not come down frequently enough to check the completed coins. It meant that Boulton was losing money on undistributed stock lying around, and there were problems of safe storage. Banks had suggested a warehouse nearer to the centre of London, but Boulton replied that this was unnecessary as: *'I deliver the coin in new Casks free of all expense & trouble at the house of the person who order it, whether they live at one end of the Town or the other or at one end of the Kingdom or the other'.*[551] This distribution was an important improvement in the supply of small change in Britain.

---

549 MS 3782-3-14, Mint Day Book 23 May 1795-16 June 1798.
550 MS 3782-12-42 Item 206, MB (Soho) to George C. Fox & Sons (Falmouth) 25 August 1797.
551 MS 3782-12-56 Item 124, Matthew Boulton (Soho) to Sir Joseph Banks (London) 29 November 1799.

Chapter Six

What Boulton Made

Regal coinage

THE Soho Mint was initially set up to make a regal coinage issue. Boulton's aim was to produce sufficient good quality copper coin for the growing industrial workforce. He had been encouraged by the Committee on Coin to think that he would receive a contract, but George III had his first bout of madness in summer 1788. After George's recovery in February 1789, the government decided that there was sufficient coin in circulation, though Boulton did not agree.[552] Then the French Revolution meant that, by January 1793, Britain was again at war with France, and coinage was put on hold. Soho Mint did not make anything for the Government until 1797.

Early attempts
Boulton's friends, Samuel Garbett and his son Francis, investigated the operation of the Royal Mint in 1782. From Garbett's report, Boulton had thought that government-appointed mint officials were charging too much and achieving little, and he could do much better.[553] Thomas Williams had originally been a rival for the coinage contract, but by October 1787 he and Boulton were making joint approaches to the Government.[554] They hoped for a consumption of 3,000 tons of copper to make coins, to use up the copper surpluses, and to make a profit for them both.[555] When asked to attend a meeting of the Privy Council for Coin in December 1787, Boulton wrote to Williams asking for advice.[556] Both Williams

---

552 MS 3782-12-97 Item 234, Copper coinage and government. Mint memorandum December 1789.
553 MS 3782-12-61 Item 45, Samuel Garbett (London) to MB (Cusgarne) 22 October 1782; MS 3782-12-108 Item 63 Collection of Facts relative to Exchanges and Coins and to Mint establishments 1792 by Samuel Garbett.
554 MS 3782-12-73 Item 69, Thomas Williams (Anglesey) to MB (Cornwall) 12 October 1787.
555 AD1583/2/76, MB to Wilson 13 October 1787.
556 MS 3782-12-3, MB Soho to Thomas Williams 2 December 1787.

and John Wilkinson arrived at Soho ready to accompany him to London, but a bout of kidney stones made it impossible for Boulton to attend, so the meeting was adjourned until January 1788.[557] At this point a very large coinage order of at least 1,000 tons per year was expected at Soho Mint.[558]

After attending the Privy Council, Boulton started to build the Soho Mint, thinking that the regal coinage contract was imminent. He reported to Watt that:

> *'I attended the Privy Council for 2 or 3 hours on 15th. The only thing that seems to be determined absolutely by them is 1st to make a new copper coinage & suppress all the old and bad. 2nd to buy the copper and the workmanship as cheap as possible & 3rd to take no profits for the Goverm[t] or allow one farthing of perquesite to the Mint officers & to put a full halfpenny worth of copper and workmanship into every halfpenny. They have promised me nothing but say they do not make a point of coining it in the Tower'.*[559]

The final agreement appeared to have been made by 8th February 1788, and Boulton wrote to Matt with enthusiasm:

> *'I was sent for to Town by Mr Pitt and the Privy Council about a new copper coinage which I have agreed for but at a very low price yet nevertheless it shall be the best Copper Coin that ever was made. I am building a Mint & new Manufacture for it ... at Soho where I shall be closed engaged for 1½ Year without going to Cornwall. Pray go to Mr Droz & see & tell me exactly what state he is in with my Sous'.*[560]

In order to show what Soho Mint would produce, pattern coins were needed, to be presented to influential people. Boulton had visited Paris in December 1786, leaving his son Matt to study there, and Jean-Pierre Droz was commissioned to engrave coin dies. Droz visited Soho in September 1787 and managed to engrave a pattern shilling die. But Boulton wanted a halfpenny die, and had sent a series of increasingly more frantic letters to find out what was happening:

October 1787 *'Pray call on Mr Droz ... and see if he has begun to engrave any dye for me'.*[561]

December 1787 *'Pray go to Mr Droz, ... and tell him I shall lose my reputation and loose the Copper Coinage unless he confines himself intirely to the completion of the dies (le Coin) ... I propose to give one to each Member of Parliament accompanied with a short proposition ... to put an end the Counterfeiting of Copper half pence'.*[562]

---

557 MS 3147-3-11 Item 18, MB (Soho) to James Watt (—) 23 December 1787.
558 MS 3147-3-12 Item 1, MB (Soho) to James Watt (Edinburgh) 8 January 1788.
559 MS 3147-3-12 Item 2, MB (London) to James Watt (Harper's Hill) 25 January 1788.
560 MS 3782-13-36 Item 21, MB (London) to MRB Paris 11 March 1788.
561 MS 3782-13-36 Item 11, MB (Truro) to MRB Versailles 2 October 1787.
562 MS 3782-13-36 Item 14, MB (Soho) to MRB Versailles 1 December 1787.

January 1788 'Pray go to Mr Droz and tell him that Belisarius never begd so hard for a halfpenny as I do, & write me by the return of the post when I may expect to receive one'.[563]

Boulton was unable to get *'my written Contract from Government until I can present to the Ministers a few <u>perfect specimens</u> & for want of which I am kept in a disagreeable suspence'.* Sadly, when he finally received the lead impressions of the halfpennies in March 1788, the die was broken in the hardening and needed to be remade.[564]

In August 1788 the hope for a regal coinage contract received a huge set back when the King became ill, and there was a possibility of a regency. Boulton followed the arguments in Parliament closely, and persisted in his plans, seeking advice on design from the leading artists of the time. But by February 1789 he was becoming increasingly worried about the prospects for his mint. An up-to-date report on George III's health indicated that he *'is perfectly recovered [in] all the powers of his mind and is recovering his strength of body daily in so much that the proceedings of the Regency Bill is stopped'.* More than £4,000 had already been spent on new technology, *'in Buildings, Engines, Coining Machine, Rolling Mills etc. etc. which I did upon the Faith of the orders I received under the seal of the Privy Council'*, but no contract ensued.[565]

Boulton continued to have a series of meeting with influential people, seeking a regal coinage contract, but also met with Thomas Williams, and agreed to coin his popular Anglesey tokens.[566] He was able to visit George III at Windsor in June 1789, accompanied by Droz, and in his diary wrote: *'the King & Queen talked with me upon the terras about France & French projects & fire engines & coin'.*[567] He also wrote to Watt:

> *'The king allows me to send him 12 penyworth which I accompanied with a paper of explanation. He looks in perfect good health & quite calm but not so fat as formerly. I have left Droz peeking at the king and the K[ing] at him'.*[568]

This enabled Droz to engrave dies for a new version of the halfpenny.

One of the supporters for a new coinage was Sir Joseph Banks (1743-1820), who had known Boulton since at least 1768. He thanked Boulton for *'the excellent & abundant specimens'* and said that: *'The workmanship also claims so decided a superiority that it will bear no comparison with any copper coin I have seen & consequently be a material security against counterfeits'.* Banks also thought that the issue, which had again been postponed due to the ill health of Lord Hawkesbury (President of the Board of Trade), would possible be discussed in November 1789.[569]

---

563 MS 3782-13-36 Item 17, MB (London) to MRB Paris 15 January 1788.
564 MS 3782-13-36 Item 24, MB (Soho) to MRB Paris 24 April 1788.
565 MS 3782-13-36 Item 28, MB (Soho) to MRB (Germany) 23 February 1789.
566 MS 3782-12-107, Boulton's 1789 Diary.
567 MS 3782-12-107, Boulton's 1789 Diary.
568 MS 3147-3-13 Item 7, MB (London) to James Watt (Harper's Hill) 23 June 1789.
569 MS 3782-12-56 Item 12, Joseph Banks (London) to MB (Soho) 21 August 1789.

However, the events of the French Revolution, starting with the convocation of the Estates General in May 1789, and culminating in the execution of Louis XVI in January 1793, were occupying the thoughts of Pitt and the government, and the regal coinage contract went into abeyance. Boulton wrote in October 1789: *'This is an epoch of great moment … The King and Queen of France are fallen from their high station at Versailles and are now little more than state prisoners in the Louvre'.*[570] An appointment with Pitt in December 1789 resulted in failure.[571] By January 1790 Boulton was again expecting to start coining 1500 tons of copper but again nothing happened.[572] In June of that year, Boulton was becoming disillusioned with the coining project. He had been let down by Droz and:

> *'my health & happiness deranged by the Conduct of our Government who have boy'd me up with hopes of contracting for 1500 or 2000 tons of Copper Coin & now after spending a great many Thousand pounds & after inventing & compleating a Coining apparatus upon new ingenious and more perfect principles than any ever yet produced in the World, yet … I perceive that I shall be disappointed'.*[573]

After this Soho Mint was used for several token orders, but did not have sufficient work to justify the expense of a steam-powered mint until the 1791 EIC order.

Thomas Wyon engraved guinea dies in 1791, and used a modified 1790 reverse Britannia die to make pattern halfpennies in 1795, possibly for a consortium of brewers.[574] However, Boulton urged the brewers to pressurize the Government for a regal coinage and repeated his offer to make copper coins. He got his wish in 1797 when finally, the government ordered an issue of copper coins from Soho Mint.

1797 coinage

Boulton's first regal coins should be seen as part of the response to the 1797 currency crisis. On 22nd February 1797 the French attempted an invasion at Fishguard. A correspondent wrote: *'Upwards of 1200 French who landed a few days ago in Pembrokeshire have been captured; the County rose in a mass and surrounded them. Two Generals and an Irish pilot were of the party'.*[575] On 26th February 1797 cash payments were suspended temporarily by the Bank of England. This had the effect of undermining the monetary system. The Bank had been under threat of failure since 1793. The only coins not in short supply, gold guineas and half guineas, were being hoarded. The number of silver coins in circulation was

---

570 MS 3782-13-36 Item 36, MB (Soho) to MRB (Germany) 26 October 1789.
571 MS 3147-3-13 Item 15 and 16, MB (London) to James Watt (Birmingham) 2 December 1789; 6 December 1789.
572 MS 3782-13-36 Item 41, MB (Soho) to MRB 4 January 1790.
573 MS 3782-13-36 Item 46, MB (London) to MRB (—) 15 June 1790.
574 MS 3782-12-66 Item 9, James Lawson (Soho) to MB (London) 23 May 1791.
575 MS 3782-12-42 Item 28, Williams (Henllis Llandovery) to MB (Soho) 27 February 1797.

very small, and many were worn and easily counterfeited. Pieces of eight (from Spanish eight *reales*) circulated freely in Britain. To alleviate the shortage of cash and to allow business to continue, the Bank issued notes, and tokens made from Spanish coins overstamped by an oval punch showing George III's head. And, as previously detailed, there was still a great shortage of small change.

On 2nd March 1797 a motion was introduced in Parliament to request a copper coinage as penny, two-penny and three-penny pieces. The three-pence was soon dropped.[576] The idea of halfpence and farthing issues was dismissed temporarily, though Boulton was convinced that a large issue of these was required.[577] The Earl of Liverpool, formerly Lord Hawkesbury, who headed the Committee for Coin responsible for re-organising the coinage, wrote to Boulton in flattering terms on 3rd March 1797:

'it has been suggested, that it may be proper in such a Moment, to have a new Copper Coinage—There is no Man who can better judge of the Propriety of this Measure, and of the Plan that ought to be adopted, in issuing a Coinage of this Nature, than Yourself; and no one will execute it with more Accuracy, and more Expedition'.[578]

He invited Boulton to attend a Privy Council meeting on 7th March to arrange for an immediate issue of copper coins.[579] By 15th March Boulton had drafted proposals for making a new coinage:

'like specimens sent; more difficult to be counterfeited, devices shielded by a flat border which is a little higher. Offer to receive the copper from the smelting furnace in its first state called tough cake copper, to roll it hot, scale it and clean it, roll it, polished etc'.[580]

The regal coinage contract was unusual in that copper two-penny and one penny coins were requested. The choice of these coins, rather than halfpennies and farthings most needed for industrial workers, was to bridge the shortage of lower value silver coins like sixpences and shillings. Soho Mint was initially asked to strike 480 tons of one penny pieces and 20 tons of two pence to follow. The contract was signed on 9th June 1797 and coining commenced ten days later. Boulton was finally able to write to his son:

'I have the pleasure to tell you that I have now finaly agreed with the Lords of the Treasury to coin 500 tons of penny pieces & to deliver 20 tons every week (which

576 G. Dyer (2002) *The Currency Crisis of 1797* British Numismatic Journal Volume 72 (2002) pp135-142.

577 MS 3782-12-42 Item 84, MB (Soho) to Sir George Stuckburgh-Evelyn (—) (March 1797).

578 MS 3782-12-42 Item 35, The Earl of Liverpool (London) to MB (Soho) 3 March 1797.

579 MS 3782-12-42 Item 40, Stephen Cottrell (Council Office, London) to MB (London) 6 March 1797.

580 MS 3782-12-42 Item 53, MB (London) to the Committee of Privy Council for Coin (—) 15 March 1797.

*will require 30 tons to be weekly rolld) from and after 15th May. I have come to a full
Explanation with Mr Williams (we are friends) & I am bound to deliver 250 ton of
copper wth is already B[ough]^t & if Mr W pleases he may deliver the other 250 ton'.*[581]

Boulton had ensured enough copper for the initial contract, but received a letter
in March 1797 from Pascoe Grenfell, Williams's partner, to say that the price of
copper could not be guaranteed, which was to lead to problems later.[582]

Figure 6:1.1 Four sizes of 1797 pattern coins.

Boulton was allowed £37 6s 8d per ton for coining, and a further 17s per ton for
casks, packing, warehousing and other expenses. Copper cost £108 per ton.[583]
Later coinage contracts in November 1799 and April 1805 and October 1807 did
not raise the price for coining much, but the cost of copper increased dramatically.

On 26th July 1797 Boulton's first regal coinage issue received royal consent.[584]
The same day, a delivery of 160 casks, value £4,000, was made to a Warehouse at
Somerset House *'to the Right Honourable the Lord Commissioners for His Majesty's
Treasury'.* It was sent by Thomas Sherratt, one of Boulton's regular carriers, via
canal to Oxford, and then on to London via the Thames.

---

581 MS 3782-13-36 Item 132, MB (London) to MRB (Soho) 9 April 1797.
582 MS 3782-12-42 Item 55, Pascoe Grenfell (London) to MB (London) 16 March 1797.
583 MS 3782-17-3, Articles of agreement for Copper for the intended new Coinage and for the
     Carriage for such Coinage 6 June 1797; MS 3782-17-4 License to coin 9 June 1797.
584 MS 3782-12-56 Item 34, Joseph Banks (London) to MB (Soho) 26 July 1797.

After over ten years of trying, Matthew Boulton was finally able to use the Soho Mint steam-powered coining press for its original intended purpose. The coins struck were the first issue of copper pennies ever struck in England. They became known as 'cartwheel pennies' due to their broad rim which was to protect the design from wear in use.

By January 1798 Boulton was able to report that:

> 'of the 500 Tons or 3000 Casks (6 of which weighs one Ton). I have the satisfaction to tell you that I have executed & put into circulation 2500 Casks so that there remains only 500 Casks of the whole quantity which I expect will be compleated in about one Month. ... I have actualy sent & deliver^d in London one Thousand & Forty one Casks which is more than one third of the whole quantity order^d. I shall begin tomorrow morning upon the Two peny pieces'.[585]

Two pence pieces were struck from January to April 1798. Casks of coins had been distributed as far as Newfoundland, the Cape Colony (South Africa) and Australia, with a final total of 43,969,204 pennies and 722,972 two pence minted.

The cartwheel pennies were readily accepted by the general public but the two pence pieces were found to be too heavy. Not only were they difficult to use, they also were very difficult to make, and despite Boulton's claims, counterfeits were in circulation by September 1797.[586] So Soho Mint was reconstructed, incorporating technical improvements to make it more efficient and quieter. This was completed in time for the 1799 issue of halfpenny and farthing coins.

Coins of 1798

The Committee on Coin was active, with Sir Joseph Banks and Lord Liverpool wanting a complete reform of silver as well as copper coinage. Boulton was consulted in April and May 1798 about various aspects of manufacture of silver coins including crowns.[587] Dies were engraved, as a demonstration of Soho Mint's ability to coin gold and silver and in April William Cheshire sent pattern crowns to Boulton for presentation to influential individuals.[588] Unfortunately progress halted when Liverpool yet again became ill. Pattern farthings were also made with the same design as the 1797 issue except that the date was below the bust on the obverse, and the value 1 FARTHING was put on the reverse.

---

585 MS 3782-12-56 Item 92, MB (Soho) to Joseph Banks (London) 14 January 1798.
586 D. Symons (2009) 'Matthew Boulton and the Forgers' in R. Clay and S. Tungate (eds.) (2009) *Matthew Boulton and the Art of Making Money* Brewin, Studley pp12-15.
587 M. Dickinson (1999) *Pattern Crowns Dated 1798* Numismatic Circular October 1999 Volume CVII No 8 p243.
588 MS 3782-12-59 Item 167, William Cheshire (Soho) to MB (London) 26 April 1798.

1798 pattern farthing   1798 Isle of Man halfpenny

Figure 6:1.2 1798 pattern farthing and 1798 Isle of Man halfpenny.

One order came from the Government in 1798. Boulton was asked to make coins for the Isle of Man, which had been sold by the Duke of Atholl to the Crown in 1765. Penny and halfpenny coins were made using the bust of George III but with a reverse showing the three-legged symbol of the Isle of Man and an inscription QUOCUNQUE IECERIS STABIT ('whichever way it is thrown, it will stand up'). Pattern coins were received for presentation at court on 3rd August 1798.[589] Most of the order was shipped in March 1799. This time, pennies were struck at 21/lb and the halfpennies at 42/lb, a total of 94,828 pence and 194,376 halfpence.[590]

1799 halfpennies and farthings

The desirability of halfpennies and farthings had been discussed between Boulton and Lord Liverpool in summer 1797, since these were the coins most required by the working population. By July 1798 the price of copper had risen, so cartwheels and other heavy copper tokens were being melted down and the copper exported or used in ships' sheathing, so that once again there was not sufficient copper coin. Lawson wrote in November 1798:

> 'I cannot but observe the increasing quantities of bad Halfpence now circulating; in getting change there is not a penny to be had, particularly at Turnpike Gates who are distributing nothing but trash'.[591]

The situation remained bad in August 1799:

---

589 MS 3782-12-59 Item 171, William Cheshire (Soho) to MB (London) 3 August 1798.
590 D. Vice (1977) *Isle of Man* Numismatic Circular p209.
591 MS 3782-12-66 Item 55, James Lawson (Workington) to MB (Soho) 3 November 1798.

'There is now no seeing a Penny piece here [Edinburgh] *and I am sure the half pence are 50 in the lb being all thin plain blanks and many of impure metal ....everywhere else nothing but rubbish'.*[592]

There was a formal proposal for a coinage of farthings and halfpennies on 17th August 1798 but written orders did not materialize until 4th November 1799. This was for 550 tons of coin with 10 halfpennies to every farthing (at 36/lb and 72/lb respectively). The price of copper had risen steeply, and it was increasingly difficult to obtain, as discussed earlier. Sir Joseph Banks was worried that Thomas Williams would attempt to disrupt the 1799 contract. He wrote: *'Nothing which is cunning and abominable ever surprises me when coupled with Williams name'.*[593] Williams was at this point at odds with Boulton as he thought he had been cheated over copper orders during the 1797 coinage contract. Boulton wrote back:

'The treasury have made another attack on my coinage & have wrote an official letter to Lord Hawkesbury desireing to know if my terms are as advantageous to the publick as those which the [Royal] *Mint offerd. N.B: the Mint cannot at this time procure either copper or Rolling or Blanks on the same terms'.*[594]

Boulton was paid at a rate of £42 per ton for coining, due to the increased number of coins per pound, plus £1 per ton for packing and an increased payment of £4 for delivery. The first shipment was sent on 27th November 1799 to Mrs Matthews.[595] Production ceased by July 1800 when 3,540 casks of halfpence and 176 casks of farthings had been sent; a total of 42,480,000 halfpennies and 4,224,000 farthings.[596]

'Regenerated' bank tokens or silver dollars

Meanwhile, the shortage of silver coins continued. An abortive effort was made by the Royal Mint in 1804 to supply silver coins by countermarking Spanish pieces of eight with an octagonal mark taken from the Maundy penny die. However, these marks could be easily applied to counterfeit coins, and the overstruck coins were withdrawn.[597]

---

592 MS 3782-12-66 Item 56, James Lawson (Edinburgh) to MB (Soho) 6 August 1799.
593 MS 3782-12-56 Item 54, Joseph Banks (London) to MB (Soho) 2 December 1799.
594 MS 3782-12-56 Item 102, MB (Soho) to Joseph Banks (London) 4 December 1799.
595 D. Symons (2009) 'Bringing to Perfection the Art of Coining' in S. Mason (ed.) (2009) *Matthew Boulton: Selling What All The World Desires* Yale University Press, London and New Haven p95.
596 MS 3782-17-5, License to coin 4 November 1799.
597 H.A. Seaby, P.A. Rayner (1949, revised 3rd edition 1968) *The English Silver Coinage from 1649* Seaby, London.

Figure 6:1.3 1804 Counter-marked 'dollar'.

Boulton suggested that the steam-powered coining presses at his Soho Mint could strike with sufficient force to completely obliterate the original design.[598] It would be quicker to overstrike the Spanish coins than to start from scratch, and they could be issued as bank tokens. He had great support for this from Sir Joseph Banks who was very impressed by the process:

'I am more than ever proud of the abilities of my worthy old friend Matthew Boulton since I saw his transformed tokens. It certainly is the chef d'ouvre of coining to destroy at one blow the impress of a Coin & to substitute another in its place. It is what has, I am confident, never before attempted & will not again be tried till the Feeble Presses of other coiners have been more strengthened indeed'.[599]

Royal approval of this clever idea was received by 6th February 1804. The Bank of England had 400,000 dollars already struck with the octagonal marks, which the Soho Mint could easily handle.[600] Dies of 40mm, 41mm and 42mm diameter were needed to overstrike Spanish reales of different sizes.[601] By 27 June 1804, 1,005,523 dollars had been overstruck, or 'regenerated' as Boulton preferred to say, plus 1,420 proof pieces struck from new silver. The order was repeated until, by April 1811, a total of 4.5 million tokens were made, all dated 1804. Boulton's claim that he could totally obliterate the old coin design proved very difficult to achieve but typically he turned this into a positive, arguing that it provided an extra protection against counterfeiting!

---

598 MS 3782-12-56 Item 126, MB (Soho) to (Lord Hawkesbury) (London) 3 February 1804.

599 MS 3782-12-56 Item 62, Joseph Banks (London) to MB (Soho) 27 January 1804.

600 MS 3782-12-56 Item 65, Joseph Banks (London) to MB (Soho) 3 March 1804.

601 M. Dickinson (1999) *Bank of England Dollars Part 1 & II* 9 & 10 p275; p310; December 2003 Volume CXI No 6 p312.

Figure 6:1.4 1804 'Regenerated' dollar.

In Ireland a mixture of old Irish copper coins and copper tokens, and English gold and silver coins was in use. Most of the tokens were produced by mining companies, such as the Cronebane token, or were counterfeit.[602] A crisis was caused in 1804 when the Post Office suddenly decided to refuse counterfeit coins, and the Government was concerned that this could lead to further rebellion in Ireland. Representatives from the Bank of Ireland discussed an issue of a six shilling dollar with Boulton on 4th April 1804 and by 24th April Küchler started to engrave the reverse die with an image of Hibernia, which was completed by 16th May.[603] The obverse was the same as for the British 'dollar'. The regeneration of nearly 800,000 dollars was commenced on 31st May and completed by 19th June, a remarkably quick response.[604] Proof dollars were struck for the bank directors, plus an extra 1,000 for Boulton to give away or sell.[605] The order was accompanied to Ireland with an escort of 12 armed soldiers.

1805-1807 Coinage Issues

Despite over 46 million coins being produced in 1799, the demand for halfpennies and farthings had not been satisfied, especially in Ireland, as no copper coins had been sent there. Boulton had been planning a further regal coinage as he knew that there was still not sufficient small change in circulation. In addition, since the Unification of Britain and Ireland in January 1801, George III had new titles. He wrote to Lawson in March 1802:

'I will not delay much time by waiting for orders but am allready preparing new Dies giving the King his new Title & makeing a new divice for the Reverse but I fear the

602 D. Vice (1994) *The 1804 Bank of Ireland Six Shilling Token* Format 50 1994.
603 MS 3782-12-56 Item 73, Joseph Banks (London) to MB (Soho) 21 April 1804.
604 D. Vice (1994) *The 1804 Bank of Ireland Six Shilling Token* Format 50 1994.
605 MS 3782-1-59 Item 147, Richard Chippindall (London) to MB (Soho) 7 June 1804.

delays of Office will be so great that it will be many Months before you see any of the New.[606]

In fact, it took three more years. Despite declining health, suffering from liver and kidney disease, Boulton kept campaigning for additional issues.[607] In September 1803 he wrote:

'they are greatly wanted in every Town in England & Scotland & I receive more than 7 letters per Week pressing me to supply them with considerable quantities of ♀ [copper] Coin. From all these letters it appears the Country is more in Want than ever because my coin has in most parts of the Island has suppressd the bad Coin & there is not half enough of the good for Current use'.[608]

Discussions about a new issue of regal coins began in spring 1804 and the Government agreed to a proposal for pence, halfpence and farthings on 19th December 1804, but then changed their mind several times. Due to Addington's resignation and the return of Pitt as Prime Minister, the copper coinage was postponed to 1805 and then to 1806.[609]

When the Irish 'regenerated' dollars were discussed in 1804, a supply of copper coins for Ireland had been suggested, but the order was delayed until 26th March 1805. By this time Boulton was suffering from very bad health, and was upset about delays and changes imposed by the Lords of the Council for Coin. They had asked him to expedite the new Irish coinage and so he had:

'ventured to prepare 200 dies for pence and to roll about 36 tons of copper. I have also cut out about 20 tons of penny blanks but when all this was done I received information that it was yet undecided whether 12 or 13 pence were to go to the Irish Shilling, in this case pence 36 per lb and halfpence 52, which threatened to rend all I had done null & void … I have neither Health, Strength or even Courage to write to you [Banks] after so long a silence'.[610]

Boulton used the obverse design featuring George III, from the 1805 pattern penny, and a harp design with the date, on the reverse. Irish penny pieces, struck at 26/lb, were shipped by canal to Liverpool and then carried to Dublin; the first delivery arriving there in June 1805. Halfpennies followed by 9th July and the final cargo of these left on 24th February 1806 along with a single batch

---

606 MS 3782-13-43 Item 92, MB (Soho) to James Lawson (Glasgow) 10 March 1802.
607 MS 3782-12-81 Item 128, MB (Soho) to Ambrose Weston (London) 31 March 1802.
608 MS 3972-12-48 Item 131, MB (Soho) to Ambrose Weston (London) 8 September 1803.
609 A. Gunstone (1982) *Bank of England Dollars* Numismatic Circular Sep 1982 Volume XC Number 7 p234.
610 MS 3782-21 Item 15, MB (Soho) to Joseph Banks (—) (3) February 1805 (*In William Cheshire's hand*).

of farthings dated 1806. In total 8,788,416 pence, 49,795,200 halfpence and 4,996,992 farthings, more than 63½ million coins, were sent to Ireland.[611]

The 1805 contract was for:

> *'1200 tons of cake copper at the rate of £169 per ton to manufacture the same into penny, halfpenny and farthing pieces at or for such price or prices. 600 tons for England and 600 tons for Ireland'.*

£4 per ton was charged for delivery, plus £1 for packing the casks containing £33 12s each, in 2s packets. Coining for the Irish pennies was charged at £44 6s 8d per ton, and the halfpennies and farthings at £49 per ton, as there were more to be struck per pound (104 in the case of the farthing).[612] Coining for England was at 24/lb for pennies, 48/lb for halfpennies and 96/lb for farthings, with coining at a slightly lower price than for Ireland, due to fewer coins per lb.[613]

The currency issues for Britain were made in 1806 and 1807, with the first coin struck being the farthing. 150 casks with total of 4,833,768 pieces were completed by 31 March 1806. Then pence followed on 28th April with deliveries starting on 7 May, to a total of 19,355,480 pennies. The halfpenny was first delivered on 28th June with a total of 87,893,526 halfpennies struck in 1806. But even with these large numbers coined, Boulton received a lot more orders for pence than were commissioned by Government.[614]

There were further orders in 1807:

> *'their Lordships having been informed by Mr Boulton that the contract … being very nearly completed and that the demand for his copper coin was still very considerable …. and that he had no doubt that a further coinage of copper to the extent of six hundred tons would be absorbed in the circulation of this kingdom'.*[615]

The same rate was charged for coining, but copper prices had reduced to £143 per ton. Halfpennies again dominated the issue, with 41,394,384 being made.[616] Distribution went on through 1807, 1808 and the first three months of 1809. During the third regal coinage a total of over 165 million coins were struck; the last major coinage made at Soho Mint as the Government decided that all coinage, not just silver and gold, should be done by the newly refurbished Royal Mint, using equipment supplied by Boulton.

---

611 R. Doty (1998) *Soho Mint* p328.
612 MS 3782-17-6, License to coin 8 April 1805.
613 MS 3782-17-7, License to coin 12 September 1806.
614 MS 3782-13-36 Item 169, MB (Soho) to MRB (London) 15 June 1806.
615 MS 3782-17-8, License to coin 2 Oct 1807.
616 R. Doty (1998) *Soho Mint* pp330-331.

Design of the Regal Coinage

It was a convention, since at least the reign of Charles II, that, on a regal coin, the bust of the sovereign should face in the opposite direction to that of the previous monarch, so this was followed at Soho Mint. George III (1760-1820), who followed his grandfather, George II (1727-1760) on the throne, faced right on all regal coinage made there. His bust was draped in 'antique' style, with long hair, usually wearing a laurel wreath but in some pattern coins he was shown with a crown. On later 1805-7 coins he had shorter hair. On some medals George III faced left, and was in contemporary dress. Inscriptions included his title as monarch in various forms, usually the simple GEORGIUS III D:G REX 'George III by the grace of God, King': abbreviated from the Latin 'Georgius Tertius Dei Gratia Rex'.

Pattern coins 1787-88

For the initial design for the regal coinage in 1787, Boulton was sent a wax model of the King:

> *'perhaps one of the most perfect likenesses ever produc'd; it was took on the Terrace* [at Windsor] *last summer, and a friend (who sees his Majesty daily) has given the artist such hints to improve on his own original model that this is look'd on as a compleat masterpiece'.*[617]

To avoid accusations of counterfeiting, Boulton asked that the reverse should not *'imitate our Money but you may put either GR that is George Rex or MB the initials of my name'.*[618] Droz engraved a shilling die with a portrait and a cipher, and thirteen pattern coins were sent. However, the die cracked.[619] In April 1787, a star and garter design for a sixpence was discussed between Garbett and Boulton.[620] It may have been engraved by Francis Eginton, who worked at Soho. Boulton's partner, John Scale, wrote to say that:

> *'Francis Eginton bids me say that before you should be at a loss for a Die-sinker, he will with pleasure exert his utmost abilities for you in that way, ... you may tell them that the 'best coin in Europe' was done by one who spent the whole of his better days in your own manufactory'.*[621]

---

617 MS 3782-12-59 Item 5 Richard Chippindall (London) to MB (Soho) 18 April 1787.

618 D.W. Dykes (2005) *Mr Garbett's Sixpence* Numismatic Circular June 2005 Volume CXIII Number 3; J.G. Pollard (1968) *Matthew Boulton and J.P. Droz* Numismatic Chronicle 1968 Volume 8 University Press Oxford p254.

619 H.A. Seaby and P.A. Rayner (1949; 3rd edn. 1968) *The English Silver Coinage from 1649* Seaby, London pp123-125.

620 MS 3782-12-62 Item 43, Samuel Garbett (—) to MB (—) April 1787.

621 MS 3782-12-72 Item 66, John Scale (Soho) to MB (London) 18 June 1787.

To improve the design, Boulton sought help from a variety of eminent artists, including Benjamin West, whose pictures proved popular with the public.[622] West came to London from America in 1763 and remained during the American War of Independence. He became historical painter to the King from 1772, and an influential presence at court.[623] Via Boulton's agent Chippindall, West agreed to support Boulton's style of design for coins. Chippindall wrote to say that:

> 'If you would be at the expense of striking two dies, one in the common style & the other in the new style which he [West] would suggest, he would accompany it with a letter to the privy council & <u>risk his own reputation on its success</u>'.

West sent a sketch of George III which 'is sure a most striking likeness & being of so recent a date'.[624]

A second letter enclosed another sketch of the King, in which:

> '[West] has left the hair flowing because he supposes it will be best for a medal, & instead of his close blue coat (the garb his last is drest in) he has given you a dress more approaching to a <u>court dress</u>'.[625]

This enabled Droz to engrave dies in 1788 and 1790 which gave a realistic likeness of the monarch. However, it was Küchler's portrait of the King which was used on the 1797 regal coinage issue, and in 1799.[626]

The reverse design on the 1788 pattern halfpennies engraved by Jean-Pierre Droz showed the figure of Britannia holding a spear, with the inscription BRITANNIA. One 1788 reverse has the date replacing the rudder in the exergue; a 1790 version has Britannia holding her arm out horizontally and a decorated oar behind the shield. Usually the rim was toothed or beaded but on some samples there was a raised rim and the edge was grained, or in some cases lettered or patterned. There were numerous other small variations made by Droz, but none of his pattern halfpennies were used in an actual regal coinage.[627]

---

622 MS 3782-12-63 Item 20, John Hodges (Soho) to MB (Plangary Green) 30 November 1780.

623 A. Boime (1987) *Art in an Age of Revolution 1750-1800* University of Chicago Press, Chicago and London p123.

624 MS 3782-12-59 Item 10, Richard Chippindall (London) to MB (Soho) 24 November 1788.

625 MS 3782-12-59 Item 11, Richard Chippindall (London) to MB (Soho) 1 December 1788.

626 MS 3782-12-59 Item 186, William Cheshire (Soho) to MB (London) 4 March 1799.

627 C.W. Peck (1970) *English Copper, Tin and Bronze Coins in the British Museum 1558-1958* Trustees of the British Museum, London pp239-245.

Figure 6:1.5 1788 pattern halfpenny.

1791 Pattern guinea coins

Boulton had made pattern guineas to demonstrate the operation of his coining presses, though he did not intend to mint gold or silver coins.

Figure 6:1.6 1791 pattern guinea.

The design came from the Royal Mint 1787 guinea and the reverse shows a crowned shield which bears the arms of England, Scotland, France, Ireland and Hanover and a legend showing the abbreviated full titles of the king in Latin: M.B. F. ET H. REX F.D. B. ET L. D. S.R.I. A.T. ET E. This translates as: 'King of Great Britain, France and Ireland, Defender of the Faith, Duke of Brunswick and Lüneburg, Arch-Treasurer and Elector of the Holy Roman Empire'. The King's German and French titles were completely abandoned after the Union with Ireland in January 1801. A thicker rim was an innovation which became a feature of the 1797 Soho regal coinage issue. Thomas Wyon, one of a family of talented engravers who got their initial training at Soho, was responsible for the dies.[628]

Sarah Sophia Banks received pattern guineas and a gauge, plus a letter explaining how the gauge should be used: *'because the guineas had been struck in collars, they are perfectly round and all exactly of the same diameter'*. This meant that they could be laid flatways into the circle, and pass through the slit, whereas the Mint guineas would not. The letter was accompanied by a diagram.[629]

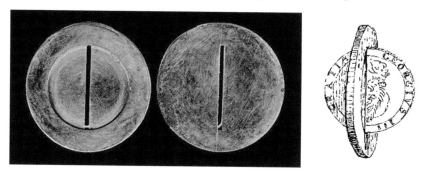

Figure 6:1.7 Guinea gauge and image from letter to Sarah Sophia Banks.

1795 Pattern coins

More pattern coins were engraved in 1795 by Thomas Wyon who used the 1791 obverse guinea and the 1790 reverse Britannia designs. The broad raised rim with incuse lettering, was intended to preserve the design from wear and to make counterfeiting more difficult. There was ornamentation and 'SOHO' beneath George III's bust.

Figure 6:1.8 1795 pattern halfpenny.

---

628 MS 3782-3-13, Mint Day Book 8th February 1791-16th May 1795.
629 MS 3782-12-56 Item 111, MB (Soho) to Miss Sarah Sophia Banks (London) 26 March 1804.

1797 'cartwheel' coins

Once Boulton had gained the regal coinage contract, a series of designs were engraved on pattern coins by Conrad Heinrich Küchler.[630] They were made in two pence, penny, halfpenny and farthing sizes, with each in proportion to the 2oz two pence. The obverses had a bust of George III with various ornamentation. Boulton wrote to ask: *'Which of the two heads should be on the money and whether any other alterations wanted'*. Advice from the Committee for Coin followed in June: *'Omit wreath & ornament but use smaller head'*.[631] On the reverse was Britannia, who sometimes wore a helmet, and held a trident, a symbol of British naval power. The coins had a broad rim, hence were known as 'cartwheels'. On the currency version, the helmet was removed, the trident moved to her left hand, and the date was placed on the rim. This design was the first use of Britannia with a trident.

Figure 6:1.9 1797 pattern penny.

The regal coinage design received favourable comment:

'The <u>proportions</u> of <u>thickness to breadth</u>, and idea of forming so accurately weight and measures. The broad and strong protecting circles & sunk letters, also the whole figure and design with the strong execution of the Britannia on the <u>Reverse are all admirable</u> and perhaps scarcely admit of any improvement'.[632]

630 C.W. Peck (1970) *Copper Coins* pp292-307.
631 MS 3782-12-42 Item 126, W. Fawkener (London) to MB (London) 2 June 1797.
632 MS 3782-12-42 Item 215, James Wright Jr. (Dundee) to MB (Soho) 1 September 1797.

Figure 6:1.10 1797 currency penny.

1799 coinage

In 1799 halfpennies and farthings were ordered by the Government from the Soho Mint. Pattern coins were made showing George III with a crown and Britannia on the reverse, with a variety of inscriptions. Some were made with a gilt finish to impress the Committee on Coin.

Figure 6:1.11 1799 pattern halfpenny.

The final design chosen for the currency halfpenny was one with a draped bust of George III as on the 1797 issue, but with a slightly different inscription: GEORGIUS III DEI GRATIA REX, and a smaller raised rim with beaded border rather than the cartwheel rim. The farthing was of the same design but 23mm in diameter rather than 30mm, and had the value 1 FARTHING on the reverse. These were the first British currency copper pieces on which the denomination appears.[633]

633 C.W. Peck (1970) *Copper Coins* pp347-350.

Figure 6:1.12 1799 currency halfpenny.

Coins from 1805

In 1805 Boulton made more pattern pennies and halfpennies, the first regal coins made since the Union of Britain and Ireland in January 1801. The design for the obverse remained very similar to the 1799 halfpenny, but with the inscription GEORGIUS III. D.G. REX. On some pattern coins the inscription GEORGIUS III. D.G. BRITANN. REX. F.D. &c. was used. The reverse showing Britannia had the inscription BRITANNIARUM ['of the Britains'] and the date 1805.

Figure 6:1.13 1805 pattern penny and proof Irish penny.

However, only Irish coins were made in 1805, with the Irish harp on the reverse rather than Britannia, and the inscription HIBERNIA.

The design for the 1806 and 1807 coins used a new portrait of George III with cropped hair, and the date was moved to the obverse. The reverse with Britannia remained the same. The penny was 33.5mm diameter, and weighed 19g, the halfpenny was 30mm and 9.5g, and the farthing 21mm and 4.75g. The only alteration for the 1807 design was the changed date.

Figure 6:1.14 1807 currency penny.

East India Company

The Honorable United East India Company (EIC) was a joint stock company holding a privileged position with the British Government. It had been formed in 1708 from two companies trading with the Indian subcontinent and China. Colonial possessions in South East Asia had been contested between Britain and France, escalating into the Seven Years War (1756-1763). But after the victory by Robert Clive, Governor General of India, at the Battle of Plassey in 1757, the EIC effectively ruled in India. British Government control was introduced in 1773, under the rule of the Governor General, Warren Hastings. After Pitt's India Act of 1784, three Presidencies were established and after a further act of 1786, the company functioned as a regularized subsidiary of the crown, subordinate in political matters to a British government Board of Trade.[634]

Boulton completed orders for the Indian Presidencies of Madras, Bombay and Bengal, for Sumatra, and for Ceylon. Despite problems with copper deliveries, adverse weather and war, Boulton was able to deliver over two hundred and twenty million coins for the EIC between 1786 and 1809.

Coins were first ordered from Boulton for Sumatra in 1786 and 1787, and then again in 1798 and 1804, for Bombay in 1791, 1794 and 1804, and for Madras in 1794, 1797, 1803 and 1808. Pattern coins were also made for Bengal in 1792 and 1809. Samples of Soho Mint products were also sent on the 1793 Macartney expedition to China.[635] These received a favourable response from the Chinese, but nothing came of this expedition in the form of orders.[636] A small private issue was also made for Claude Martin for Lucknow, Northern India, ordered in 1796, but not delivered until 1799.[637] A final coinage was made for Ceylon, which came into the possession

---

634 Information in this section is from F. Pridmore (1975) *Part 4 India: Volume 1 East India Company Presidency Series* Spink and Son.

635 MS 3782-12-75 Item 49, Zaccheus Walker (Birmingham) to MB (London) 18 October 1792.

636 MS 3782-12-39 Item 288, James Cobb (East India House, London) to MB (Soho) 22 October 1794.

637 D. Vice (1988) *The Indian Token Coinage of Major-General Claude Martin* Format 37 September 1988.

of the EIC in 1796 during the Napoleonic Wars, and due to its strategic importance, was declared a crown colony. Coins for Ceylon were made in 1802, and dies for a further coinage in 1804, which was postponed, and then cancelled.

East India Company Designs

Designs for the East India Company issues had to incorporate both the political and religious affiliations of the various areas served, and the range of languages spoken. In Sumatra, a Persian inscription in the Malay language was used. Arabic script was used for Bombay, and in 1792 for Bengal. The Madras and Ceylon coins however had Latin or English inscriptions. In 1809, Bengali, Hindi and Urdu were used on Bengal pattern coins, and Arabic and Sanskrit on medals for the EIC College. The reverses of the various EIC issues were simpler, and in general showed the date and value in a variety of languages.

Boulton also had to take into account the variety of coins used; in Madras there were gold pagodas or mohurs and silver fanams, with copper cash coins. In Bombay and Bengal, the silver rupee dominated, but there were different weight standards. The rupee was variously divided into 1/48 and 1/96-rupee coins, or pie or pice, also known as dubs. Ceylon used a system of stuivers and rix-dollars. Sumatran coins came in four values of kepings.

For East India Company coins a system of 'grains' weight was used. Boulton's first coinage for Sumatra in 1786 was for coins of 100, 150 and 50 grains weight, or 9.75g, 6.50g and 3.25g, with diameters of 28mm, 25mm and 20mm. With the addition of a 200 grain coin, weighing 13g with 30mm diameter, these continued to be the standard size for most EIC coin issues made at Soho Mint. In 1803 an extra small coin, valued at one cash, weighed only 0.65g. An exception was a pattern coin for Bengal at 5.5 grain (0.35g).

1804 Sumatra (4, 2 and 1 keping)   1804 Bombay (2, 1 and ½ pice)

1803 Madras (20, 10, 5 and 1 cash)   1802 Ceylon (1/48, 1/96
and 1/192-rupee)

Figure 6:2.1 EIC coinage.

Many designs incorporated the EIC heart-shaped balemark on one side, with slight variations depending on the area and date of issue. This motif was established in 1783 by John Marsden, the elder brother of the language expert at the EIC, William Marsden, who supplied the denominations, their proportions and the inscriptions.[638] It was used in 1786, 1787 and 1798 on Sumatra coins but also on the 1791 and 1794 Bombay issues, and on the 1792 hexagonal pattern Bengal, and the 1794 and 1797 Madras coins.

1787 Sumatra   1791 Bombay   1792 Bengal

Figure 6:2.2 Balemarks of the East India Company.

The EIC had been granted a coat of arms in 1698, first used as the obverse for 1794 Madras coins. From 1803, versions of this consolidated the design on all EIC issues made for India and Sumatra, and on EIC medals, so that the coins would be easily recognised; like the modern symbol used on the reverse of all Euro coins. The broad rim was replaced with a small raised beaded rim. Dies were engraved by Noel-Alexandre Ponthon and Conrad Heinrich Küchler.

1797 Madras   1804 Sumatra   1804 Bombay

Figure 6:2.3 Coat of Arms of the East India Company.

---

638 MS 3782-12-59 Item 2, William Chippindall (London) to MB (Truro) 12 September 1786.

Sumatra

The East India Company had established a base in the late seventeenth century in Sumatra, an island in western Indonesia. Its capital Bengkulu (Bencoolen) was established in 1685 as a pepper-trading centre, which was never profitable. Most Sumatrans were Muslims and the languages spoken were varieties of Malay. The first coins issued there in 1783, were struck locally, and were based on the Spanish silver dollar divided into 400 kepings.

The 1786 coinage for Sumatra was Boulton's first attempt at coining in quantity, and was suggested to him by Thomas Williams.[639] The blanks were prepared in Birmingham from copper supplied by the EIC.[640] Nearly three million coins of three sizes were struck on hand presses made by Anthony Robinson in Birmingham, and installed in London by Joseph Harrison under Boulton's direction. However late delivery of the copper and technical problems delayed the contract.[641] This order was one stimulus for the Soho Mint. The coins were very simple in design, merely the EIC balemark and date on the obverse, and on the reverse the value of the coin and the Hejira date in Persian. Hejira (or Islamic year) dates from the flight of Muhammad from Mecca to Medina in AD 622. The reverses were the same for all issues from 1786, 1787, 1798 and 1804, but the obverse changed to the coat of arms in 1804.

1786 Sumatra obverse   1787 Sumatra reverse   1798 Sumatra reverse

Figure 6:2.4 Sumatran coins of the EIC.

Another order for 30 tons, around 12 million coins, was made on 12th May 1787. The copper was delivered by December 1787, but again delays meant that the order was not completed on time. On 20th February 1788 Boulton wrote:

John Harrison *'promised me that all the ♀ [copper] pieces for the India co would be finished by 31st Jan and though we have worked night & day for a fortnight, & have yet 8 ton to coin and the last day of receiving it is on Fryday ye 29th'.*[642]

639 MS 3782-12-73 Item 66, Thomas Williams (London) to MB (Soho) 12 July 1786.
640 B. Gould (1969) *Matthew Boulton's East India Mint in London 1786-1788* Coin and Medal Bulletin No 612, (August 1969) p270-277.
641 MS 3792-12-63 Item 43, John Hodges (Soho) to MB (Chacewater) 23 September 1786.
642 MS 3147-3-12 Item 9, MB (London) to James Watt (Harper's Hill) 20 February 1788.

This was so the order could go on the spring sailings to India. A third member of the Harrison family, William Harrison, completed it by May 1788.

A further order, for 15 tons of coins to the same design and weights as the original coinage, was made in 1798. The obverse design was changed when dies for the 1804 Sumatra and Bombay coinages were made by Phillp.[643] The coins were struck in two batches very early in 1804. The first portion was shipped between 3rd and 31st January 1804 and another between 6th March and 28th April. These Sumatran coins were at 50, 100 and 200 grains.[644] A total of over 28 million coins were struck for Sumatra between 1786 and 1804.

India: Bombay Presidency

Bombay, now known as Mumbai, had originally been ceded to Britain in 1661 as part of the Dowry of Catherine of Braganza, the Portuguese princess, when she married Charles II. The Bombay Presidency, in western and central India, came under British control later. This area was partly Muslim, but was also contested by the Hindu Maratha Empire.

The request for the first Bombay coinage came via Robert Wissett of the East India Company in December 1790. It was dealt with very quickly. Designs were approved by 18th February 1791. Boulton wrote:

> *'Pray tell Mr Lawson to proceed as fast as possible in preparing cutting out tools, dies and die holders for East India bits of 50 grains, of 100 grains and 200 grains. He must also get all the four presses finished ready for striking the said E.I. pieces'.*[645]

For speed, Boulton wrote: *'I dare not attempt to strike the pieces in collers, as it's necessary we should strike 250 per minute, or 300, untill the order is compleated, and I fear collers will delay us'.*[646]

1791 Bombay obverse   1794 Bombay reverse

Figure 6:2.5 Bombay coinage of the EIC.

---

643 MS 3782-12-58 Item 128, William D. Brown (Soho) to MB (Soho) November 1802.
644 R. Doty (1998) *Soho Mint* pp299-301.
645 MS 3782-13-36 Item 52, MB (East India House) to MRB (Soho) 13 January 1791.
646 MS 3782-13-36-53, MB (London) to MRB (Soho) 17 January 1791.

Four weeks later the first shipment of eighty casks of 1½ pice pieces, struck at 47/lb, left Soho for London. Pice coins, struck at 70/lb, were sent in batches on 13th April and 19th April 1791. In November 1791 double pice coins at 35/lb, and half pice coins at 140/lb were sent. In total 100 tons of copper, 17 million coins, were struck.[647]

The Bombay coinage issued in 1794 had the same design as the 1791 coinage except for the date change. They were made in the first four months of 1794, but this time the one and a half pice coin was only made as a pattern. For the reverses of 1791 and 1794, and the 1791 hexagonal pattern coins for Bengal, the design was a pair of scales with an Arabic inscription *Adil* ['Peace']. The size of the coins was the only indication of value. The Hegira date was added on the 1804 Bombay issue, as on the earlier Sumatran coins.

A total of more than 8 million coins were sent along with an order for Madras. The final coinage for Bombay was made in 1804 with a different obverse design. The original plan had been to issue a unified currency for India which was abandoned. The Bombay order was struck in two batches along with an order for Sumatra. The first portion was shipped between 3rd and 31st January 1804 and another between 6th March and 28th April.[648]

India: Bengal Presidency

The Bengal Presidency consisted of west Bengal with a mainly Hindu population, and east Bengal where Muslims predominated. The principal city, Calcutta, now known as Kolkata, had its own mint for high value coins. To cut costs of coining, the cowrie shell was used instead of low-value copper coins.

In 1792 it was proposed that a coinage should be made for Bengal. Boulton

'offered to Coin Copper pieces of the Value of Cowrees which are reckoned after the rate of 1280 to a rupee [or 5½ grains each] *... I have thought of the means of making such Coins very Cheap, at least at such Expence'.*[649]

These pattern coins introduced a completely new idea in coining as they were to be hexagonal. Specimens were wanted within the fortnight to show to the new Governor General who was about to depart for Bengal. The design was to be: *'the same as before ...... the device must be left to your fancy or after consideration. the company's mark and the Scales as for Bombay'.*[650]

Fifty coins were sent on 26th September 1792. But a miscalculation had been made, and the smallest coin of 5.5 grain (0.35g) was worth four cowries. It was impossible to coin at a smaller size and so the attempt was abandoned. More

647 R. Doty (1998) *Soho Mint* pp305-306.
648 R. Doty (1998) *Soho Mint* p325.
649 MS 3782-13-36 Item 88, MB (Truro) to MRB (Soho) 19 September 1792.
650 D. Vice (1995) *A Pattern Cowrie for Bengal Presidency* Format 58 1995.

pattern coins were made in 1809 which showed the standard EIC coat of arms on the obverse, and the value inscribed three languages to suit three religions: in Hindi (Hindu) and Punjabi (Sikh) with the central inscription in Urdu (Muslim). But, due to rising copper prices, delays in translations by Wilkins the language expert at the EIC, the illness of John Phillp and Boulton's death, the order did not materialise.[651]

Figure 6:2.6 1809 India Bengal one pie pattern coin.

India: Madras Presidency

The Madras Presidency covered a large area of southern India and had a mainly Hindu population. The capital, Madras, is now known as Chennai. An order for Madras coins was made in 1794, and again in 1797. The design of the Madras coins was by Sir Charles Wilkins, Librarian to the East India Company. Two values of coins were made: 1/48-rupee coins and the 1/96-rupee coins at 30mm and 24mm diameter respectively. The dies were engraved by Ponthon and had a legend on a broad rimmed coin, later used by Boulton on the 1797 cartwheel issues.

1794 Madras obverse   1794 Madras reverse   1797 Madras reverse

Figure 6:2.7 Madras coinage of the EIC.

---

651 R. Doty (1998) *Soho Mint* p332.

By September the issue was in full production.[652] Copper for the order was sent via the EIC, 20 tons coming from Freeman and Co and 37 tons from Mines Royal Co.[653] By December 1794 over 9 million coins had been shipped to St. Botolph's Wharf in London, for onward dispatch. The second Madras order was struck just before the regal coinage of 1797, with an identical design to the first, except for the date. A total of over ten million coins was sent from 15th December 1796 to 9th February 1797, and a further six million by May 1797. The 1797 issue arrived in Madras in August on the company's ships *Houghton* and *Earl Talbot*.[654]

In 1803 more coins for Madras were struck. This time the designs featured the EIC coat of arms and an inscription giving the value in Persian and in Roman numerals and the word CASH, with one, five, ten and twenty cash values. Ten and twenty cash were also issued in 1808. The dies were engraved by Conrad Heinrich Küchler and John Phillp in combination.[655] Delivery of the coins started in November 1802 and was completed 23 May 1803. This was a very large order of nearly 38 million coins. The smallest one cash coins were struck at 720 per pound and needed special coining tools. They were also too small to pack as rouleau and were therefore packed loose into casks.

The 1808 Madras issue was more problematic as there were difficulties with the supply of copper. Also 22 ton of copper were used to make more than two million surplus 20 cash coins. Over 86 million were dispatched by June, despite a cargo of 10 cash coins being lost in a shipwreck.[656]

Figure 6:2.8 1808 Madras 20 cash.

652 MS 3782-13-36 Item 110, MB (Cheltenham) to MRB (Soho) 2 September 1794.
653 MS 3782-12-39 Item 249 Chas Thomas Coggan (East India House) to MB (Soho) 12 September 1794.
654 R. Doty (1998) *Soho Mint* pp311-312.
655 MS 3782-12-59 MS 3782-12-59 Item 112-117, MB (Soho) and Richard Chippindall (London) 23 August to 28 September 1802.
656 R. Doty (1998) *Soho Mint* p332.

Ceylon (now Sri Lanka)

The Ceylon coinage from Soho Mint in 1802 was ordered by Governor North, who wanted coins of three denominations, all of the same design except for the value. The largest was 1/48 equal to 48 stuivers to the rix-dollar, and the smallest was valued at 1/192 rix-dollar and was made at 184 to the lb. The order came to Soho Mint via William Huskisson, agent of the EIC and a friend of Alexander Davison, already a customer of Soho Mint. A total of over six million coins were dispatched from Soho Mint on 10th May 1802 in 256 casks.[657]

The design was completely different to the EIC coinage for India and Sumatra, with an elephant on one side and a decorated inscription on the other, used for coins of three values.

Figure 6:2.9 1802 Ceylon 1/192 rix-dollar.

Dies were prepared for a further order with the same denominations dated 1803 and 1804.[658] However this coinage was postponed as coinages for Madras, Bombay and Sumatra were given preference, due to unrest in Ceylon. Then further issues for Ireland and Britain from 1804 meant that the coinage was never resumed.[659]

1809 East India Company College Medals

Boulton was approached by Nathaniel Marchant on behalf of the EIC in November 1806 to make medals for the East India Company College, to be awarded to students with proficiency in Persian and in Sanskrit. The college had been set up at Hertford Castle, Haileybury, Hertfordshire to train future administrators for India. From 1805-1858, it provided general and vocational education for youths of sixteen to eighteen who were nominated by EIC Directors. Attendance was

657 R. Doty (1998) *Soho Mint* p324.
658 MS 3782-12-56 Item 113, MB (Soho) to Sir Joseph Banks (London) 5 April 1804; MS 3782-12-56 Item 84, Sir Joseph Banks (Overton) to MB (Soho) 22 September 1804.
659 MS 3782-12-56 Item 73 Sir Joseph Banks (London) to MB (Soho) 21 April 1804.

generally for four six-month terms. These young men were employed in India to keep accounts and were responsible for correspondence with London. Every letter to the Head Office was completed in triplicate to ensure delivery, two copies going by two different sailing ships, and the other went overland.

The designs for the EIC College medals were by Dr Charles Wilkins, the orientalist at the EIC, who also provided the gold. They were engraved by Küchler. One with an Arabic inscription ('Seeking knowledge is more important than seeking gold'), showed the EIC coat of arms on the obverse, and the other with an inscription in Sanskrit, ('Highest intelligence and happiness result from giving'), showed an Indian female figure wearing an elephant scalp headdress on the obverse.

Arabic inscription

Sanskrit inscription

Figure 6:2.10 1809 East India Company Medals.

Major General Claude Martin Coins

A private issue was ordered by Claude Martin for the Lucknow area of northern India, with copper, silver and gold pieces of four sizes. Although the commission first was given to Soho Mint in 1796, through a variety of circumstances, the dies were not engraved until 1798.[660] Samples were sent to Raikes, his agent in February 1799.[661] The issue was ready by September 1799 and the order, 11,000 in total, was delivered just weeks before Martin died.[662] All four sizes have a similar design, as seen in the drawings by Küchler.[663]

Figure 6:2.11 Sketch for Claude Martin coins.

Figure 6:2.12 Claude Martin '4 knob' coins.

660 D. Vice (1988) *The Indian Token Coinage of Major-General Claude Martin* Format 37 September 1988.

661 MS 3782-12-59 Item 182, William Cheshire (Soho) to MB (London) 22 February 1799.

662 MS 3782-12-59 Item 192, William Cheshire (Soho) to MB (Cheltenham) 7 September 1799.

663 MS 49 Ref 82934, Sketch by C.H. Küchler Timmins Album Volume 1 Item 33.

The smallest size die, 32mm diameter, was engraved by Küchler with Martin's portrait facing left, and the larger three had dies engraved by Alexander Mackenzie in India, with Martin facing right, but were struck at Soho Mint. The pieces had to be struck by hand using the special large heavy presses which were normally reserved for striking proofs, medals and the multiplication of dies, as Mackenzie had not made suitable dies for use in the steam-powered press.

British Tokens

Tokens, also known as commercial or provincial coins, were made, not for a government or ruling authority, but for a variety of private individuals and organizations. Boulton was not initially interested in token issues. He wrote to his Cornish agent, Thomas Wilson, in September 1789:

> 'As to makeing Specimens of Coin for Cornwall I must decline it as I never will rest untill I have accomplished a National Coinage of which I hope to give you a favourable Acc[oun]t very shortly'.[664]

But, as the prospect of a government contract receded, Boulton agreed to make tokens at the Soho Mint.

At least thirty-five different types of tokens were made at Soho Mint for individuals who wished to remedy the shortage of small change. This includes Boulton's associates Thomas Williams of Anglesey, John Wilkinson, the ironmaster, and William Roe of the Macclesfield Company. They ordered tokens to pay the wages in their large and booming mining and engineering establishments. Other orders came from towns, such as Glasgow and Dundee in Scotland, Hornchurch in Essex and Bishop Stortford in Hertfordshire. Many were not intended for a wide distribution.

Most token issues were made at 28-29mm in diameter for the halfpenny size and 33mm for the penny size but were gradually made at a lighter weight as the price of copper rose. The original 1787 Anglesey halfpenny tokens contained half an ounce of copper, as did the 1791 Cornish tokens, made at 32 per lb. As James Conder wrote:

> 'the Halfpennies of Anglesey, Macclesfield, Edinburgh, Dundee, Cronebane and several others, formed originally a good and respectable medium; and were even heavier than any other coins of that denomination, that had ever previously issued from our national mint'.[665]

---

664 AD1583-3-92, Boulton to Wilson 5 Sep 1789.
665 J. Conder (1799) *An Arrangement of Provincial Coins, Tokens and Medalets*, Jermyn, London.

Boulton was often instructed by his customers as to the weight they wanted. In 1789 Cronebane tokens were made at 36 per lb. Later issues were made at 46 per lb. By 1802, the Enniscorthy halfpenny tokens were made at 55-60 per lb, nearly half the weight of the first tokens.

Unlike official coinage, tokens were initially marked clearly with their nominal value, and bore a legend stating where they could be redeemed, i.e. exchanged for an equivalent value of regal coin or goods, unlike the copper coinage of the Royal Mint. The image needed to be authoritative, so that the tokens could be used with confidence in the knowledge that they would be accepted in retail outlets. Because their quality and weight were of a high standard, some tokens were used throughout Britain. Eighteenth-century tokens were most commonly issued in the denomination of a halfpenny, with some penny issues.

The boom period for token production at the Soho Mint lasted until 1796, with some further orders in 1801-1804, but Boulton's steam powered presses were more suitable for orders of millions of coins. Smaller companies started to issue tokens after 1790, often intended as advertisement, which carried no promise of repayment and were used locally. From 1794 a market in specious tokens for collectors also grew. There was no intention of passing these tokens as currency, and issues were often limited to around six dozen pieces. Boulton refused to make specious tokens but did produce proof tokens for collectors.

Dalton and Hamer, who wrote the standard work on tokens between 1910 and 1918, estimated that there were at least seven thousand varieties of eighteenth-century tokens.[666] Along with Boulton, the Birmingham manufacturer Westwood dominated the market from 1789-1792, but by 1795 their coining business finished. Seventeen other manufacturers were listed by Pye as working in Birmingham in 1801 but most made very few issues. The most productive, Peter Kempson (1755-1824) and William Lutwyche (1754-c1801) made 72 and 75 issues each, and were better placed to deal with low volume issues for local shopkeepers and businesses.[667]

Many engravers worked for several manufacturers; John Gregory Hancock and Thomas Wyon worked for Boulton at times, but also worked for Kempson and Edward Thomason. Noel-Alexandre Ponthon, initially employed at Soho, worked for Lutwyche later, as did Peter Wyon.[668] Kempson and Lutwyche sometimes worked together, and at other times produced tokens independently.[669] One token manufacturer, Thomas Mynd, was married to Matthew Boulton's sister Catherine, and may have had work passed on to him by Boulton.[670]

---

666 R. Dalton and S.H. Hamer (1910-15) *The Provincial Token-Coinage of the Eighteenth Century* in several volumes.

667 C. Pye (1801) *Provincial Copper Coins or Tokens issued between the Years 1787 and 1796* Pearson, Birmingham.

668 R.C. Bell (1966) *Tradesmen's Tokens and Private Tokens (1785-1819)* Corbitt and Hunter, Newcastle p176.

669 L. Forrer (1904-1916) *Biographical Dictionary of Medallists* in 6 volumes p503.

670 D.W. Dykes (2000) *The Tokens of Thomas Mynd* British Numismatic Journal Volume 70 2000 pp90-102.

Boulton tried to make tokens difficult to counterfeit profitably by making them full weight, and with edge inscriptions, but counterfeit tokens were made. Tokens became scarcer after Soho Mint's regal coinage issues of 1797 and 1799, as Conder pointed out: *'the massy national coinage, now on the anvil of fabrication for Government, by that ingenious and useful member of society Mr Boulton, is likely soon to supplant the whole'.*[671] However the rising price of copper led to the melting down of heavier copper pieces, such as cartwheel pennies, and Wilkinson and Anglesey tokens, thus causing further shortages. So, there were more issues of tokens from Soho Mint around 1800-1803. Tokens were eventually banned from circulation by 1818.[672]

1787-1792 Anglesey Tokens

The first large scale initiative to remedy the shortage of small change had been taken in 1787 by Thomas Williams (1739-1802), known as the 'Copper King' and also in Anglesey as Twm Chwarae Teg ('Tom Fair Play'). Like Boulton, he had created an industrial organization which integrated many aspects of mining and manufacturing, and he was instrumental in influencing Boulton's entry into coining. One important aspect of his tokens was the 'WE PROMISE TO PAY THE BEARER' inscription, which made them very popular, as they could be redeemed for gold coins.

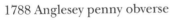

1788 Anglesey penny obverse   1787 Anglesey penny reverse

Figure 6:3.1 Anglesey penny tokens.

Anglesey tokens, known variously as Druid tokens, or Parys Mine Company tokens, were not only the first, but also the most numerous. The first prototypes may have been struck using fly presses at Holywell owned by Williams, but by

---

671 J. Conder (1799) *An Arrangement of Provincial Coins, Tokens and Medalets,* Jermyn, London.
672 R.C. Bell (1964) *Commercial Copper Coins 1811-1819* Corbitt and Hunter, Newcastle.

summer 1787 production had moved to Birmingham.[673] The Parys Mint was set up in Williams's warehouse at 9 Great Charles Street and run from 28th March 1787 by Charles Wyatt, a former apprentice at Soho Manufactory.[674]

Penny tokens were made in 1787, 1788 and 1791, and halfpennies in 1788, 1789, and 1792. From 1789 these tokens were made at Soho Mint. Some were struck on blanks previously cut and edge marked at the Parys Mint.[675] Most Druid dies were engraved by John Gregory Hancock in Birmingham, who continued to work freelance for Soho Mint.[676] In total around 250 tons of pennies were made, plus approximately 50 tons of halfpennies (9 million penny and 3,584,000 halfpenny tokens) according to a whole list of authorities, though no contemporary evidence for this amount has been seen.[677] Soho Mint coined at least 29 tons of copper for Anglesey.[678]

The Anglesey token, first used in 1787, showed a Druid's head within an oak wreath, which came from Thomas Williams's seal. On the reverse there was an entwined cipher, with a variety of inscriptions, as the dies were made individually.

Figure 6:3.2 1791 Anglesey halfpenny token.

1787-1795 Wilkinson Tokens

Matthew Boulton had been acquainted with John Wilkinson (1728-1808), an exact contemporary, since December 1766.[679] Wilkinson was born in Cumberland, where

673 J.H. Morris (2003) *The Battle of the Tokens, 1789-1799: The Hibernian Mining Company v. The Associated Irish Mine Company* Mining Heritage Trust of Ireland.

674 G. Selgin (2005) *Charles Wyatt, Manager of the Parys Mint: A Study in Ingratitude* British Numismatic Journal Volume 75 pp113-120.

675 MS 3782-3-13, Mint Day Book 8 February 1791-16 May 1795.

676 MS 3782-12-74 Item 183, Zaccheus Walker (Birmingham) to MB (Buxton) 4 September 1789.

677 G. Selgin (2003): Hawker (1996); D. Vice (1989) *The Soho Mint and the Anglesey Tokens of the Parys Mine Company* Format 38 March 1989.

678 MS 3782-3-13, Mint Day Book 1791-1795.

679 MS 3782-12-23 Item 81, Letter forwarded to Boulton. John Wilkinson to John Florry 5 December 1766.

his father was an over-looker for Little Clifton iron furnace. John Wilkinson invented a box iron, used to frill the cuffs worn by dandies, and with the profits, his father set up an iron works. The family then moved to Bradley, near Bilston, Staffordshire where they set up a coal fired iron furnace in the 1750s. In 1757 with partners, he erected a blast furnace at Willey near Broseley in Shropshire. Later at Bersham near Wrexham, they had an iron foundry, where rails were cast for the wagons from the Coalbrookdale foundry.[680] Wilkinson also made the accurate cylinders used in Boulton and Watt steam-powered engines from 1775 until 1795. These engines were used in the Cornish copper industry, in iron foundries and elsewhere.[681]

Wilkinson was instrumental in arranging a collaboration between Williams and Boulton in 1787. But when the regal contract did not materialise, Wilkinson advised that Boulton should '*push all private channels that offer'd*' and then he would be in a better position later. He also recommended that the Government should provide the copper, as prices were rising.[682]

Wilkinson's penny tokens, sometimes known as Willeys, were ordered by Wilkinson from Thomas Williams in 1787, and were struck in Birmingham.[683] Unlike the Anglesey pennies these tokens weighed around half an ounce, rather than an ounce, and Wilkinson was quickly forced to issue them as halfpence.[684] Soho Mint took over their production in 1789. Hancock dies, with the date 1788, were initially used. However, John Westwood was also producing tokens for Wilkinson, with a different reverse, the Vulcan design. Boulton complained to Wilkinson in October 1790:

'*You say you have been petitioning Westwood for 15 cwt. of coin weekly; allow me to remark that I expended more than ten guineas in Dies to coin for you …nevertheless if you choose to order any quantity of Halfpence worth engraving new Dies for, … I will contract to make you as many per week as you please*'.[685]

Wilkinson in turn complained that the tokens were too heavy:

'*4 in the pound less in number than those struck by Westwood, and even those were deem'd too heavy by people in general. However … I desired they might be thirty six to the pound wt and this number I request you will adhere to*'.[686]

After this Dumarest prepared new dies from the original Hancock design and Boulton made around 6cwt of tokens for Wilkinson in 1790.[687] Over 5 tons of

---

680 D. Vice (1990) *The Tokens of John Wilkinson* Format 40 March 1990.
681 R.C. Bell (1963) *Commercial Coins 1787-1804* Corbitt and Hunter, Newcastle pp144-148.
682 MS 3782-12-73 Item 167, John Wilkinson (Court) to MB (Soho) 4 December 1788.
683 R.C. Bell (1963) *Commercial Coins 1787-1804* p147.
684 D. Vice (1990) *The tokens of John Wilkinson* Format 40 March 1990.
685 MS 3782-12-73 Item 169, MB (Soho) to John Wilkinson October 1790.
686 MS 3782-12-73 Item 171, John Wilkinson (Broseley) to MB (Soho) 11 December 1790.
687 D. Vice (1990) *The Tokens of John Wilkinson* Format 40 March 1990.

tokens were dispatched by 22nd February 1791, also dated 1790. They were struck at 32 per lb, but later issues were reduced to 36 per lb. Further Wilkinson tokens were made in 1792, 1793 and 1795. The details of the various issues can be seen in the Mint Day Book, and a total of nearly nine tons were produced, costing £839 6s 11½d.[688] All these orders have the same design apart from the date.

After 1795, due to a dispute between the Wilkinson brothers, no further tokens were ordered. William Wilkinson, who been working in France since around 1782, returned and found that his brother had been cheating him. John Wilkinson had also made engines without paying Boulton and Watt the correct premium. The agreement to break up their association was finalised by December 1795.[689] Boulton seemed to have been expecting this. He had predicted in 1789 that ultimately Wilkinson would act against B&W.[690]

Figure 6:3.3 1793 Wilkinson halfpenny token.

1789 Cronebane Halfpenny Token

Once Boulton realized in 1789 that the regal coinage contract would not materialize imminently, he started to make tokens for a variety of customers, including the Associated Irish Mine Company, run by Roe and Co of Macclesfield. Charles Roe (1714-1781) was one of the major players in the copper industry, having originally been a silk manufacturer near Macclesfield.[691] In 1758 the Macclesfield Copper Company was formed by Roe and fourteen other partners, but was still often referred to as Roe and Co. They had a copper works on Macclesfield Common, where there were convenient shallow coal seams for smelting the copper ore, bought from the Duke of Devonshire's mine at Ecton in the Peak District. The

688 MS 3782-3-13, Mint Day Book 8th February 1791-16th May 1795.
689 MS 3782-12-73 Item 178, John Wilkinson (Brymbo) to MB (Soho) 8 December 1795.
690 MS 3147-3-13 Item 8, MB (London) to James Watt (Soho) 6 July 1789.
691 D. Bentley Smith (2005) *A Georgian Gent and Co. The life and times of Charles Roe* Landmark, Ashbourne.

company later owned the Cheadle Copper and Brassworks in Staffordshire, and established smelting facilities in 1768 near Liverpool. These were moved to Neath near Swansea in 1790 by Roe's son William. The Company operated copper mines at Alderley Edge, Cheshire, from 1759-1768, plus mines at Coniston in Cumbria, which were worked intermittently until 1795. In particular they ran the Mona Mine, Anglesey from 1764, but the lease was acquired by Thomas Williams in 1785.

In 1787, the Macclesfield Company took over the lease of the Cronebane copper mine, near Wicklow, Ireland, where a rich lode of copper was discovered in 1788. Operations there continued to 1808, with an annual output of 1000 tons of copper ore between 1787 and 1797. During the Irish Rebellion from May 1798 to September 1798 mining ceased, and the loss in production cost around £60,000.[692] In March 1789 the Company had ordered 42 tons of tokens from John Westwood for use at the Cronebane mine, and for their works at Macclesfield.[693] But as Westwood was unable to complete the contract, 10 tons of ready milled and lettered blanks, for both sets of tokens, were sent to Soho, ready for annealing, cleaning and striking. The dies for the Macclesfield tokens were not ready, but the order for Cronebane tokens was completed at Soho.[694]

The Cronebane tokens were the first in the world to be produced by a steam-powered coining press at Soho Mint. Hancock, who engraved the dies for both issues, was asking for three guineas per pair for 'sinking the dies with St Patricks head and ye Miners arms on reverse'.[695] Macclesfield Company were later invoiced for a total of 1,674,185 coins; over 20 tons struck at 36/lb.[696]

There were many varieties of the Cronebane token, as Boulton's team had not yet mastered the mass multiplication of dies. Details were put in by hand, so the positions of the crosier and date relative to the legend may differ.[697] The reverse design with the symbols of the copper industry, the windlass, picks and shovels was very appropriate for a copper mine issue.

The initial production at the Soho Mint was not always completely accurate, as can be seen in the mis-strike of the Cronebane halfpenny below. This problem was soon remedied however with the introduction of a collar in the coining press.

692 J.H. Morris (2003) *The Battle of the Tokens, 1789-1799: The Hibernian Mining Company v. The Associated Irish Mine Company* Journal of the Mining Heritage Trust of Ireland 3, 2003 pp41-54.

693 D. Vice (1991) *The Cronebane Token of the Associated Irish Mine Company* Format 42 March 1991.

694 D.W. Dykes (1999) *John Gregory Hancock and the Westwood Brothers: An Eighteenth Century Token Consortium* British Numismatic Journal Volume 69 p173-186.

695 MS 3782-12-108 Item 53, Mint Book 1788 p99.

696 MS 3782-3-13, Mint Day Book 8th February 1791-16th May 1795.

697 R.C. Bell *Commercial Coins* p232.

1789 Cronebane mis-strike   1789 Cronebane halfpenny

Figure 6:3.4 1789 Cronebane halfpenny token.

1791 Cornwall Halfpenny Token

Matthew Boulton was heavily involved in the Cornish copper mining industry as described previously. John Vivian, Deputy Governor of the Cornish Metal Company, who commissioned the Cornish token, thought in September 1790 that:

> 'we could circulate 100 tons, but the Committee of course will not think it right to contract for so much at first. I think the best way will be for us to deliver you Cake Copper at £84 per ton; you to roll and finish, so that you have only to say the price at which you will deliver the Coin: And a Milling on the Edges I think is handsomer than an inscription'.[698]

It was decided to use the Druids Head, originally engraved by Dumarest for an Anglesey token, as the obverse, probably to unite the copper industries of Anglesey and Cornwall. Boulton did not send a pattern reverse until 9th February 1791.[699] Vivian criticised the design: *'the Motto makes it looks too crowded, and that it had better be omitted altogether'*. The tokens were sent to Cornwall in October 1791.[700] On 3rd January 1792 Vivian reported that:

> 'We have put our half-Pence into circulation; they are so greedily sought after that we wish to have more as soon as possible. According to your engagement, when I had the Pleasure to meet you at Bristol, Eight tons more ought by this time to be coined. When can JV expect them? I beg you to coin only 20 tons of our Copper, but let it remain in Cakes 'til you hear again from me'.[701]

---

698 MS 3782-12-73 Item 39, John Vivian (Truro) to MB (Soho) 22 September 1790.
699 MS 3782-12-73 Item 41, MB (Soho) to John Vivian (Truro) 9 February 1791.
700 MS 3782-12-73 Item 46, MB (Soho) to John Vivian (Truro) 8 November 1791.
701 MS 3782-12-73 Item 47, John Vivian (Truro) to MB (Soho) 3 January 1792.

However two days later Vivian wrote: *'I strongly suspect we shall not be able to put so large a Quantity of Coin in circulation as we expected: therefore I beg you to coin no more 'til you hear again from me'.*[702] And by 2nd February 1792 the whole order was countermanded: *'The Co. have determined to put a Stop to their Coin; And I am authorised to offer you the Copper, which was delivered to you for that Purpose, at £94 per ton'.*[703] In the end only around 1 ton of Cornish halfpennies were coined.[704]

Figure 6:3.5 1791 Cornwall halfpenny token.

1793 Leeds Halfpenny Token
The Leeds token was ordered by Henry Brownbill, a watchmaker and silversmith in Leeds. Its other sponsor was Samuel Birchall on 31st December 1792. Birchall was author of one of the earliest books on the eighteenth-century token series, published in 1796.[705] The die engraver was Noel-Alexandre Ponthon, who copied Hancock's die of St Patrick, used in the Cronebane token; he removed the crosier and replaced it with a wool-comb to make Bishop Blaise, the patron saint of Leeds. Boulton wrote to his son in January 1793: *'take St Patrick from the Chronebane dye, may Serve for Bishop Blazes head, of which you may consult with Ponthon & Lawson'.*[706] The reverse die shows the Cloth Hall in Leeds built in 1758.[707]

The first batch of halfpenny tokens was dispatched on 12 March 1793 and the second five weeks later. In total 172,233 tokens were struck plus 150 proofs in copper, bronzed copper and silver.[708] The mint was very efficient at completing

702 MS 3782-12-73 Item 48, John Vivian (Truro) to MB (Soho) 5 January 1792.
703 MS 3782-12-73 Item 49, John Vivian (Truro) to MB (Soho) 2 February 1792.
704 MS 3782-3-13, Mint Day Book 8 February 1791-16 May 1795.
705 S. Birchall (1796) *A descriptive List of the Provincial Copper coins or Tokens issues between the years 1786 and 1796 arrange alphabetically.*
706 MS 3782-13-36 Item 94, MB (London) to MRB (Soho) 18 January 1793.
707 R.C. Bell (1963) *Commercial Coins 1787-1804* Corbitt and Hunter, Newcastle p205.
708 MS 3782-12-7, Letter book 1786-1788.

this order; only seven weeks passed between the first letter to the dispatch of the tokens. The dies were charged at £10 10s and the copper cost £105 per ton.[709]

Figure 6:3.6 1793 Leeds halfpenny token.

1793-1796 Inverness Halfpenny Token

These tokens were ordered in four successive years for Mackintosh, Inglis and Wilson, sail-cloth, sacking and bagging manufacturers of Citadel Works, Inverness. The dies were engraved by Küchler. The first two shipments, sent on 13th December 1793 and 19th November 1794 were made at 42/lb. A third lighter weight issue, struck at 46/lb, was sent on 31st October 1795, with a final order on 25th February 1796, a total of 377,554 tokens with four different dates. The Inverness orders were sent via Taylor and Mander who were also involved in an order for Southampton.[710] The 1791 Southampton token was the first to use Lawson's recent invention of a rising and falling collar, and thus had a sharp edge.

The obverse design for the Inverness token showed the emblems of England and Scotland, the rose and the thistle, tied by a ribbon, representing their Union. In the 1793 version the date was on the reverse, but it was moved to the obverse for the 1794-1796 issues. The cornucopia represented 'plenty', and beneath it was a representation of a stone, preserved in the Royal Burgh of Inverness since the fifteenth century. It stood at the foot of the town cross and when water was carried from the river Ness in a wooden tub, or cudden, the women found the stone (clach) convenient for resting the cudden on while exchanging gossip. It became known as the cudden stone or in Gaelic 'clach-na-cudden' as on the reverse of the 1795 version.[711]

---

709 MS 3782-3-13, Mint Day Book 1791-1795.
710 MS 3782-3-14, Mint Day Book 1795-1798.
711 R.C. Bell (1963) *Commercial Coins 1787-1804* p205.

1793 Inverness halfpenny obverse   1793 Inverness halfpenny reverse

1794 Inverness halfpenny obverse   1795 Inverness halfpenny reverse

Figure 6:3.7 1793-5 Inverness halfpenny token.

1794 Lancaster Halfpenny Token (Daniel Eccleston)

In the eighteenth century Lancaster was an important port, the fourth largest for the slave trade after Bristol, London and Liverpool. The Lancaster token was made for Daniel Eccleston (1745-1821), who had spent several years in Antigua and Barbados, acting as an agent for his brother, Isaac, who exported both sugar and cotton. Eccleston was also a coin collector, and finally settled in Lancaster, where he worked as a liquor merchant and insurance broker. He was an enlightened polymath, studying electricity and agriculture, and believed in equality of religion, rights for women and free trade. He had campaigned against war with France and against slavery, and was an activist for the poor.[712]

---

712 Thanks to Dr Caroline Downes, University of Salford, for information about Daniel Eccleston.

Just over a ton of Lancaster tokens were produced at 48/lb. They were sent to Liverpool by Worthing & Gilbert's canal boat in seven casks containing 109,247 copper halfpenny tokens. The engraving of the dies cost 5 guineas, the coining expenses were £44 10 6d and the total cost £57 2s 6d.[713] There was an order for a further two tons to be struck, but the die cracked, and the order was not completed. Eccleston was still corresponding with Boulton about the bill in Dec 1800.[714]

The portrait of Eccleston on the obverse shows him without a wig, which was a political statement in support of democracy. The reverse image shows three important aspects of eighteenth-century British economy, agriculture, manufacturing, and commerce, symbolised by a plough, a flying shuttle, and ship's rigging. The engraver was Noel-Alexandre Ponthon. The tokens were struck with a raised 'cartwheel' rim, in the style of the later 1797 regal copper coinage.

Figure 6:3.8 1794 Lancaster halfpenny token.

1796 (dated 1794) Penryn Volunteers Halfpenny Token

The importance of artistic merit in engraving can be seen in the beautiful and complex design of the Penryn Halfpenny tokens ordered by Sir George Chapman George and dedicated to Sir Francis Bassett (1757-1835). The Bassett family had been living in Cornwall for seven hundred years and had considerable interests in the Cornish copper mines. Bassett opposed some of Boulton's plans to regulate the mining industry and prevent overproduction of copper.

As commander of the Penryn Volunteers, Bassett raised a force of miners to defend Falmouth from Spanish and French fleets in 1794, and became Baron de Dunstanville in June 1796. He also erected a battery of four twelve pounder cannons at Portreath Bay on the north Cornish coast as a defense against privateers. The Penryn tokens produced at Soho Mint were dispatched in September 1796.

---

713 MS 3782-3-13, Mint Day Book 1791-1795 p190 25 August 1794.
714 MS 3782-12-45 Item 441, Daniel Eccleston (Lancaster) to MB (Soho) 28 December 1800.

Figure 6:3.9 1796 Penryn halfpenny token.

Undated (1794/5) London Ibberson Halfpenny Token

Christopher Ibberson was the proprietor of the 'George and Blue Boar' in the West End of London. This was the terminus to many of the stage coaches serving the north and served an essential role in the British transportation network.[715] An order for half a ton of halfpenny tokens was sent to Soho Mint on 20th December 1794, and pattern coins, engraved by Ponthon, were dispatched to London in February 1795. But the order was cancelled.[716] The design was criticized; Boulton wrote: *'Tell Bush & Ponthon that Mr Ibbertson say the Boar looks more like a Mouse upon his half penny'.*[717]

The Ibberson halfpenny was included in sets for collectors. This token had edge lettering, which was gradually abandoned on other token issues through the later 1790s.[718]

Detail of boar crest from Ibberson token.

---

715 J.S. Whiting *Trade tokens* p84.

716 MS 3782-13-36-172, MRB (Soho) to MB (London) 9 February 1795.

717 MS 3782-13-36 Item 117, MB (London) to MRB (Soho) 5 February 1795.

718 R.G. Doty (1986) *Notes of the Ibberson Token* Numismatic Circular Vol. XCIV Number 2 March 1986 pp39-40.

Figure 6:3.10 1794-5 Ibberson halfpenny token.

1800 Pen-y-darran Works Tokens

Tokens were made of five values: five shillings, two shillings and sixpence, one shilling, sixpence and three-pence values, and were to be used at the company shop for the Pen-y-darran Ironworks at Merthyr Tydfil.[719] These works were established in 1784 by Jeremiah, Thomas and Samuel Homfray, the sons of Francis Homfray (1725-1798). Homfray, a pioneer in the smelting of copper, had also been successful in the iron trade in Coalbrookdale and at Cyfartha. Samuel Homfray (1762-1822) ordered tokens in May 1800. He wrote to Boulton:

Figure 6:3.11 1800 Pen-y-darran two shilling pattern token.

---

719 N. and A. Cox (1994) *The Tokens, Checks, Metallic Tickets, Passes and Tallies of Wales 1800-1993* p208.

'I am in want of a sort of a coin to pass amongst our Workmen. Mr Scale will explain the meaning of it to you.... & if you could get one by way of specimen by next week I can then take a peep at it, as I intend myself the pleasure of seeing you some time in the week if it is convenient to you'.[720]

The tokens were very simple in design, merely a statement of value and the place where they could be used. They were not intended for use anywhere except at Pen-y-darran.

1801 (dated 1800) Enniscorthy Halfpenny Token

The Enniscorthy tokens were engraved by Küchler for R. Woodcock, a banker from County Wexford in Ireland. The first order left Soho on 7th Feb 1801 (118,716 tokens) and the second on 27th Feb (536,588 tokens). The reverse design refers to an incident in 1798 when United Irishmen revolted in Dublin and in the south. The rebels were organised in a large camp of around 15-20,000 on Vinegar Hill, Wexford. They were attacked and routed in June 1798 by General Lake with 13,000 British troops. The bodies of about 500 men are buried in a pit at the foot of Vinegar Hill.[721]

Figure 6:3.12 1801 Enniscorthy halfpenny token.

1803/4 (dated 1802) Tullamore-Charleville One Shilling One Penny Token

The last token issue made at the Soho Mint was for Charles William Bury, Viscount Charleville. His seat, Charleville Forest Castle, was at Tullamore, fifty miles west of Dublin, Ireland.[722] The tokens for one shilling and one penny were ordered in October 1802 by Frederick Trench on behalf of Lord Charleville. The dies for this token had input from three engravers. John Phillp began the dies at Soho,

---

720 MS 3782-12-45 Item 249, Samuel Homfray (Hyde) to MB (Soho) 5 May 1800.
721 R.C. Bell *Commercial Coins* p231.
722 D. Vice (1991) *The Tullamore Token of Viscount Charleville* Format 43 1991.

but the mint received an extensive order from Ceylon for which he was needed. Therefore, the partly completed dies were sent to Küchler to finish. Boulton wrote:

> *'You will receive by Conveyance a Medal Die that I wish Mr Kuckler to engrave for which Purpose it is accompanied by 2 Drawings & an impression from Lord Charleville's Seal. The latter of which will be the most certain Guide for Mr Kuckler to work from as the Heraldry of the Shield is not quite compleat in the Drawings'.*[723]

At that time Küchler was working in London for Scott and Smiths, but was not happy. Chippindall reported that:

> *'Mr Kuckler [was] here this afternoon & after reading your note & examining the dies. Kicked – swore & grumbled until his fit had a little subsided – during which I let him vent his displeasure at being set to amend the workings of a Boy – after which he became a little rational – & by some maneuvering on his own account took away the die although he had before said he would not touch it'.*[724]

Küchler made little progress and the dies were returned to Soho. As Phillp was still busy, the dies were sent to Hancock to complete.[725] Tokens were dispatched to Ireland in February 1803, and a further order for 6,000 tokens was made on 24th May 1804, but this was delayed due to striking the silver Irish Bank tokens. 4,100 pieces were struck in 1803 and 6,051 in 1804.[726]

Figure 6:3.13 '1802' Tullamore one shilling one penny token.

---

723 MS 3782-12-59 Item 121-122, MB (Soho) to Richard Chippindall (London) 25 October 1802.
724 MS 3782-12-59 Item 122, Richard Chippindall (London) to MB (Soho) 26 October 1802.
725 MS 3782-12-59 Item 125, MB (Soho) to Richard Chippindall (London) 12 November 1802. MS 3782-12-59 Item 226, William Cheshire (Soho) to MB (—). 30 November 1802.
726 MS 3782-12-108 Item 69, Medal ledger p105.

Foreign Coins

Europe

The largest order came from France, and a variety of other orders were suggested, including coins for Portugal, Russia, Würtemberg (now part of Germany) and Denmark which were not completed except as pattern coins. Medals were made to commemorate the Death of Gustav III of Sweden in 1793 and in 1799 for Ferdinand IV of Naples and Sicily.

France

At the start of the French Revolution in 1789 Boulton had hoped to coin for the new French government, as copper coinage was in very short supply in France as well as in Britain. He wrote to various individuals, including John Motteux, to ask them to use their influence to obtain a coinage contract.[727] Mirabeau, who was in charge of the National Assembly in January and February 1791, was contacted.[728] Boulton went so far as to empower his Paris agent, Francis Swediaur to treat with the National Assembly *'for the coining of the whole of the money of that kingdom'* or alternatively to sell them his coining equipment. As the church had been abolished by the National Assembly, Swediaur was also asked to: *'purchase of all their bells'* so that the metal could be made into coins.[729] At this point things were happening fast in France, and by the time the letter arrived Mirabeau was no longer in charge.

However, one of the first large orders that Boulton received at the Soho Mint was for the Monneron Brothers from Paris. The contract proved vital to the survival of the Soho Mint in its early days. Between November 1791 and September 1792, he managed to strike well over seven million 2 and 5-sol copper tokens for France, several thousand copper medallions, and an unknown quantity of tokens and medals in silver and silver gilt.

The Monneron family was introduced by Swediaur who wrote:

'There are three brothers… all three have been in the East Indies and have made their fortune…, especially Louis, who was agent of the Company at the Cape of Good Hope, and on his return married a very rich woman at l'Orient. He is member of the National Assembly for Paris, and is known for his activity and abilities, is rekoned to be worth about a million of livres. The two other brothers are likewise men of activity, one of them … is also a member of the National Assembly for Vivarais, and his brother Pierre is his suppleant'.[730]

---

727 MS 3782-12-91 Item 1, MB to John Motteux 3 January 1791.
728 MS 3782-12-91 Item 113, MB to Francis Swediaur 14 February 1791.
729 MS 3782-12-91 Item 110, MB to Francis Swediaur 7 February 1791.
730 MS 3782-12-91 Item 115, Francis Swediaur to 'Andrew Smith' pseudonym for MB 27 February 1791.

As a result of the evolving events of the French revolution, this contract was rather problematic. In December 1791 a paragraph appeared in the British newspapers about *'the failure of the House of Monnerons Bankers at Paris & the same that is concern'd with Boulton in a Copper Coinage'*. Boulton was worried about his financial reputation, though he had *'a Ballance in my hands in their fav[ou]r to ye amount of 26,000£ Sterling'*.[731] Again in March 1792 Boulton received a report that Pierre Monneron had *'ordered his coach man at Midnight to the Bois de Boulogne & there he put an end to all his miseries'* due to the collapse of their bank, the Caise Patrotick.[732] He had left his wife and three small children ill with small pox. In fact, later reports showed that Pierre had fled to his *'Old Friend Tipoo'* [Tipu Sultan] in India. *'If he had stayd 2 Days longer all would have been well as his Brother at Port L'Orient offerd to lend him 50 Thos £ Sterling to which add the arrival of a Ship from L'Isle de France that brought him half a million of Livres in dollars Indies'*.[733] Coining for the Monneron brothers ceased in September, but medal production continued.

Between August 1791 and 2nd September 1792 Soho Mint produced more than 197 tons of tokens for the Monneron brothers which ensured a more technically efficient process. Tokens were first sent in November and December 1791 as 2-sol (32mm diameter; 16g) and 5-sol (40mm; 28g) tokens. New 5-sol dies were ready by May 1792. James Lawson wrote to report progress:

> *'Only one set of dies finished for the reduced 5 sols and the originals are locked up in your rooms so if the 22 tons of small are to be coined up I need the originals, but if there is to be a new reverse the sooner the inscription could be had the better. ... Sending 2 gross of medal blanks'.*[734]

Designs for the Monneron issues had to be altered due to the changing events of the French revolution, for example in 1792 Boulton wrote: *'the following alterations must be made: L'AN III de la Liberty must be changed to L'AN IV de la Liberty as by a decree of the Nat[l] Assembly the year of Liberty is to commence on New Years Day'*.[735] Several versions of both two and five sol pieces were made.

Various engravers were involved in the Monneron tokens and medals. Some dies were engraved by Noel-Alexandre Ponthon at Soho, including the 1791 and 1792 Liberté 2-sol.[736] The 5-sol Pacte Federatif and the Serment du Roi obverses were engraved in France by Augustin Dupré and dies were ready by May 1792.[737]

---

731 AD1583/4/112, Boulton to Wilson 3 December 1791.
732 MS 3782-13-36 Item 67, MB (London) to MRB (Soho) 4 April 1792.
733 MS 3782-13-36 Item 73, MB (London) to MRB (Soho) 12 April 1792.
734 MS 3782-12-66 Item 33, James Lawson (Soho) to MB (London) 19 April 1792.
735 MS 3782-13-36 Item 61, MB to MRB (Soho) 3 January 1792.
736 MS 3782-12-91 Item 7, Monneron (Paris) to MB (Soho) 17 September 1791.
737 MS 3782-12-66 Item 36, James Lawson (Soho) to MB (London) 4 May 1792.

Figure 6:4.1 1791 Monneron 2-sol 'Liberté' token.

1792 Monneron 5-sol
Pacte Federatif

1791 Serment du Roi 'Je Jure'

Figure 6:4.2 Monneron tokens.

The tokens were sold as 'medals' with the reverse inscription **MEDAILLES DE CONFIANCE** (of trust), which was altered to **MEDAILLE QUI SE VENDE** (which sell) on both the 2-sol and 5-sol tokens to avoid them being confiscated.[738]

---

738 R. Margolis (1988) *Matthew Boulton's French Ventures of 1791 and 1792: Tokens for the Monneron Frères of Paris and Isle de France* British Numismatic Journal Volume 58 1988 pp102-109.

1792 Monneron 5-sol reverse   1792 Monneron 5-sol reverse

Figure 6:4.3 Inscriptions for 5-sol tokens.

New dies engraved by Ponthon, were made with the image of Hercules on the obverse, and a pyramid on the reverse and they were struck by 26th August 1792.[739] Originally the inscription was to be in Latin but by this stage of the Revolution Boulton was advised that: '*Mr P* [Ponthon] *on receipt of your instructions for the Hercules reverse of the Pyramid thinks a mixture of French and Latin will not be by any means proper. It is understood that the French have rejected everything Latin*'.[740] However by the time this token was struck, the National Assembly had abolished private tokens, so this version was not sent to France but was sold as part of the Soho Mint sets for collectors.

Figure 6:4.4 1792 Monneron 5-sol 'Hercules' token.

---

739 MS 3782-12-66 Item 39, James Lawson (Soho) to MB (London) 26 August 1792.
740 B. Gould (1972) *Noel-Alexandre Ponthon: Medallist and Miniaturist* Seaby's Coin and Medal Bulletin 1972 Seaby London pp312-319.

In October 1791 there were also plans to make to make a series of historic medals celebrating famous French men for Mr Janvier Monneron but only two designs were actually made, as the personalities of the Revolution went quickly out of favour as the revolution progressed.[741] The dies for the Lafayette and Rousseau medallions were engraved by Rambert Dumarest who worked on commission for Boulton both in Paris and in Birmingham.

1791 Rousseau Medal

1791 Lafayette Medal

Figure 6:4.5 1791 Rousseau and Lafayette Medals.

Russia

Boulton had been negotiating with representatives of Empress Catherine about supplying a mint for St Petersburg when she died in November 1796. A medal, only 29mm in diameter, was issued by Soho Mint in 1797 to commemorate her death with a legend in Russian Cyrillic script, and a Russian double-headed eagle on the reverse.[742] The design may have been by John Phillp, and the engraver Küchler.[743]

Catherine's son Paul I (1754-1801) hated his mother, and cancelled the Russian Mint project. Paul had joined the Second Coalition against France in

741 MS 3782-12-91 Item 10, Monneron to MB (Soho) (in French) 10 October 1791.
742 MS 3782-12-108 Item 69, Medal ledger p84.
743 BMAG 2003-0031-69, Phillp album Russian arms no date 182x143mm.

1798, but in 1801 he formed the League of Armed Neutrality with Scandinavia and Prussia to enforce free trade. This threatened British imports of timber, iron ore and steel. After Paul's assassination on 11th March 1801, his son, Alexander I (1777-1825) reversed the policies of his father and commissioned Boulton to make pattern coins as part of the mint contract.[744] Chippindall wrote: *'He [Mr Hoy] shewed me a very excellent Bust of the Emperor Alexander wth he says is a very striking likeness & wth he seem'd to wish you to see'.*[745] A series of letters followed and the bust and wax models were sent to Soho by April 1803.[746] Two versions were engraved by Küchler with different busts and reverses, and pattern coins were ready in 1804. The St Petersburg Mint was operative by 1807, but not used for a general coinage as Boulton had hoped.[747]

1796 Catherine II

1796 Catherine II

Figure 6:4.6
1796 Catherine II
of Russia medal.

Design by John Phillp

744 R. Doty (1998) *Soho Mint* p113, p116.

745 MS 3782-12-59 Item 105, Richard Chippindall (London) to MB (Soho) 16 November 1801.

746 MS 3782-12-59 Item 130, Richard Chippindall (London) to MB (Soho House) 28 November 1802; Item 131 30 November 1802; Item 139 25 March 1803; Item 140 6 April 1803.

747 R. Doty 'The Industrialisation of Money' in M.M. Archibald, MR Carrell (eds.) (1993) *Metallurgy in Numismatics 3*, Royal Numismatic Society Special Publication 24, London, pp169-176.

1804 Alexander I Pattern Rouble   1804 Alexander I Pattern Rouble

1804 Alexander I Pattern Imperial   1804 Alexander I Pattern Imperial

Figure 6:4.7 1804 Alexander I of Russia.

Portugal (and Brazil)

John, King of Portugal, (1767-1826) was also King of Brazil from 1816, but acted as Prince Regent there from 1799. Boulton supplied blanks suitable for Portuguese reis in 1796 and 1798 to a firm called Lucena and Crawford in London. Over 800,000 blanks were made from around 6½ tons of copper.[748] Following the invasion of Portugal by the French in 1807, the whole royal family fled to Brazil with the assistance of the British. Around the same time, following reforms introduced by John, a pattern coinage was made for Brazil. The dies were probably engraved by John Phillp, and samples sent to M.A. Paiva, the London

---

748 D. Vice (forthcoming) p73.

agent for the Portuguese government.[749] An order was also given for a complete mint with a ten horse-power rotative engine, four coining presses, six cutting out presses, and dies, punches, drawings of buildings etc. The final agreement was drawn up on 16th June 1810 but not executed.[750] Soho Mint also supplied pattern coins for several other South American countries after Boulton's death.

Africa

'1791' Sierra Leone

The Sierra Leone coinage was important for two reasons; it was the first decimal issue produced in Britain, and it was made for a colony of freed slaves, fifteen years before the British abolished the slave trade in 1807.

Portuguese traders had first reached Sierra Leone in 1460, and various companies were set up to trade goods such as gold, ivory, and slaves, who were used in America and the West Indies to produce sugar, tobacco, coffee, indigo and cotton. Until 1772, slaves brought from Africa could be owned in Britain, but a case brought before the Chief Justice of the King's Bench, Lord Mansfield, decided that the condition of slavery did not exist under English Law and ten to fifteen thousand slaves living in England and Wales, were freed. Later these were joined by slaves who had fought on the British side in the American War of Independence (1775-1783).[751] Many were living in poor conditions.

In 1786 Boulton and Watt were asked to give their opinion on plans by Henry Smeathman: *'to open a new and beneficial system of commerce with Africa'*; with favourable opportunities for: *'Blacks and Persons of Colour'*. Smeathman continued: *'the Public will be relieved from a great burthen, for the greater part of those unfortunate persons come to the Parish. ... Upward of 340 have entered voluntarily to go with me'*. This letter offers an interesting perspective on race relations at the time: *'Many of the Black Men have white wives and the Black Women white husbands, and there are among them all kinds of useful tradesmen'*.[752] However this attempt to found a colony for freed slaves was unsuccessful.[753]

Following this, the Sierra Leone Company, in which Boulton owned two shares worth £50, was established in June 1791 by Granville Sharp and others as a colony for freed slaves. A coinage was requested from Soho Mint to help *'establish regular habits of industry and traffic'*.[754]

---

749 R. Doty (1998) *Soho Mint* pp167-183.

750 F.F. Gilboy (1990) *Misadventure of a Mint: Boulton, Watt and Co and the 'Mint for the Brazils'* British Numismatic Journal Volume 60 1990, pp113-119.

751 D. Vice (1983) *The Coinage of British West Africa & St Helena 1684-1958* Format 58, Birmingham p4.

752 MS 3219-23-24, Henry Smeathman (London) to James Watt 21 June 1786.

753 F. Pridmore (1966) *Notes on Colonial Coins: The Coins of the Sierra Leone 1791-1807* Numismatic Circular Volume LXXIV No 9 September 1966 pp206-208.

754 D. Vice (1983) *The Coinage of British West Africa & St Helena 1684-1958* Format 58, Birmingham p22.

The Sierra Leone coinage was based on the Spanish-American dollar with a complex series of coins. They were issued in denominations of 1, 10, 20, 50 cents, 1 penny and 1 dollar. The 1 cent was minted in copper, the rest in silver. The dollar die was charged at 10 guineas, and for the 10 and 20 cent dies at 3 guineas each; but there was no charge for the one cent, 50 cent and penny dies. The total coinage consisted of less than a million pieces, and the first coins were sent to the Sierra Leone Company on 27th December 1792, with more following in 1793, 1796, 1802, 1803 and 1806, although all were dated 1791.[755] One of the reasons that the order was accepted was to provide *'Ponthon with a little work till I return'*. Boulton wrote:

> *'I have promised to make about £50 worth of ½ pence for the Sirra Liona C° which must be done in about a fortnight. … No inscription on ye edge but may be struck in plain collers & the first 100 must be clean scratched blanks and good specimens as present to ye proprietors'.[756]*

Figure 6:5.1 Comparison of sizes '1791' Sierra Leone copper coins.

The coins entered circulation at a time when millions of slaves were still being transported across the Atlantic by British ships. All coins had the same design except for indication of value, and the dies were engraved by Noel-Alexandre Ponthon. The obverse shows the Lion of Sierra Leone and on the reverse, there is a wonderful image of a white hand and a black hand, clasped in friendship. The model of the hands was sent from London in October 1792.[757] This pointed to growing opposition to slavery. Boulton himself had taken out a subscription of two guineas against the slave trade in 1789.[758]

---

755 MS 3782-3-13, Mint Day Book 8 February 1791-16 May 1795.
756 MS 3782-13-36 Item 82, MB (London) to MRB (Soho) 28 August 1792 & Item 84 3 September 1792; Item 86 MB (Truro) to MRB (Soho) 13 September 1792.
757 MS 3782-12-59 Item 41, Richard Chippindall (London) to MB (Soho) 27 October 1792.
758 MS 3782-12-107, Boulton's 1789 Notebook.

Sierra Leone 20 cent proof   Sierra Leone 50 cent proof

Figure 6:5.2 '1791' Sierra Leone 20 and 50 cent proof coins.

1796 and 1801 'Gold Coast' (African Company of Merchants)

The Royal African Company, established in 1672, was restructured in 1750 as the Company of Merchants Trading to Africa. British merchants could join on paying a fee of 40s. The company had maintained forts for the slave trade until 1731, when it abandoned slaving in favour of trafficking in ivory and gold dust. Its successor was the African Company of Merchants who operated on the west coast of Africa between the Ivory Coast and Togo, now part of Ghana. Coins were struck at Soho Mint for this company in 1796 and 1801. The issue consisted of silver coins of four values with more or less the same design. The obverse has the GR cipher, similar to the 1787 pattern shilling. The reverse design, with individuals wearing native head-dresses, features the elephant and castle from the company coat of arms.

The first request for a coinage was made in June 1796 by Governor Dabiel. The order was made quickly so that it could be sent to Africa aboard a 'man-of-war'. The company provided its own silver and the coining costs were £15. The order recorded on 21st December 1796 was for 1,080 ackeys, containing half an ounce of silver, 2,162 half ackeys, 2,882 quarter ackeys and 5,762 tackoes at one sixteenth of an ounce. The dies of four sizes, engraved by Küchler, cost £15 15s, and a total of 11,886 coins were struck.[759] Bronzed specimens were struck for collectors. On the 1796 issue the larger three coins had PARLIMENT spelt incorrectly.[760] A new order was made in 1801 when the spelling of Parliament was corrected.[761]

---

759 MS 3782-3-14, Mint Day Book 1795-1798 p40 21 December 1796.
760 J.H. Remick (1965) *The Coinage of the Gold Coast 1796-1818* Numismatic Circular March 1965 Volume XXIII Number 3 p60.
761 D. Vice (1983) *The Coinage of British West Africa & St Helena 1684-1958* Format 58, Birmingham.

one ackey obverse   one ackey reverse   one tackoe reverse

Figure 6:5.3 African Company of Merchants coins.

West Indies

Boulton was asked to make coins for several places in the West Indies, including Barbados, Bermuda and the Bahamas. Further coin issues for the West Indies were proposed in 1797 but not followed up, because Boulton was worried about the legitimacy of the issues.[762]

1793 Bermuda Halfpenny

Unusually, Bermuda had no indigenous population at the time of the first British settlement in 1609, and the islands became a British colony in 1707. When a new capital in Bermuda was planned in 1793, John Brickwood was hired to commission a coinage from Soho Mint. Discussions began in November 1792 and the order for £200 sterling was authorized by George III in February 1793. Boulton used a die of George III produced by Droz for the obverse. The three-

---

762 MS 3782-12-59 Item 91-92 Richard Chippindall (London) to MB (Soho) 24 April 1797; 25 April 1797.

masted ship on the reverse was by Ponthon.[763] The die cost £3 3s out of a total bill of £184 19 6d. The coins were made at 34 to the lb (13.25g each), a similar size to the British halfpenny. Over 81,000 coins left Soho on 8th May 1793 in seven casks, but around half the coins were captured by the French en route.[764]

Figure 6:5.4 1793 Bermuda halfpenny.

1806 Bahamas Halfpenny

The Bahamas had a history of piracy, blockade running and ship wrecking. At the peak of operations, in 1703-1718, at least twenty commanders, including the notorious pirate, Edward Teach (better known as Blackbeard), had sailed illegally from the capital, Nassau. The islands became a British colony in 1718, when the British clamped down on piracy.[765]

American Loyalists settled in the Bahamas after the end of the American War of Independence. They brought their slaves with them and established plantations. The slave trade was abolished by the British in 1807; slavery in the Bahamas was abolished in 1834. The Bahamas became a haven for freed slaves, as Africans liberated from illegal slave ships by the Royal Navy were resettled there, and they constituted the majority of the population.

The Bahamas halfpenny was first discussed in 1802, but nothing was done until summer 1804. The island's agent, George Chalmers, approached Soho Mint's London agent, John Mosley, who mistakenly thought the order was for Bermuda, and so it took until 1806 to sort out the final contract.[766] The coins were made at 48 pieces to the lb; the same as the 1806 British halfpenny, and the order was sent

---

763 D. Vice and F Pridmore (1976) *Bermuda copper coinage 1793* Numismatic Circular Volume LXXXIV No.10.

764 MS 3782-3-13, Mint Day Book 8th February 1791-16th May 1795 Bill to John Brickwood Esq. p121 7 May 1793.

765 D. Vice (1977) *Bahamas Copper Coinage* Numismatic Circular Volume LXXXV No. 10b p425.

766 R. Doty (1998) *Soho Mint* p329.

out in November 1806. The colony received 120,317 coins but the coinage was not successful as the population did not trust copper coins. The obverse die engraved by Küchler was the same as for the 1806 halfpenny; the reverse design was the colony's seal, showing a merchant vessel under full sails with two fleeing pirate ships.

Figure 6:5.5 1806 Bahamas halfpenny.

America

United States of America

Boulton appears to have had hopes of coining for the United States of America at an early stage of the development of Soho Mint, which resulted in much correspondence in 1786-1788.[767] The possibility reoccurred in 1790, but though a fascinating story, nothing came of it.[768] By 1793, when Boulton's nephew Zaccheus Walker visited the United States, the opportunity had passed as the Philadelphia Mint was founded in 1792.[769] A further proposal was made in 1797 when Robert Fox, one of Boulton's copper suppliers, sent a Soho Mint penny to the United States, and was asked by the Secretary of State at Philadelphia *'to asertain by thy assistance the expense of coining any given quantity of pence & half pence etc'*.[770] This did not result in a coinage but copper blanks were made at Soho Mint for the United States from May 1797 on. The order included *'Rolling, cutting and annealing, milling round edges, delivery at Bristol £120 1s 3½d. 28 casks. Entry and fees at Custom House, town dues'*. The total paid was over £600 in June 1797. A further order was sent in February 1798 with a total cost £1338 19s. Orders for coining blanks continued until at least 1819.[771]

---

767 MS 3782-12-74 Item 121, Zaccheus Walker (Birmingham) to MB (Chacewater) 28 September 1786. MS 3782-12-108 Item 53, Mint Book 1788 p68, p83 and p93.
768 MS 3782-12-75, Item 9 Zaccheus Walker (Birmingham) to MB (London) 30 June 1790.
769 MS 3782-12-75, Item 57 Zaccheus Walker (Birmingham) to MB (London) 18 April 1793.
770 MS 3782-12-42, Item 282 George C. Fox & Sons (Falmouth) to MB (Soho) 11 December 1797.
771 MS 3782-3-14, Mint Day Book 1795-1798 p189.

1798 Washington Medals

Boulton also made a series of 'Seasons' medals to mark the presidency of George Washington (1732-1799), President of the United States from 1789-1797. A total of 720 medals were made. All were engraved by Küchler. The medals showed three aspects of American life, a shepherd, a farmer and a spinner. They were intended to be presented to American Indian chiefs to show them the benefits of so called civilised society.

Shepherd   Farmer   Spinner

Figure 6:5.6 1798 George Washington Medals.

1796 pattern Myddleton Kentucky Token

There were also pattern tokens for Kentucky in 1796 with a figure ('Plenty') in Roman dress who was holding a spear, and was reaching out to a mother and two children. Only 50 tokens were produced. The dies were engraved by Ponthon and Küchler.[772]

1796 dated '1794' Canada

Tokens were engraved for Canada by Ponthon, again for a copper company, but they did not get further than the pattern stage.

Figure 6:5.7 pattern tokens for Canada.

---

772 R. Doty (1998) *Soho Mint* p310.

Medals

Boulton had decided to produce medals at the Soho Mint to keep the engravers and key workers employed, and his mint in the public eye. Medals were in general made to celebrate public events, and were collected by general members of the public as well as by connoisseurs. Some medals were commissioned, but many were made on a speculative basis. Most were engraved by Conrad Heinrich Küchler. Medals were usually around 48mm in diameter, and were made in a variety of metals. The largest was for Gustav III of Sweden, at 56mm diameter and the smallest was one made to commemorate Catherine of Russia, at 29mm diameter.

Royal Events

1789 Restoration of the King's Health Medal

An early medal made at Soho Mint was to celebrate the Restoration of the King's Health. The obverse, with a portrait of George III, was engraved by Jean-Pierre Droz. After recovering from his first bout of 'madness' in June 1788, a celebration was held in April 1789. However, the medal arrived too late in London. Despite this, Boulton received thanks and congratulations from several correspondents. Chalmers wrote that he was *'happy to hear that he* [MB] *is to strike another medal of the King, still more like the monarch, who everyone venerates as a good man, an able magistrate and a benificent prince'.*[773]

1795 (incorrectly dated 1797) Marriage of the Prince of Wales Medal

Another unsuccessful medal, incorrectly dated, was suggested by Küchler to celebrate the forthcoming wedding of the Prince of Wales to Princess Caroline of Brunswick. Boulton had originally met the Prince in July 1789.[774] In February 1795 Boulton visited the Prince who *'showed me his princisses picture & has consented to have a Medal struck upon his Marriage & has consented to sit of a drawing of his profile'.*[775] Boulton criticised the likeness made by Küchler:

> *'I am sorry to say that the Prince of Wales strikes me as the head of a Citizen Aldermⁿ for the Hair has too much the appearance of a Wig and it is not a good Sembl of the Prince ... there is a heaviness in the Counten & not that of Vivact, w^h marks it'.*

He wanted to have *'the most perfect and finished likeness of the Prince and Princess'* and requested a consultation with Richard Cosway, painter to the Prince.[776]

---

773 MS 3782-12-34 Item 71, Mr Chalmers (Office for Trade, Whitehall) to MB (Soho); Item 72, Stephen Cottrell (Grosvenor Place, London); Item 73, William Fawkener (Whitehall, London); Item 74, George Rose; Item 75, Richard Chetwynd (Whitehall, London); Item 76, Mr Steel (Treasury Chambers, London) 1-4 May 1789.

774 MS 3782-13-36 Item 32, MB (London) to MRB (Germany) 14 July 1789.

775 MS 3782-13-36 Item 118, MB (London) to MRB (Soho) 12 February 1795.

776 J.G. Pollard (1970) *Matthew Boulton and Conrad Heinrich Küchler* p280.

The marriage took place on 8th April 1795 but Küchler did not complete the dies until 10 May, a month late. Boulton decided against issuing any medals so long after the event. To make matters worse, the wrong date, 1797, appeared on the medal by mistake. The royal couple separated after a year, and it seems that the surviving medals were only struck for collectors, on Matthew Robinson Boulton's instructions.[777]

Figure 6:6.1 1795 Marriage of the Prince of Wales medal.

As always Boulton showed a strong interest in the visual quality of the images. The reverse showing the shields of Great Britain and Brunswick-Wolfenbuttel, and the background with extensive view of London including St. Paul's, are amazingly detailed. The medals were struck in a variety of finishes, including bronzed and gilt versions.

1795 Queen Charlotte's Birthday 'Frogmore' Medal

A more successful enterprise was a series of medals made for the birthday of Queen Charlotte (1744-1818). It was celebrated in style on 19th May 1795 at Frogmore, her residence near Windsor. The whole family of the House of Orange and vast numbers of the nobility were present according to a report in the *Gentlemen's Magazine*.[778] To commemorate the event, the King wanted a series of medals, but he was told *'that it was impossible'*. To which the King replied *'that if Boulton could be favour'd he was sure he wd do them, as nothing was impossible wth him'*.[779] Boulton was determined that it should be accomplished. An account is given in a memorandum by Sarah Sophia Banks in September 1804.[780]

777 D. Vice (forthcoming) p35.

778 *Gentlemen's Magazine* May 1795, p435 according to Laurence Brown (1980) *A Catalogue of British Historical Medals 1760-1960 Volume 1: The Accession of George III to the Death of William IV* Seaby, London p92.

779 MS 3782-13-36 Item 126 MB (London) to MRB (Soho) 13 May 1795.

780 Note by Sarah Sophia Banks *Mem: Mr Bolton Sep'r 1804*. Unclassified SSB Papers in British Museum.

Three different obverses were used with the same reverse. The die of the King's head had already been engraved by Droz for the 1789 Recovery Medal, and the Prince and Princess of Wales busts for the abortive Marriage Medal. However a die with the Queen's bust was made in London very rapidly by Küchler, and the reverse die with a simple inscription was made at Soho by Ponthon.[781] Boulton requested that:

> 'Mr Bush to Matt all the flesh & head well and let the Ground be well polished in order to make the greater contrast' ... 'Though we are defective in Engraving yet I beg the Manufacturing part may be as well done as in the best medals'.[782]

It was important to his reputation to produce as perfect a job as the time allowed, to impress the King.

The medal ledger records that J. Wyatt at Windsor received '50 medals in silver P&P of Wales, 50 medals in silver Kings Head and 50 medals Queen with a total bill of £135, including cases'.[783] After this commission Boulton wanted to obtain a good likeness of the Queen, presumably for future orders and Richard Chippindall, Boulton's London agent was able to oblige on 25th June 1795. But no further medals were produced using Charlotte's image.[784]

Figure 6:6.2 1795 Queen Charlotte medal.

1800 Preservation of George III Medal

Boulton made a further medal featuring George III after an attempt to assassinate him at the theatre on 15th May 1800. The idea was suggested by Chippindall, who had been asked for medals to sell by London retailers. But again, the medals

---

781 MS 3782-13-36 Item 127, MB (London) to MRB (Soho) 14 May 1795.
782 MS 3782-13-36 Item 128, MB (London) to MRB (Soho) 15 May 1795.
783 MS 3782-12-108 Item 69, Medal ledger p22 18 May 1795.
784 MS 3782-12-59 Item 78, Richard Chippindall (London) to MB (Soho) 25 June 1795.

needed to be made quickly as the best sales would be up until the King's birthday on 4th June. Two dies had already been made by Küchler showing *'one head in ye antique stile & the other the more modern in his dress wig'*.[785] Chippindall thought that many would sell including a few made as silver or gilt, and tin medals for the military.[786] Four versions of this medal were made, with the two different busts of the king and two inscriptions: REGE INCOLUMI POPULUS LAETUS ('Be glad that the King is safe') or PERSPICIT ET PROTEGIT ('He observes and defends').

Figure 6:6.3 1800 Preservation of George III medal.

1801 Union of Britain and Ireland Medal

There are also two versions of the Union of Britain and Ireland obverse, one showing George III as on the preservation medal, but with a slightly different inscription, the other with him in antique dress. The reverse shows a seascape background with Britannia clasping hands with Hibernia.

Figure 6:6.4 1801 Union of Britain and Ireland medal.

---

785 MS 3782-12-59 Item 98, MB (Soho) to Richard Chippindall (London) 25 May 1800.
786 MS 3782-12-59 Item 99 and 100, Richard Chippindall (London) to MB (Soho) 27 and 29 May 1800.

1802 Peace of Amiens Medal

Britain had been at war with France since 1793, for most of the time that Soho Mint had been in production. In 1799, Napoleon Bonaparte made truce proposals, but these were rejected by the Prime Minister, William Pitt, and the British Foreign Secretary, Lord Greville. However, Pitt resigned in February 1801, when he could not get George III to agree to Catholic Emancipation, and the new Foreign Secretary, Lord Hawkesbury, reopened discussions with the French. The Treaty of Amiens was signed on 25th March 1802. The terms of the preliminary agreement required Britain and France to restore most colonial possessions captured since 1794. France was to restore Egypt to Ottoman control, to withdraw from most of the Italian peninsula and to preserve Portuguese sovereignty. The British retained Ceylon, and both sides were to be allowed access to Cape of Good Hope in South Africa.

However, the war broke out again in 1803, with both sides claiming violations of the peace treaty. On 17th May 1803, a day before the official declaration of war and without any warning, the Royal Navy captured all the French and Dutch merchant ships stationed in Britain, seizing more than £2 million of commodities and taking their crews as prisoners. In response to this provocation, on 22nd May, the First Consul ordered the arrest of all British males between the ages of 18 and 60 in France and Italy, trapping many travelling civilians. Both acts were denounced as illegal by all the major powers.

Boulton used the 'modern' version of George III's bust on the Peace of Amiens medal. The reverse shows Peace standing with an olive branch in her left hand, setting fire to a pile of arms.

Figure 6:6.5 1802 Peace of Amiens medal.

Medals of the French Revolution

Initially opinion in Britain had been favourable towards the French Revolution. However, the suspension of the monarchy and then the executions of Louis XVI and then Marie Antoinette altered public opinion.[787] Many contemporary prints were made, such as those by Jacques-Louis David, and the *'Final separation of Louis XVI from his family'* engraved by P.W. Tomkins.[788] A companion picture of Marie Antoinette going to her execution was also made.

Busts of the King and Queen of France were engraved by Ponthon, but Boulton thought their depictions looked too young, and so Küchler took over. The portrait source may have been by the French court medallist Benjamin Duvivier. Küchler also engraved the bust of Marie Antoinette alone. One medal made at Soho Mint featured the King and Queen of France saying farewell to their family. Two other medals were made, one to show Louis XVI's execution on 21st January 1793 in the Place de la Révolution which was later renamed Place de la Concorde. The second medal depicts Marie Antoinette on her way to the guillotine in October 1793.

1793 Execution of Louis XVI Medal

Boulton wrote in March 1793:

> *'I am now preparing a medal with a fine head of King and Queen of France on one side with a view of the execution of the king on the other, accompanied by the guards & an immense crowd of spectators in the act of savagely rejoicing'.*[789]

The portrayal of Louis' execution on the reverse by Ponthon was highly influenced by Boulton's comments.

Figure 6:6.6 1793 Execution of Louis XVI.

---

787 D. Bindman (1989) *The Shadow of the Guillotine*, British Museum, London 1989, pp22-23.
788 J.G. Pollard (1970) *Matthew Boulton and Conrad Heinrich Küchler* Numismatic Chronicle Volume X p273.
789 MS 3782-12-59 Item 48, MB (Soho) to Richard Chippindall (London) 12 March 1793.

'Tell Mr Ponthon that in the Die of the Execution of the King he must leave the body lying down & the Executioner must hold up in one hand the Head (holding it by the Hair) shewing it to the people'.

He also gave the inscription.[790] The medal was 55mm in diameter.

1794 (dated 1793) Execution of Marie Antoinette Medal

The medal featuring the bust of Marie Antoinette held a political message, as well as being a work of art, as it was trying to rehabilitate her reputation. She had been seen as an extravagant flirt responsible for the excesses of the French monarchy, but was now portrayed facing a horrific death. The classical buildings in the background initially were government offices, and later the western side was the Hôtel de Crillon where Marie Antoinette took piano lessons.[791]

Figure 6:6.7 1793 Execution of Marie Antoinette medal.

Military victories

Initially Britain remained on the sidelines during the events of the French Revolution. However, a succession of military conflicts, known as the French Revolutionary Wars, lasting from 1792 until 1802, and the Napoleonic Wars from 1803-1815 brought the United Kingdom into conflict with France from February 1793. The war was between the French Republic and several European powers forming a variety of coalitions, and the field of conflict spread worldwide. Napoleon seized power in 1799, and became First Consul of France, and Emperor of the French from 1804. Soho Mint made several medals celebrating military and naval successes against the French.

---

790 MS 3782-13-36 Item 103, MB (London) to MRB (Soho) 19 June 1793.
791 D. Bindman (1989) *The Shadow of the Guillotine* British Museum, London pp22-23.

1792 Marquis Cornwallis Medal

Charles Cornwallis, 1st Marquess Cornwallis (1738-1805) was a British Army general who fought in the American War of Independence (1775-1783), and surrendered to a combined American and French force at the Siege of Yorktown in 1781. This effectively ended active hostilities. He served as Governor-General in India from 1786-1793, where he reformed the East India Company. He concluded the 'Permanent Settlement' of Bengal in 1793 which installed a less corrupt bureaucracy run by the EIC. He was then Master-General of Ordnance responsible for British artillery, engineers, fortifications, military supplies, transport and field hospitals, and later Commander-in-Chief in Ireland from 1798, where he oversaw the response to the Irish Rebellion and helped bring about the Act of Union in Ireland. He was chief signatory to the 1802 Peace of Amiens.

The American Revolution sparked off problems in India in the form of the Second Anglo-Mysore War (1780-1784), where the chief combatants were Tipu Sultan (1750-1799), ruler of Mysore, in southern India, and, on the other side, the British. This conflict was bloody but inconclusive and ended in a draw in 1784, but was continued again during the Third Anglo-Mysore War (1789-1792). The 1792 Cornwallis Medal was struck to commemorate the victory of Cornwallis and his Indian allies over Tipu Sultan, a key French ally. Tipu was made to surrender half his possessions and to pay an indemnity, and his sons were delivered to Cornwallis as hostages, as shown on the reverse of the medal. An account was given in the *Gentleman's Magazine* and a painting was produced by Henry Singleton. The die was engraved by Küchler and completed by November 1794.[792] Several suggestions for a suitable inscription on the medal came from Sir George Shuckburgh-Evelyn, 6th Baronet (1751-1804), who acted as Member of Parliament for Warwickshire from 1780-1804. He was a fellow of the Royal Society and, like Boulton, interested in astronomy.[793]

Figure 6:6.8 1792 Marquis Cornwallis medal.

---

792 J.G. Pollard (1970) *Matthew Boulton and Conrad Heinrich Küchler* pp276-277.
793 MS 3782-12-39 Item 261, G. Shuckburgh-Evelyn (Shuckburgh Park) to MB 20 September 1794.

By 1797 Richard Wellesley (1760-1842), a colleague of William Pitt, was appointed Governor-General in India. Both Cornwallis and Wellesley had the desire to form a great empire in India to compensate for the loss of the American colonies in 1783. Wellesley's rule in India resulted in an enormous and rapid extension of British power.

1801 (dated 1799) Seringapatam Medal

The Fourth Mysore War (1798-1799) involved the same combatants as the Third. The British troops were under the command of Richard Wellesley's brother, Arthur Wellesley (1769-1852), later the Duke of Wellington. He had 4,000 Europeans and 26,000 East India Company troops, mainly local sepoys, plus ten battalions and over 16,000 cavalry supplied by the Nizam of Hyderabad. With the capture of the capital, Seringapatam, and the death of Tipu Sultan, French influence in India was finally extinguished. The East India Company ordered a medal from Soho Mint to commemorate this victory, to be awarded to troops engaged in the battle; in gold for Indian princes, generals and senior officers; silver-gilt for intermediate officers including majors and senior EIC officials; silver for captains; bronzed for native commissioned and European non-commissioned officers, and white metal (pewter) for corporals and other ranks, both British and Indian. The obverse design included the lion of Britain and the tiger of Mysore, with an Arabic inscription ('The lion of God is the conqueror'). The reverse shows the battle with the date in a Persian inscription.

Figure 6:6.9 1801 Seringapatam medal.

William Brown wrote from Soho Mint in August 1800: *'I have given the sketch of the lyon and tyger to Mr. Kückler, who promises to do his best. Mr. Busch is preparing to strike a few tin medals in the mint'*. He went on to calculate prices for *'copper bronzed;*

gilt, silver, and gold' medals.[794] But they were still waiting for the inscription, expected from Charles Wilkins of the EIC, ten days later: *'Mr. Küchler strongly urges me to remind you of the inscription for the Seringapatam medal, which you promised to send him'.*[795] The eventual version was 'Seringapatam, God given 28th day of the month zikadah, in the Hejira year 1213'.

1799 Count Alexander Suvorov Medal [alternative Suworow]

Count Alexander Suvorov (1729-1800) was one of the most successful of Russian generals. He was dismissed by Paul I, but at the insistence of the coalition leaders, Paul was forced to reinstate Suvorov as field marshal. Suvorov was given command of the Austro-Russian army and sent to drive France's forces out of Italy. In 1799, he succeeded in reversing all of the gains Napoleon had made during 1796 and 1797. The medal was made to commemorate his victories. Since 1994, the Russian Federation has awarded a medal, named after Suvorov, to troops for courage in combat.

Figure 6:6.10 1799 Alexander Suvorov medal.

Naval victories

Soho Mint produced several medals to celebrate naval victories. These included one to commemorate the victory of the Glorious First of June in 1794 by Lord Howe, the 1798 British Victories (Army and Navy Victories) Medal and one dated 1800, the Earl St Vincent's Medal celebrating his defeat of the Spanish fleet in 1797. There were several medals marking the spectacular career of Horatio Nelson (1758-1805), who first went to sea at the age of twelve, and rapidly rose to the rank of Captain by the age of twenty-one.

---

794 MS 3782-12-58 Item 99 William D. Brown (Soho) to MB (London) 4 August 1800.
795 MS 49 Timmins collection Reference 82934 Volume 1 Item 31, MB (Soho) to J Willis Esq (India House) 14 November 1800.

1794 Lord Howe, 'Glorious' First of June Medal

Lord Richard Howe (1726-1799) served in the British Navy from 1739 on. He fought in the West Indies, during the Jacobite Revolution, and gained a reputation for his role in a decisive British naval victory during the Seven Years War. A naval commander through the American Revolution, he later commanded the Channel fleet in 1793. In 1794 Lord Howe defeated a French fleet of twenty-five ships, escorting a grain convey. His fleet of twenty-two ships captured seven enemy ships.

Figure 6:6.11 1794 Lord Howe medal.

1798 British Victories Medal

This medal featured George III on the obverse, and Britannia on the reverse, holding victory aloft, surrounded by captured arms, trophies and colours. The inscription, 'MARI VICTRIX TERRAQUE INVICTA' (Victorious at sea, unvanquished on land) indicated that the medal was to celebrate a variety of British victories over the French.

Figure 6:6.12 1798 British Victories medal.

1798 Davison's Nile Medal

One commissioned medal was made to celebrate Nelson's victory over the French at the Battle of the Nile. Bonaparte had invaded Egypt in July 1798. On 1st August 1798, a scouting vessel found the French fleet anchored close to shallow water in Aboukir Bay to the south of Alexandria. Nelson, on board the *Vanguard,* divided his fleet of fourteen battleships into two lines and ordered them to sail down on either side of the enemy. Of the thirteen French ships of the line and four frigates, only four ships escaped. This victory gave the British control of the Mediterranean.

Soho Mint was commissioned by Alexander Davison, Nelson's prize agent, to make medals for everyone who served in the action. Medals were struck in gold for Nelson and his captains, silver for lieutenants and warrant officers, in gilt copper for petty officers, and in tin or pewter for the seamen and marines. A series of letters passed between William Cheshire at Soho and Matthew Boulton in London during November and December 1798 discussing the designs.[796] The medals were eventually dispatched on 3rd March 1799.[797] The final bill showed a cost of £112 14s for engraving and completion of 25 gold, 154 silver, 506 gilt and 6,530 tin medals, with the gold and silver costing £334 6s, paid by profits from the captured ships.[798]

Figure 6:6.13 1798 Davison's Nile medal.

1805 Boulton's Trafalgar Medal

Britain faced a serious threat of invasion by Napoleon's forces, until the Battle of Trafalgar in 1805 destroyed the main French and Spanish fleets and gave

---

796 MS 3782-12-59 Item 176, William Cheshire (Soho) to MB (London) 19 November 1798 and Item 181, 9 December 1798.

797 MS 3782-12-59 Item 183-185, William Cheshire (Soho) to MB (London) 25-28 February 1799; 3 March 1799.

798 MS 3782-6-195 Item 50, Bill to Alexander Davison 15 May 1801.

Britain control of the seas. The Trafalgar medal is probably the most famous of Soho's medals. It was produced at Boulton's own expense for presentation to the marines and seamen who took part in the action. 19,000 medals were prepared, with 16,163 in tin or white metal. A few were made in silver and gold for presentation at court.

Nelson died, struck by a musket ball, as the victory was won on 21st October. Great care was taken by Boulton to get a lifelike portrait of Nelson and several dies were engraved. The first die was based on a sketch by Lady Beechey, from the portrait of Nelson painted in 1801, by her husband, Sir William Beechey, but this was not liked by Nelson's family. A second attempt from a miniature from Lady Hamilton and a drawing by de Koster (da Costa) was also not accepted, and the final version was engraved by Küchler from a wax by Catherine Andras, modelled from life in 1805.[799]

Figure 6:6.14 Trial strikes for the Trafalgar medal.

Boulton wrote to Sir William Beechey in 1806:

> *'Although the Heros of Trefalga conquered the French and Spaniards, yet nevertheless feeble as I am, I am now prepared to conquer them by the presence of their immortal and unconquerable commander; specimens of which I send you herewith in silver, copper and grain tin; but I beg you will view them as they lye in their boxes and touch the edges only'.*[800]

Lady Anne Beechey acknowledged their receipt with thanks in December.[801]

---

799 D. Vice (1997) *Boulton's Trafalgar Medal* Format 55; Nicholas Goodison (2007) *MB's Trafalgar Medal* Birmingham Museum and Art Gallery, Birmingham City Council.

800 W. Roberts (1907) *Sir William Beechey RA*, London, p68. Thanks to Val Loggie for this reference.

801 MS 3782-12-51 Item 198, Lady Anne Beechey to MB (Soho) 11 December 1806.

1805 Trafalgar medal alternate version   Trafalgar die face

Figure 6:6.15 1805 Trafalgar medal and die.

The reverse was based on a design by Richard Cleveley, a marine artist, who wrote to Boulton to say it was taken as the *Royal Sovereign* was going into action partly enveloped in smoke. The edge was inscribed TO THE HEROES OF TRAFALGAR FROM M:BOULTON.

Figure 6:6.16 1805 Trafalgar medal.

Local Volunteer Organisations

Many volunteer associations had been raised during the French Revolutionary Wars to protect the country from the threat of invasion. Boulton made several medals, including ones for the Birmingham Loyal Association, the Manchester and Salford Volunteers and the Nottinghamshire Yeomanry.[802] He also made a

---

802 MS 3782-12-108 Item 69, Medal ledger p110 12 September 1804.

halfpenny token in 1796 featuring the Penryn Volunteers, commanded by his old acquaintance from Cornwall, Sir Francis Bassett.

1802 Nottinghamshire Yeomanry Medal

The Loyal Nottingham Volunteer Infantry was raised in June 1794 and was used to quell a food riot in April 1795. In 1801 all officers and around 500 NCOs and privates were transferred to the local militia and the rest disbanded. Medals made at Soho Mint were presented to the Corps by Lord Newark on 13th May 1802 in commemoration of their important service. A drawing in the Sarah Sophia Banks collection at the British Museum shows the design for this medal with its inscription FOI LOI ROI ('Faith, Law and King').[803]

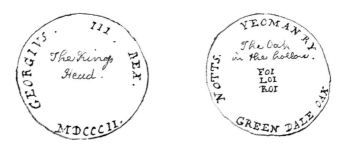

Figure 6:6.17 Design for Nottingham Yeomanry medal.

Figure 6:6.18 1802 Nottingham Yeomanry medal (an actual gold medal, not gilt).

1802 Birmingham Loyal Association Medal

This medal was produced in 1802 for presentation to the members of the Birmingham Loyal Association (BLA) and of the Loyal Birmingham Light Horse

---

803 Uncatalogued notes in Sarah Sophia Banks collection, Prints and Drawings, British Museum. Thanks to Dr Catherine Eagleton for her help in viewing this collection.

Volunteers (LBLHV), who together comprised the first generation of volunteer units raised in Birmingham. The BLA was an infantry force, 10 companies strong with around 550 members. The LBLHV was the cavalry force, probably just one troop, so something like 100 strong. Both were raised in 1797 as a response to possible invasion by the French, and disbanded in 1802 following the Peace of Amiens, when it was assumed their services would no longer be needed. Medals were individually inscribed with the name of the recipient.

When the peace broke down, a completely new volunteer unit, the Loyal Birmingham Volunteers, was formed in 1803. Matthew Boulton's son, Matt was an officer in this unit.

Figure 6:6.19 1802 Birmingham Loyal Association medal.

'Society' medals

Medals were made at Soho Mint for various groups or societies, including Agricultural Societies. Medals were given for skill in ploughing, rearing of prize cattle, and so on. The issuing of such awards can be seen as relating to a growing emphasis on meritocracy in various areas of British life. Boulton also made medals for Friendly Societies set up to give support to individuals in time of need, including the St Albans Female Friendly Society and the Hafod Friendly Society. He made tokens for the Ipswich Theatre, Westminster Fire Office and Linwood Meeting Rooms, generally engraved by John Phillp.

1794 Essex Agricultural Society Medal

The medal ordered by Louis Majendie for the Essex Agricultural Society in December 1793 was the first private commission made at Soho Mint, rather than a speculative medal. The dies, engraved by Küchler, were delivered to Chippindall on 20th June 1794.[804]

---

804 J.G. Pollard (1970) *Matthew Boulton and Conrad Heinrich Küchler* p276.

The obverse design featured Britannia, holding a wreath in her extended right hand and a cornucopia in her left. She is seated next to the lion of Britain in a peaceful agricultural landscape with fields, cottages, windmill and haystacks. The edge was engraved: STRUCK IN THE MINT OF M. BOULTON.

Figure 6:6.20 1794 Essex Agricultural medal.

Very specific orders were given for one medal to be struck in silver with the reverse inscribed:

> '(*between the wreath and Edge*) *to Filmer Honeywood Esq MDCCVIIII and at the bottom No 1: within the wreath should be The Best Ram. The engraving to be neatly and distinctly executed and the medal put into a real shagreen case*'.

Majendie enclosed a diagram.[805] This medal was finally on its way in January 1795.[806] The Medal ledger book shows that various other Essex Agricultural Society medals were ordered up until at least May 1808.[807]

1797 (dated 1793) Board of Agriculture Prize Medal

Another agricultural medal was ordered by the Board of Agriculture in September 1797.[808] Boulton had corresponded with the Board on various matters, including the powering of grain mills using steam engines. The medals were examined in November by Sir John Sinclair, who asked '*that you will send us specimens in copper, silver and gold as quickly as possible*'.[809] Medals were made individually and could

805 MS 3782-12-39 Item 243, Mr Majendie (Hedingham Castle) to MB (Soho) 7 September 1794.
806 MS 3782-13-36 Item 114, MB (London) to MRB (Soho) 30 January 1795.
807 MS 3782-12-108 Item 69, Medal ledger p22.
808 MS 3782-12-42 Item 221, Sir John Sinclair (Edinburgh) to Boulton & Watt (Birmingham) 6 September 1797.
809 MS 3782-12-42 Item 263, Sir John Sinclair (London) to Boulton & Watt (Birmingham) 8 November 1797.

be engraved on the edges with the name of the recipient.[810] A bill for £44 15s for engraving the dies, the preparation of the gold, and engraving the medal, was presented to the Board of Agriculture on 7th October 1799.[811] The medals were awarded until at least 1803. The design of this medal has been described earlier.

Figure 6:6.21 1797 Board of Agriculture medal.

1801 (dated 1800) Staffordshire Agriculture Society Medal

Medals similar to that for Essex were made for the Staffordshire Agricultural Society and for the Drayton Agricultural Society. There are variations in the positioning of the lion who lies on a shield for Staffordshire, and partially hides behind a raised shield in the Drayton version. The Staffordshire Agricultural Medal was possibly ordered by Richard Dyott as president, as his name appears faintly in pencil on a design diagram.[812]

Figure 6:6.22 Design and trial strike for Staffordshire Agricultural Society.

---

810 MS 3782-12-59 Item 184, William Cheshire (Soho) to MB (London) 28 February 1799.
811 MS 3782-6-195, Bill to Board of Agriculture 7 October 1799.
812 MS 49 Timmins collection Reference 82934 Volume 1 Item 34.

1798 Hafod Friendly Society Medal

Colonel Thomas Johnes (1748-1816) was the owner of an estate, Hafod Uchtryd, twelve miles south-east of Aberystwyth. The grounds were laid out in sympathy with the 'picturesque principles' fashionable at the time. Johnes tried out new ideas and experimental methods in farming and forestry and was one of the chief supporters of the Cardiganshire Agricultural Society, founded in 1784.[813] He corresponded with Boulton on a variety of topics in 1797 including plated zinc and a discovery of cobalt.[814] At Hafod he built a church and a school for girls, and established a friendly society to support workers in times of illness or unemployment. The sale of 20 silver and 100 bronzed medals was recorded in the medal ledger book, and the engraving of the dies cost £7 7s.[815]

The obverse inscription in Welsh SOBRWYDD DIWYDRWYDD A BRAWDGARWCH means sobriety, diligence and brotherhood, and the clasped hands indicate friendship. The reverse gave details of when the society was established.

Figure 6:6.23 1798 Hafod Friendly Society.

1803 St Alban's Female Friendly Society Medal

Both the Hafod and the St Alban's medals were engraved by John Phillp. The actual medal made for the St Alban's Friendly Society was different from the alternative designs seen in the Phillp Album, held at Birmingham Museum and Art Gallery.

---

813 The Hafod Trust www.hafod.org.
814 MS 3782-12-42 Items 258 & 279, Colonel Thomas Johnes (Hafod) to MB (Soho) 4 November 1797, 2 December 1797.
815 MS 3782-12-108 Item 69, Medal ledger p106.

Figure 6:6.24 1803 St Alban's Female Friendly Society.

1803 (dated 1798) Boulton's Medallic Scale Medal

Following the Peace of Amiens, Boulton was again investigating the possibility of coining for the French government.[816] But Droz had presented a paper to the Napoleonic National Institution in 1802, claiming for himself what Boulton considered his techniques.[817] Droz also produced a medal in Spanish asserting that he had invented a method of multiplying dies as he was hoping to obtain a contract in Spain for the Paris Mint. The medallic scale medal, in French, was intended to counteract these claims, a multilingual argument carried out on medals.

The medal was engraved in France by Rambert Dumarest. In November 1802 Boulton wrote:

> 'I have some thought on striking a piece (of money in relief) of the size of my peny piece provided Mr Dumarest would engrave _my head_ expeditiously; in the Reverse I purpose to make 4 Aides expressive as to Size of pence, ½ pence, farthings & ½ farthings'.

The letter included a diagram with four circles to show the four sizes.[818]

The medal was not completed when war with France recommenced but in September 1803 Boulton promised to send a sample to his lawyer, Ambrose Weston. He wrote:

> 'from the love of Truth, I have been induced to Engrave a Medal of my own dear self: upon the reverse & Edge of which, I have recorded the history & effects of my Mint: otherwise it will be claimd by the french ... I will give you a Medal, which may serve as a record a thousand years hence & it may also serve as a mark of my having existed upon this Planet whether my Executors may lay a flat Stone over my Dust or not'.[819]

---

816 MS 3782-13-51, MB (Soho) to Zaccheus Walker Jr (Paris) 6 November 1802.
817 J.G. Pollard (1968) _Matthew Boulton and J.P. Droz_ pp247-248.
818 MS 3782-13-51, MB (Soho) to Zaccheus Walker Jr (Paris) 1 November 1802.
819 MS 3782-12-80 Item 131, MB (Soho) to Ambrose Weston (London) 8 September 1803.

The obverse of the medal shows a bust of Matthew Boulton facing right with the inscription: MATT. BOULTON E[SQR.] F.R.S. L[N] & ED. FR.I. &. A.S. Boulton was elected a Fellow of the Royal Society of London on 25th November 1785, and a Fellow of the Royal Society of Edinburgh, Fellow of the Royal Institute and Academy of Science.[820]

The reverse shows rings with numbers, and an inscription in French describing the history and powers of Soho Mint's steam-powered coining press. In translation this reads:

'Matthew Boulton erected at Soho, England in 1788, a steam powered machine to strike coins. In 1798 he set up a much better one with eight new presses. These circles and numbers indicate the diameter and number of pieces struck per minute by eight children without fatigue, of the smallest or greatest volume, or of 8 different combinations. One can increase efficiency to the necessary degree'.

Figure 6:6.25 1803 Boulton's Medallic Scale medal.

820 www.royalsociety.org GB 117 The Royal Society, Item EC/1785/12.

Conclusion

MATTHEW Boulton deserves most of the credit for improvements in coining technology at Soho Mint in the eighteenth century, which led in turn to improvements in coining practises throughout the world. He survived problems with copper supply, lack of orders, and difficulties with engravers. He trained a team of engineers and technicians in a completely new technology and succeeded in producing over 600 million coins for countries worldwide.

The Soho Mint, more than any other of Boulton's business affairs, utilized his talents as an engineer, industrialist, artist, businessman and one of the eighteenth century's foremost networkers. He had great organisational ability and attention to detail and was able to coordinate collaborative effort. He could communicate his ideas to a team of individuals who were inspired by his enthusiasm for the Soho Mint project.

His capacity to motivate his workers, to persuade governments, to keep royalty happy, and to obtain foreign orders proved to be essential for the survival of the mint. Peter Ewart wrote:

> 'He possessed above all other men I have ever known the faculty of inspiring others with a portion of that ardent Zeal with which he himself pursued every important object he had in view, and it was impossible to be near him without becoming warmly interested in the success of his enterprises'.[821]

It was due to his perseverance and drive that the Soho Mint finally succeeded in the face of multiple difficulties, which would have discouraged anyone else. James Lawson concluded in a memorial written for Boulton's son: 'no one I have ever known has had that continued & unwearied Perseverance to accomplish the object as your Worthy Father'.[822]

Lack of small change had threatened to derail industrial progress at the end of the eighteenth century. Matthew Boulton was able to solve this problem, making major improvements not only in the technological aspects of minting practices, but also in the transport of the raw materials needed, and in the distribution of

---

821 MS 3782-13-120 Folder 5, Mint Inventions Peter Ewart (Manchester) to MRB (Soho) 9 November 1809.
822 MS 3782-13-120 Folder 4, Lawson (London) to MRB (Soho) 12 December 1809.

the completed products. By the time he obtained a regal coinage contract in 1797, Boulton was sixty-nine years old, with failing health. But despite this, he went on to produce 321 million coins for the British government in the next ten years, which the Royal Mint were unable to do.

It was the Cornish copper industry that had provided the first major use of the Boulton and Watt steam-engine, but it was also important for providing many of the engineers who set up the mint. Copper was an essential raw material, and one reason for the development of the Soho Mint was the over-supply of copper in the late 1780s. The Privy Council for Coin were finally persuaded to award contracts to Boulton and the Soho Mint, rather than to the Royal Mint, because of his expertise in all aspects of the metal industries.

The development of the rotative engine, used to power the coining apparatus, was only one of the Soho Mint's technical improvements. In addition to using steam-powered, Boulton introduced automation and standardisation for the first time in minting. Each of the new coin presses had an automatic layer-in which fed in the blanks and removed the finished coin. The whole process could be rapidly repeated. Progress in one area of the metal industries was strongly linked to another, such as the introduction of crucible steel by Huntsman, and its use in die making. Boulton's practical investigations into annealing and hardening steel, led to standardized dies, an important aspect often overlooked in making coins.

The hoped-for regal coinage contract had been hampered by global events such as the French Revolution and the wars that followed, plus unforeseen events such as the 'madness' of George III. This meant that Boulton had to diversify his customer base, and obtain contracts for private tokens issues and foreign coins, and to make medals. For certain orders, the amounts produced were negligible compared to the millions of coins struck for the British Government and the East India Company, but nevertheless they proved important in the development of the mint, both technically and artistically. These commissions were gained by Boulton's ability as a publicist, through personal contacts, and because of his reputation as a reliable supplier. Sales to collectors were also important in keeping the Soho Mint in the public eye, and in retaining key workers. Copper tokens were accessible to collectors who were not especially wealthy, but the more expensive medals produced at the Soho Mint were also popular with the elite of society. His influence lasted after his death, as many coin and medal producers had been trained at Soho Mint.

The aesthetic aspects of Boulton's coins were of high quality, with a huge range of designs for customers from many walks of life. Boulton took a personal interest in design, and his search for perfection in details, such as inscriptions, and the accuracy of the images, made the Soho pieces popular with influential individuals, and encouraged contemporary interest in collecting coins, medals, and tokens. The designs on the regal coins were seen as representative of Britain, and of excellent quality. One appreciative recipient of coin wrote: *'The specimens of the intended copper pence are, like all your productions, strong marks of the superior excellence of the English artists over those of any other country'.*[823] This would have been very satisfying to Boulton, who had achieved the reform of coinage and its distribution, which had defeated others.

A great part of the innovations at the Soho Mint were due to Matthew Boulton's personal attributes. His great knowledge of the mechanical and metallurgical arts, his leadership, and his determination were recognized at the time by his co-workers:

> *'That the management & methodizing of the whole was exclusively his [Boulton's] own; & that to his indefatigable energy & perseverance in pursuit of this the favourite & nearly the sole object of the last twenty years of the active part of his life is to be attributed the perfection it has ultimately attained'.*[824]

All members of the Soho team admired Boulton's technical skills acknowledging that *'the first idea of applying the power of the steam engine to the purposes of coining originated with Mr Boulton'*. Southern also said that all improvements in *'making & hardening dies and in annealing were MB's own'*.[825]

Ewart attributed much of the progress to Boulton, and also appreciated his personal qualities:

> *'His judgement in the selection of objects to which machinery might be applied with the greatest advantage & in suggesting not only the leading points, but the subsidiary part also, to which the chief attention ought to be directed, was most conspicuous; and amidst a variety of different plans for attaining the same object, he had a quick perception of that which was most likely to succeed, and great promptitude in his determination to carry it into effect. In none of his enterprises were these qualities more conspicuous than in the prosecution of his favourite object, the bringing to perfection the Mint Machinery'.*

Ewart continued:

> *'The urbanity of his manners and his great kindness to young people in particular, never failed to leave the most agreeable impression on the minds of all around him; and most truly may it be said that he reigned in the hearts of those that were in his employment'.*[826]

The Soho Mint was one of Matthew Boulton's proudest achievements; in two portraits painted between 1792 and 1801 he is holding a coin or medal, and

---

823 MS 3782-12-42 Item 197, John Barton (Office for Trade, Whitehall, London) to (MB) (—) 5 August 1797; MS 3782-12-42 Item 139, Brook Watson (London) to MB (Soho) 14 June 1797.
824 MS-3782-13-120, Minutes of a meeting held at Soho on 7 January 1810.
825 MS 3782-13-120, Mint Inventions and Improvements 7 Jan 1810.
826 MS 3782-13-120 Folder 5, Mint Inventions Peter Ewart (Manchester) to MRB (Soho) 9 Nov 1809.

in the third he is leaning on the Mint record book.[827] However, after his death in 1809, the Soho Mint declined, finally closing in 1849. Both the Mint and Manufactory were demolished and the coining apparatus was sold to Calcutta in 1823. Only the coins, medals and tokens remain. However, his legacy was the coining technology and die-making techniques that were adopted across the world. He can truly be said to be the founder of modern money, with uniformly sized coins, straight edges and standardized images.

Figure 7.1 1798-1801 Matthew Boulton leaning on his Mint book.

It seems fitting that the final words in this book should be those of James Watt who wrote, in Matthew Boulton's obituary, that:

'Had Mr B done nothing more in the world than what he has done in improving the coinage, his fame would have deserved to be immortalised; and if it is considered that this was done in the midst of various other important avocations, & at an enormous expense for which he could have no certainty of an adequate return, we shall be at a loss as to whether to admire most his ingenuity, his perseverance or his munificence'.[828]

---

827 1792 Charles Frederick von Breda Oil on canvas BMAG 1987F106; 1798-1801 Lemuel Abbott Oil on canvas BMAG: 1908P20; 1798 Sir William Beechey Oil on canvas BMAG: 2003.007.44 (1810 copy).

828 James Watt's Memorial to Matthew Boulton written on 17 September 1809 H.W. Dickinson, *Matthew Boulton*, Cambridge, 1937, p205.

Acknowledgements

THIS book is the result of research undertaken for a PhD, awarded in 2011 by the University of Birmingham, financed by an Arts and Humanities Research Collaborative Doctoral Award with the Birmingham Museums and Art Gallery. Thanks especially to Dr David Symons for all his help. Information from archives, numismatic and historical literature, scientific, technological, art historical and transport sources, is brought together with research into museum artefacts; the dies, coins, medals and tokens produced at Soho Mint. Over 2,000 examples from Soho Mint were viewed at locations such as Birmingham Museum and Art Gallery, Birmingham Assay Office, Avery Museum, Birmingham Think Tank and the British Museum. Field work at sites associated with various aspects of the metal industries complements the archival studies of Matthew Boulton's involvement in the extraction and supply of copper, iron and steel.

The number of coins struck, and the weight of copper used for each order were recorded. All figures given for numbers of coins, medals, or tokens produced are taken from David Vice's forthcoming monograph. I thank David for allowing me a preview of this outstanding piece of scholarship.

Sources

Field work

Places associated with the Soho Mint were visited, such as Handsworth, where Soho Mint and Manufactory were located, the canal system in Birmingham, and Soho House where Boulton lived. Greater understanding of the processes necessary to provide the raw materials for Soho Mint was provided by visits to the copper mining areas in Cornwall, Anglesey and the Peak District, to various ports used to ship copper ore, and to Thomas Williams's Greenfield copper works at Holywell, Flintshire. In addition, important iron manufacturing sites at Ironbridge, Shropshire, and at Carron, near Falkirk, Stirlingshire plus Wilkinson's ironworks at Bersham, Clwyd, were visited. These were useful in understanding the processes of iron and steelmaking. A visit to the Royal Mint at Llantrisant, Pontyclun, Wales, to see coining equipment at work proved very instructive.

Archives

One of the reasons that Matthew Boulton has been studied by so many researchers is the availability of the wide-ranging holdings of business records, letters, plans, patents, diaries, newspaper cuttings, ledgers, diagrams and so on, which are known as the Archives of Soho, held by the Library of Birmingham. Both sides of the correspondence are often available due to the use of James Watt's copying machine.

Soho Mint records exist from 1791-1850, and consist of 183 volumes of various sizes and 25 archival boxes. They include daybooks, packing books, consignments and weight books, order books and notebooks. The Soho documents are far too extensive to investigate comprehensively, but certain sections have been studied in detail, including correspondence from various employees and customers, the Mint record books, Boulton's experimental notebooks and diaries, and his letters and notes on the copper industry.

There is also a wealth of information in a variety of other less well-known archives, now available electronically. The Cornwall Heritage Trust holds a collection of around 1,100 letters from Matthew Boulton and James Watt to and from Thomas Wilson, their mining agent in Cornwall. The collection of letters spans the years 1780-1803 and have references starting AD1583.[829] They

---

829 Cornwall Heritage Trust at www.cornish-mining.org.uk/story/boulton.htm.

offer a viewpoint of the start of Boulton's coining activities and his links with the copper industry. Valuable information is also available on the Anglesey Industrial Heritage Trust on copper mining.[830] A useful contribution was made by a collection of letters and documents concerning Sir Joseph Banks and his connection with Boulton.[831]

Secondary Sources

A considerable volume of literature has been written about aspects of the life of Matthew Boulton and the Soho Mint. The most significant volume has been completed by Richard Doty. David Vice has also done much important work, and numerous articles detail individual coin, medal or token issues made there. George Selgin covers the problems caused by lack of copper and silver coin. There are also books about the Royal Mint by J. Craig and C.E. Challis.

The studies of the iron and copper industry by K.C. Barraclough, J.R. Harris and H. Hamilton proved particularly useful when considering the preparation of the raw materials. Hamilton discussed the history and industrial organization of the brass and copper industries in Birmingham. Harris concentrated on the career of Thomas Williams of Anglesey, the 'Copper King', whose story is interlinked with Boulton. Barraclough, meanwhile, has analysed the production of steel.

---

830 Anglesey Industrial Heritage Trust at www.angleseymining.co.uk; www.parysmountain.co.uk.
831 State Library of New South Wales, Australia at www.sl.nsw.gov.au/banks

Selected Bibliography

FOR a full list of sources see Sue Tungate PhD thesis awarded December 2011 available at: www.etheses.bham.ac.uk/3202/9/Tungate_11_PhD_minusvol2.pdf

There are also further accounts in:

Richard Clay and Sue Tungate (eds.) (2009) *Matthew Boulton and the Art of Making Money* Brewin, Studley.

Sue Tungate (2009) 'Matthew Boulton's Mints: Copper to Customer' in: S. Mason (ed.) (2009) *Matthew Boulton: Selling What All The World Desires* Yale University Press, London and New Haven pp80-88.

Sue Tungate (2009) 'Technology, Art and Design in the Work of Matthew Boulton: Coins, Medals and Tokens produced at the Soho Mint' in M. Dick (ed.) (2009) *Matthew Boulton: A Revolutionary Player* Brewin, Studley pp185-200.

Sue Tungate (2013) 'Workers at the Soho Mint' in S. Baggott and K. Quickenden (eds.) *Matthew Boulton – Enterprising Industrialist of the Enlightenment* Ashgate, Farnham.

R.R. Angerstein (2001) *R.R. Angerstein's Illustrated Travel Diary, 1753-1755 Industry in England and Wales from a Swedish Perspective* translated by Torsten and Peter Berg, Science Museum, London.

T.S. Ashton (1924) *Iron and Steel in the Industrial Revolution* Manchester University Press, Manchester.

S. Baggott and K. Quickenden (eds.) *Matthew Boulton – Enterprising Industrialist of the Enlightenment* Ashgate, Farnham.

K.C. Barraclough (1984) *Steel Making before Bessemer Volume 1: Blister steel; Volume 2: Crucible Steel the growth of technology* Metals Society, London.

R.C. Bell (1963) *Commercial Coins 1787-1804* Corbitt and Hunter, Newcastle.

R.C. Bell (1964) *Copper Commercial Coins 1811-1819* Corbitt and Hunter, Newcastle.

R.C. Bell (1966) *Tradesmen's Tickets and Private Tokens 1785-1819* Corbitt and Hunter, Newcastle.

C.E. Challis (ed.) (1992) *A New History of the Royal Mint* Cambridge University Press, Cambridge.

D.R. Cooper (1988) *The Art and Craft of Coin-making: A History of Minting Technology* Spink, London.

J. Conder (1799) *An Arrangement of Provincial Coins, Tokens and Medalets,* Jermyn, London.

J. Craig (1953) *The Mint: A History of the London Mint from AD 287-1948* Cambridge University Press, Cambridge.

R. Dalton and S.H. Hamer (1910-1918) *The Provincial Token-Coinage of the 18th Century Illustrated* in 14 parts, Stationers Hall, London.

M. Dick (ed.) (2009) *Matthew Boulton: A Revolutionary Player* Brewin, Studley.

H.W. Dickinson (1936; republished 1999) *Matthew Boulton* Cambridge University Press, Cambridge; TEE Publishing, Warwickshire.

R. Doty (1998) *The Soho Mint and the Industrialization of Money* British Numismatic Society Special Publication No 2, London.

C. Evans and G. Rydén (eds.) (2005) *The Industrial Revolution in Iron: The Impact of British Coal Technology in Nineteenth Century Europe* Ashgate, Aldershot.

N. Goodison (1974 amended 2002) *Matthew Boulton Ormolu* Christies, London.

H. Hamilton (1926; 2nd ed. 1967) *The English Brass and Copper Industries to 1800* Cass, London.

J.R. Harris (1964) *The Copper King: A biography of Thomas Williams of Llanidan* Liverpool University Press, Liverpool.

J.R. Harris (1998) *Industrial Espionage and Technology Transfer: Britain and France in the Eighteenth Century* Ashgate, Aldershot.

E. Hopkins (1989) *Birmingham: The First Manufacturing Town in the World 1760-1840* Weidenfeld and Nicholson, London.

J. Mokyr (2009) *The Enlightened Economy: An Economic History of Britain 1700-1850* Yale University Press, London and New Haven.

S. Mason (ed.) (2009) *Matthew Boulton: Selling What All The World Desires* Yale University Press, London and New Haven.

J. Morton (1983) *Thomas Bolton and Sons Limited 1783-1983 the bicentenary history of a major copper and brass manufacturer* Morland Publishing, Ashbourne.

C.W. Peck (1970) *English Copper, Tin and Bronze Coins in the British Museum 1558-1958* Trustees of the British Museum, London.

H.A. Seaby and P.J. Seaby (1949 edn.) *A Catalogue of Copper Coins and Tokens of the British Isles* B.A. Seaby Ltd. London.

G. Selgin (2008) *Good Money: Birmingham Button Makers, the Royal Mint, and the Beginnings of Modern Coinage 1775-1821* The University of Michigan Press, Ann Arbour.

J. Uglow (2002) *The Lunar Men: Friends who Made the Future* Faber and Faber, London.

Appendix

Chronological List of Coins, Medals and Tokens made at Soho Mint till 1820

THE date of production and name of the item is given, followed by the engraver and the total number of pieces made if known.[832] The items in italics are requests which were found during research, for orders which were discussed but not started.

1772 'Otaheite' Medal also known as Resolution and Adventure Medal or Captain Cook's Second Voyage to the Pacific Medal (BHM 165; Eimer 744) **41-44mm John Westwood Senior TOTAL 2,144**

1774 Regimental Medals 37th Foot (Hampshires) Sir Eyre Coote Medal **45 x 56mm**; oval **40 x 52mm**; **50mm John Westwood TOTAL 22**

1781 Admiral Rodney Medal (BHM 230) **34mm Thomas Moore/William Wilson**

1786 Sumatra (Bencoolen) three keping, two keping, one keping **William Castleton 28mm; 25mm; 20mm TOTAL 2,944,620**

1786 *Request from Charles Borel, South Carolina for five tons of copper coin.*[833]

1787 Sumatra; three keping, two keping, one keping **William Castleton 27mm; 25mm; 20mm TOTAL 7,250,000**

1787 (possibly not struck till after 1815) Siege of Gibraltar (General Eliott/Lord Heathfield) Medal (BHM 247; Eimer 794) **59mm Jean-Pierre Droz**

1787 pattern Shilling **25mm Jean-Pierre Droz** (ESC 1242)

---

832 Numbers of pieces made come from R. Doty (1998) *The Soho Mint;* D. Vice (forthcoming) and from a variety of archive sources found during research.

833 MS 3782-12-74 Item 121, Zaccheus Walker (Birmingham) to MB (Chacewater) 28 September 1786.

1787 pattern Sixpence **20.5mm Francis** or **John Eginton** (ESC 1641)

1787 pattern Halfpenny (drawing only) **Jean-Pierre Droz**

1787 Anglesey Penny Token (D&H Anglesey 11-85) **33mm John Gregory Hancock** (not struck at Soho Mint)

1787 (struck 1789) Wilkinson **Forge** Halfpenny Token (D&H Warwickshire 340-358; 360-368) **29mm John Gregory Hancock**

1787/9 *Request from John H Mitchell, South Carolina for terms for coining for the whole of USA.*[834]

1788 pattern Halfpenny (Peck 935-945; 962-970) **31mm Jean-Pierre Droz**

1788 pattern Sixpence **20.5mm John Eginton/Jean-Pierre Droz** (ESC 1642)

1788 *Request from Otto Jacob Finck from Altona, Denmark for Schleswig coin.*[835]

1788 *Request from James Jarvis for terms for federal coinage for the USA.*[836]

1788 Anglesey Penny Token (D&H Anglesey 86-140, 169-243) **33mm John Gregory Hancock** (made later using old blanks)

1788 Anglesey Halfpenny Token (D&H Anglesey 273-279, 281-352) **29mm John Gregory Hancock** (not all struck at Soho Mint)

1788 (struck 1789) Wilkinson **Forge** Halfpenny Token (D&H Warwickshire 375-384) **29mm John Gregory Hancock TOTAL 19,296**

1788 (struck 1789) Wilkinson **Ship** Halfpenny Token (D&H Warwickshire 336) **28mm John Gregory Hancock TOTAL 100**

1789 *Counters ordered by Mr Constable for whist, 'on one side a Head of the King with Motto George the Beloved & on the reverse a figure of a drooping Britannia with the figure of Health in the Act of raising her up'.*[837]

1789 Restoration of the Kings Health Medal (BHM 331; Eimer 827) **34mm Jean-Pierre Droz**

1789 Cronebane Halfpenny Token (D&H Wicklow, Ireland 3-31) **29mm John Gregory Hancock TOTAL 1,674,185**

1789 Anglesey Halfpenny Token (D&H Anglesey 355-376) **29mm John Gregory Hancock TOTAL 915,382**

1790 pattern Halfpenny (Peck 948-961; 971-976) **31mm Jean-Pierre Droz**

1790 pattern Sixpences **21mm Eginton/ Jean-Pierre Droz** (ESC 1645)

1790 Wilkinson **Forge** Halfpenny Token (D&H Warwickshire 385-388) **29mm Rambert Dumarest/ John Gregory Hancock TOTAL 404,217**

1790 Anglesey Halfpenny Token (D&H Anglesey 378) **29mm Dumarest after John Gregory Hancock**

1791 pattern Guinea **24mm Thomas Wyon Senior**

1791 India Bombay Presidency double pice, one and half pice, one pice, half pice **30.5mm; 27mm; 24mm; 21mm Dumarest? TOTAL 17,232,100**

---

834 MS 3782-12-108 Item 53, Mint Book 1788 p68.

835 MS 3782-12-108 Item 53, Mint Book 1788 p86.

836 MS 3782-12-108 Item 53, Mint Book 1788 p68 and 93.

837 MS 3782-12-59 Item 17, Richard Chippindall (London) to MB (Soho) 9 May 1789.

1791 Southampton Halfpenny Token (Taylor Moody and Co) (D&H Hampshire 89) **29mm Dumarest TOTAL 194,489**

1791 Anglesey Halfpenny Token (D&H Anglesey 386-397) **29mm Dumarest TOTAL 1,150,784**

1791 Anglesey Penny Token (D&H Anglesey 255) **33mm John Gregory Hancock/Dumarest TOTAL 34,320**

1791 Cornwall Halfpenny Token (Cornish Copper Co, John Vivian) (D&H Cornwall 2) **29mm Dumarest TOTAL 76,562**

1791 Glasgow Halfpenny Token (Gilbert Shearer and Co) (D&H Lanarkshire 2) **29mm Dumarest TOTAL 483,903**

1791 pattern Barbados Pineapple Penny **32mm T Wyon**

1791 pattern Monneron 'Liberty Sous La Loi'; 'Confiance' two sol (Margolis 1; 2) **32mm Noel-Alexandre Ponthon**

1791/2 Monneron 'Vivre Libre' Year III 1792; 'Confiance' five sol (Margolis 8) **40mm Augustin Dupre/Ponthon**

1792 Monneron 'Vivre Libre' Year IV 1792; 'Confiance' five sol (Margolis 9) **40mm Dupre/Ponthon TOTAL 7,561,483**

1792 Monneron 'Vivre Libre' Year IV 1792; 'Qui Se Vend' five sol (Margolis 10) **38mm Dupre/Ponthon**

1792 Monneron 'Liberté Sous La Loi'; 'Qui Se Vend' two sol (Margolis 11) **32mm Ponthon** Estimate **TOTAL 3,225,600**

1792 Monneron 'Hercules' 'Les Francais' 'Qui Se Vend' five sol (Margolis 12) **40mm Dupre/Ponthon TOTAL 460**

1792 Monneron Respublica Gallica 'Hercules' 'La Sagesse Guide' two sol (Margolis 14) **32mm Dupre/Ponthon TOTAL 362**

1792 (dated 1791) Monneron Serment Du Rois 'Je Jure' Medal (Margolis 18) **34/35mm Dupre TOTAL 612**

1791 Monneron 'Acceptation' Medal (similar to Sermont du Roi) **36mm Dupre** (not listed by Margolis)

1792 (undated) Monneron Rousseau Medal (Margolis 19) **34/35mm Dumarest (obverse); Ponthon (reverse) TOTAL 756**

1792 (dated 1789/90/91) Monneron Lafayette Medal (Margolis 20) **35mm Dumarest (obverse); Ponthon (reverse) TOTAL 2,699**

1792 '1791' Sierra Leone one dollar, fifty cent; twenty cent; ten cent, one cent, one penny **36mm; 31mm; 24mm; 19mm; 29mm; 32mm Ponthon TOTAL 736,806**

1792 *Offer by Ralph Mather on Soho's behalf to supply Mint and coinage to Thomas Jefferson for the USA.*[838]

1792 pattern Bengal cowrie coinage **15mm; 10mm Ponthon**

---

838 MS 3782-12-75 Item 57, Zaccheus Walker (Birmingham) to Matthew Boulton (London) 18 April 1793.

1792 (dated 1791) Anglesey Penny Token (D&H Anglesey 386-397) **29mm John Gregory Hancock TOTAL 34,320**

1792 Wilkinson **Forge** Halfpenny Token (D&H Warwickshire 389) **29mm Dumarest based on John Gregory Hancock TOTAL 27,184**

1792 Wilkinson **Ship** Halfpenny Token (D&H Warwickshire 336) **30mm John Gregory Hancock TOTAL 100**

1792 Soho Manufactory Medal **32mm Droz**

1792 *Proposed medal for the Royal Academy.*[839]

1792 *Request from Col Thomas Johnes for a Prize Medal for Cardiganshire Society of Husbandry.*[840]

1793 Louis XVI Farewell/Final Interview Medal (Pollard 1) **48mm Conrad Heinrich Küchler TOTAL 423**

1793 Execution of Louis XVI (Death) Medal (Pollard 2) **51mm Küchler/ Ponthon TOTAL 488**

1793 Death of Gustav III of Sweden Medal (Pollard 3) **56mm Küchler TOTAL 423**

1793 Bermuda Halfpenny **30mm Droz/Ponthon TOTAL 81,942**

1793 Leeds Halfpenny Token (Henry Brownbill) (D&H Yorkshire 33-35, 37, 41) **29mm Ponthon TOTAL 179,448**

1793 Inverness Halfpenny Token (Mackintosh, Inglis and Wilson) (D&H Inverness 1) **29mm Küchler TOTAL 122,577**

1793 Wilkinson Forge Halfpenny (D&H Warwickshire 409-416) **28mm Dumarest based on John Gregory Hancock TOTAL 92,553**

1794 (dated 1793) Execution of Marie Antoinette Medal (Pollard 4) **48mm Küchler TOTAL 429**

1794 (dated 1792 or 1793) Marquis Cornwallis Medal (Pollard 5; BHM 363; Eimer 845) **48mm Küchler TOTAL 457**

1794 pattern Canada Halfpenny **29mm Ponthon**

1794 Lancaster/Eccleston Halfpenny Token (D&H Lancashire 57) **29mm Ponthon TOTAL 104,752**

1794 Inverness Halfpenny Token (Mackintosh, Inglis and Wilson) (D&H Inverness 2) **28.5mm Küchler TOTAL 96,668**

1794 Essex Agricultural Society Medal (Pollard 7) **45mm Küchler TOTAL 50** to 1808

1794 India Bombay Presidency double pice, pice and half pice (pattern one and half pice) **30mm; 28m; 25mm; 20mm Ponthon? TOTAL 8,653,390**

1794 India Madras Presidency (Northern Circars) 1/48-rupee, 1/96-rupee **30mm, 24mm Ponthon TOTAL 13,559,018**

1794 *Request for spanish silver pistorinas and half pistorinas from Mr Aniswick, Albion St, Black Friars Bridge.* This order could have been for colonies in the West Indies.[841]

---

839 T. Stainton (1983) *The Proposed Academy Medal of 1793* British Numismatic Journal Vol 53 1983 pp187-197.

840 MS 3782-12-38 Item 73, Colonel Thomas Johnes (Swansea) to MB (Soho) 8 May 1793.

841 MS 3782-12-59 Item 63, Richard Chippindall (London) to MB (Soho) 29 March 1794.

1794/5 Ibberson London Halfpenny Token (D&H Middlesex 338-343) **29mm**
  Ponthon

1795 (dated 1794) Lord Howe and the Glorious First of June Medal (Pollard 8;
  BHM 383; Eimer 855) **48mm Küchler**

1795 *Lord Hood Medal designs sent 22.1.1795 by Küchler.*[842]

1795 pattern Halfpenny (Peck 1036-1046) **30-31mm T. Wyon based on Droz**

1795 Wilkinson Forge Halfpenny Token (D&H Warwickshire 420-423) **29mm**
  Dumarest/John Gregory Hancock TOTAL 86,488

1795 Hornchurch, Romford, Essex Halfpenny Token (George Cotton) (D&H
  Essex 33-4) **28mm Ponthon TOTAL 10,563**

1795 (undated) pattern Swainson Vegetable syrup, London Token (D&H
  Middlesex 907) **28mm Ponthon**

1795 (dated 1797) Marriage of Prince of Wales Medal (Pollard 9; BHM 392;
  Eimer 865) **48mm Küchler TOTAL 50**

Undated 1795 Dundee Halfpenny Token, W. Croom Engraver: Ponthon
  TOTAL 52,805

1795 Queen Charlotte Frogmore Medal (Pollard 10; BHM 389; Eimer 864)
  34mm Küchler/Ponthon TOTAL 50

1795 Queen Charlotte Birthday: George III Frogmore Medal (BHM 390) **35mm**
  Droz/Ponthon TOTAL 50

1795 Visit of Prince and Princess of Wales to Frogmore Medal (BHM 401)
  47mm Küchler/Ponthon TOTAL 50

1795 *Hutton Jackson & Magrath of Angle Court in Friday Street, London, for a Silk Manu-*
  factory, with Weavers Arms for the obverse and bale of silk with a Shuttle for the reverse.[843]

1795 *George Bowser, one ton of Halfpennies for Lockwood Morris & Co LM &Co*
  cypher and T &Co on reverse with edge inscription to read 'Payable at 26 Bush Lane,
  London'.[844]

1796 (dated 1791) Sierra Leone ten cent, one cent **19mm; 29mm Ponthon**

1796 Medallic dies for Anton Schaeffer **79mm Küchler**

1796 Catherine II of Russia Medallet (Pollard 11) **29mm Küchler TOTAL 33**

1796 pattern Myddleton Kentucky Token **29mm Ponthon/Küchler TOTAL 50**

1796 Inverness Halfpenny Token (D&H Invernesshire 4) **28.5mm Küchler**
  TOTAL 85,254

1796 (dated 1795) Bishop's Stortford Halfpenny Token (D&H Hertfordshire 4)
  28.5mm Küchler TOTAL 24,814

1796 '1794' Penryn Volunteers Halfpenny Token (D&H Cornwall 4) **28mm**
  Küchler TOTAL 19,173

1796 Gold Coast one ackey, half ackey, quarter ackey, tackoe **31mm; 24mm;**
  19mm Küchler TOTAL 11,886

---

842 J.G. Pollard (1970) *Matthew Boulton and Conrad Heinrich Küchler.*
843 MS 3782-12-75 Item 94, Zaccheus Walker (Birmingham) to MB (London) 29 January 1795.
844 MS 3782-12-40 Item 17, George Bowser (London) to MB (Soho) 14 January 1795.

1796 *Request from Sir Joseph Banks for Rumford Medal.*[845]

1796 *Proposed Jersey coinage.*[846]

1796/7 Major General Claude Martin coins (BHM 424) **43mm; 38mm; 34mm; 26mm Küchler/Alexander Mackenzie**

1797 *Proposed coin for West Indian islands for Mr Bundack, East Cheaping.*[847]

1797 *Possible coinage for the United States.*[848]

1797 Blanks for cents United States Mint, Philadelphia **TOTAL 425,535**

1797 dated 1793 Board of Agriculture Prize (Pollard 6; Eimer 853) **48mm Küchler**

1797 *Request for sample coins from John Ashworth; to take to dominions of the Vizier of Aude.*[849]

1797 India Madras (Northern Circars) Presidency 1/48-rupee, 1/96-rupee **32mm; 24mm Küchler based on Ponthon? TOTAL 16,535,202**

1797 Cartwheel Two pence (Peck 1064-1077) **42mm Küchler TOTAL 722,180**

1797 Cartwheel Penny (Peck 1083-1133) **36mm Küchler TOTAL 43,969,204**

1797 pattern Penny (various) **36mm Küchler**

1797 pattern Halfpenny (Peck 1152-1160) **31mm Küchler**

1797 pattern Farthing (Peck 1186-1190) **25-26mm Küchler**

1798 Blanks for cents United States Mint **TOTAL 926,834**

1798 Blanks for Lucena & Crawford, Portugal 36 to lb (221,929); 72 to lb (295,686); 120 to lb (242,400) **TOTAL 760,015**

1798 Hafod Friendly Society Medal 41mm **John Philp TOTAL 120**

1798 pattern Guinea **24mm Küchler**

1798 pattern Shield Crown/Dollar (ESC 168-180) 42mm **Küchler**

1798 pattern Farthing (Peck 1202-1206) **25-26mm Küchler**

1798 Mrs Mary Linwood, Linwood Concert Rooms tickets **TOTAL 100**

1798 Sumatra three keping, two keping, one keping **27mm; 24mm; 20mm Küchler? TOTAL 2,562,345**

1798 Isle of Man Penny **33mm Küchler TOTAL 95,045**

1798 Isle of Man Halfpenny **27mm Küchler TOTAL 193,234**

1798 The Second Presidency of George Washington 'Seasons' Medals **TOTAL 720**

'Shepherd' Medal (Pollard 12) **48mm Küchler**

'Farmer' Medal (Pollard 13) **48mm Küchler**

'Spinner' Medal (Pollard 14) **48mm Küchler**

1798 Battle of the Nile (Davidson's Nile Medal) (Pollard 15; BHM 447; Eimer 890) **48mm; 47mm; 45mm Küchler TOTAL 7,316**

---

845 MS 3782-12-56 Item 31, Sir Joseph Banks (London) to Matthew Boulton (Soho) 30 November 1796.

846 MS 3782-12-73 Item 122-123, Thomas Williams (Anglesey) to MB (Soho) 6 September 1796; MB to Williams 15 September 1796.

847 MS 3782-12-59 Item 91-92, Richard Chippindall (London) to MB (Soho) 24 and 25 April 1797.

848 MS 3782-12-42 Item 282, George C. Fox & Sons (Falmouth) to MB (Soho) 11 December 1797.

849 MS 3782-12-42 Item 15, Captain John Ashworth (—) to MB (Soho) 2 February 1797.

1798 British Victories (Army and Navy Victories) Medal (BHM 458: Eimer 897) **48mm Küchler**

1799 Blanks for cents United States Mint **TOTAL 2,526,501**

1799 pattern and currency Halfpenny (Peck 1218-1253) **30mm Küchler TOTAL 42,480,000**

1799 pattern and currency Farthing (Peck 1268-1280) **23mm Küchler TOTAL 4,224,000**

1799 pattern Christian VII Denmark coins **39mm; 34mm; 27mm; 21mm; 18mm Küchler**

1799 Count Alexander Suvorov Medal (Pollard 17) **48mm Küchler TOTAL 348**

1799 Ferdinand IV of Naples and Sicily Medal (Pollard 18; BHM 479; Eimer 908) **48mm Küchler TOTAL 611**

1799 South Devon Militia Defence of Waterford Medal **31mm Küchler TOTAL 596**

1800 Earl St Vincent's Medal (Battle 1797) (Pollard 19; BHM 489; Eimer 919) **47mm Küchler TOTAL 637**

1800 Preservation of George III from Assassination Medal (Pollard 23; BHM 482, 483, 484 and 485; Eimer 916) **48mm Küchler TOTAL 217**

1800 Pen-y-darran Works token (five shillings, two shillings and sixpence, one shilling, sixpence and three-pence) **34mm; 32mm; 30mm; 29mm; 26mm Phillp**

1800 Blanks for half cents United States Mint (188,382); cents (947,710) **TOTAL 1,136,092**

1801 Blanks for cents United States Mint **TOTAL 4,207,008**

1801 (dated 1800) Staffordshire Agricultural Society Medal (Pollard 21) **47mm Küchler TOTAL 200**

1801 (dated 1800) Enniscorthy Halfpenny Token (D&H Wexford 1-4) **28mm Küchler TOTAL 655,304**

1801 dated 1796 Gold Coast one ackey, half ackey, quarter ackey, tackoe **34mm; 31mm; 24mm; 19mm Küchler TOTAL 13,200**

1801 Union of Britain and Ireland (Pollard 24; BHM 523, 524 and 525; Eimer 927) **48mm Küchler TOTAL 316**

1801 (dated 1799) Seringapatam Medal (Pollard 20; Eimer 903) **48mm Küchler TOTAL 51,165**

1801 Preparation for Peace of Amiens Medal (BHM 513; Eimer 941) **48mm Küchler**

1801 *Request from Mr James Braithwaite of Kendal for 50,000 pieces of base silver Danish money which MB advised him to decline it as it is contrary to the Laws of the Kingdom & of Nations.*[850]

1802 *Discussion of possible coinage for France.*[851]

---

850 MS 3782-12-46 Item, 352-23a, Request for Danish money 5 November 1801.
851 MS 3219-4 Item 124 MB (Soho) to James Watt (Frankfurt) 10 October 1802.

1802 Peace of Amiens Medal (Pollard 25; BHM 534, 535 and 536; Eimer 941) **48mm Küchler or Dumarest TOTAL 204**

1802 Birmingham Loyal Association Medal (Eimer 943) **47mm John Gregory Hancock**

1802 Nottinghamshire Yeomanry Medal (Pollard 26; Eimer 945) **36mm Küchler TOTAL 246**

1802 Manchester and Salford Volunteers Medal (Eimer 944) **36mm Küchler TOTAL 106**

1802 Blanks for cents United States Mint **TOTAL 2,812,664**

1802 Ceylon rupee 1/48-rix dollar, 1/96-rix dollar, 1/192-rix dollar **30mm; 23mm; 18mm Küchler TOTAL 6,440,121**

1802 '1791' Arnold Works token (Davison and Hawksley) (crown (five shillings), half a crown, one shilling, and sixpence) **43mm; 30mm; Peter Wyon TOTAL 22,489**

1802 Sierra Leone ten cents **24mm Dies based on Ponthon**

1803 India Madras Presidency twenty cash, ten cash; five cash; one cash **31mm; 25mm, 21mm; 11mm Phillp/Küchler TOTAL 37,936,629**

1803 Sierra Leone ten cents **24mm Dies based on Ponthon**

1803 St. Albans Female Friendly Society Medal **42mm Phillp TOTAL 200**

1803 (dated 1798) pattern Fridericus II Duke of Würtemberg thaler **44mm Küchler TOTAL 100**

1803 Ipswich Theatre **41mm Phillp TOTAL 4,000**

1803 (dated 1798) Boulton's Medallic Scale Medal (Pollard 27; BHM 462; Eimer 901a/b) **42mm; 41mm Dumarest/Küchler**

1803 Boydell's Shakespeare Medal (Pollard 28; BHM 553 and 554; Eimer 950) **48mm Küchler/Phillp**

1803 trial strike Duke of Bridgewater Medal **48mm Phillp?**

1803 Blanks for United States Mint (1,186,387); cents (1,868,011) **TOTAL 3,054,398**

1804 *Enquiry from Antigua for silver and copper coin.*[852]

1803/4 (dated 1802) Charleville-Tullamore one shilling and one penny token (D&H Kings County 1-4) **36mm John Gregory Hancock. TOTAL 10,211**

1804 Ceylon rupee 1/48 rix-dollar, 1/96 rix-dollar, 1/192-rix dollar **30mm; 23mm; 18mm Küchler TOTAL 66**

1804 Sumatra four, two and one keping **30mm; 26mm; 20mm Phillp TOTAL 9,775,025**

1804 India Bombay Presidency double pice, one pice, half pice **30mm; 26mm; 20mm Phillp TOTAL 12,240,550**

1804 pattern Alexander I of Russia rouble **41mm Küchler TOTAL 59**

1804 pattern Alexander I of Russia imperial **27mm Küchler TOTAL 77**

---

852 MS 3782-12-56 Item 69, Sir Joseph Banks (London) to MB (Soho) 28 March 1804.

1804 pattern Bank of England Regenerated Garter Dollar Token (ESC 181-9) **41mm Küchler TOTAL 70**

1804 Bank of England Regenerated Britannia Five Shilling Dollar Token (ESC 190-3) **40-42mm Küchler TOTAL 4,496,192 (up till 1811)**

1804 Bank of Ireland Regenerated Six Shilling Dollar Token **42mm Küchler TOTAL 791,561**

1805 Dies for Royal Visit to Soho Medal (Pollard 29a)

1805 Boulton's Trafalgar Medal (Pollard 30; BHM 584; Eimer 960) **48mm Küchler TOTAL 14,000**

1805 pattern Penny (Peck 1288-1292) **34-35mm Küchler**

1805 pattern Halfpenny (Peck 1301-1306) **30mm Küchler**

1805 Irish Penny **33mm Küchler TOTAL 8,788,416**

1805 Irish Halfpenny **27-28mm Küchler TOTAL 49,795,200**

1806 Irish Farthing **20mm Küchler TOTAL 4,996,992**

1806 (dated 1800) Drayton Agricultural Society Medal **47mm Küchler TOTAL 53**

1806 Bahamas Halfpenny **28mm Küchler TOTAL 120,317**

1806 currency Penny (Peck 1320-1343) **34mm Küchler TOTAL 19,355,480**

1806 currency Halfpenny (Peck 1356-1377) **28mm Küchler TOTAL 87,893,526**

1806 currency Farthing (Peck 1386-1395) **21mm Küchler TOTAL 4,833,768**

1807 St. Albans Female Friendly Society Medal **42mm Phillp TOTAL 50**

1807 currency Penny (Peck 1344-1345) **33-34mm Küchler TOTAL 11,290,168**

1807 currency Halfpenny (Peck 1378) **28mm Küchler TOTAL 41,394,384**

1807 currency Farthing (Peck 1399) **21mm Küchler TOTAL 1,075,200**

1807 (made till 1840) Royal Society of Arts Medal

Pallet Prize Medal **63 x 52 mm Küchler TOTAL 386 silver and 1 gold**

Minerva Medal: **43mm G.F. Pidgeon TOTAL 278 silver, 94 gold**

Isis Medal: **39mm Thomas Wyon Junior TOTAL 120 silver and 94 gold**

1808 India Madras Presidency twenty cash, ten cash **31mm; 25mm Phillp TOTAL 86,515,344**

1808 Dies for Haiti coinage

1809 *Request for recoinage for Guernsey*[853]

1808 on East India Company College Prize for Persian Medal (Pollard 31) **37mm Küchler TOTAL 34**

1808 on East India Company College Prize for Sanskrit Medal pattern (Pollard 32) **37mm Küchler TOTAL 57**

1809 pattern India Bengal Presidency one pice, half pice **27mm; 21mm Phillp**

1809 pattern Brazil 960 reis **41mm Küchler**

1809 Death of Matthew Boulton Medal (BHM 659) **45mm P. Wyon**

1809 (made 1817?) Death of Matthew Boulton Medal (Roux/Thomason) (BHM 660; Eimer 1000) **102mm P. Wyon**

---

853 MS 3782-13-8 Item 58, Bowerbank, Monkhouse, & Co. (London) to MRB (Soho) 17 June 1809.

1809 Matthew Boulton Obsequies Medal (BHM 662; 663; Eimer 1002; 1003) **40mm; 41mm Küchler TOTAL 532**

1809 Matthew Boulton 'Farewel' (sic) Medal (Pollard 33; BHM 661; Eimer 1001) **48mm Küchler**

1809 Blanks for cents United States Mint **TOTAL 1,886,637**

1810 pattern coin for Penang **T. Wyon Junior**

1810 Lord Radnor's Jubilee Medal for George III (Pollard 34; BHM 684; Eimer 1008) **48mm Küchler TOTAL 685**

1810 George III Jubilee (Frogmore) Medal (BHM 686; Eimer 1007) **48mm Phillp TOTAL 1710**

1811 (dated 1803) Westminster Fire Office token **Phillp TOTAL 218**

1811 pattern 'Regenerated' Dollar Bank token (five shillings and sixpence Britannia) George III **Phillp/based on Küchler**

1811 pattern 'Regenerated' Dollar Bank token (five shillings and sixpence oak wreath) George III **Phillp/Küchler**

1811 Blanks for cents United States Mint **TOTAL 1,770,221**

1812 Blanks for Brazil? Ordered by Abraham Rhodes at 32 per lb (1,638,336); at 81.5 per lb (5,215,920); at 120 per lb (1,369,386) **TOTAL 8,223,642**

1812 Blanks for Portugal ordered by J.C. Harris 36 per lb for 10 reis **TOTAL 741,744**

1813 (dated 1808) Beilby Christ's College Medal (BHM 632, 633 and 634; Eimer 991) **42mm; 43mm; 50mm Küchler/Phillp/Pidgeon**

1813 Isle of Man Penny **based on Küchler**

1813 Isle of Man Halfpenny **based on Küchler**

1814 (dated 1807) Macauley and Babington (Abolition of the Slave Trade) token (Eimer 984) **36mm Pidgeon/Phillp** (reverse) **TOTAL 50,000**

1814 (dated 1809) John, Prince Regent of Portugal/'Cayenne seized' Medal **51mm Pidgeon TOTAL 257**

1815 Blanks for cents United States Mint **TOTAL 461,659**

1816 (dated 1801) Highland Society Medal (BHM 512) **Pidgeon**

1816 Blanks for cents United States Mint **TOTAL 1,866,637**

1817 Blanks for cents United States Mint **TOTAL 2,333,296**

1817 Blanks for Brazil May & Lukin at 32 per lb (1,092,224); at 81.5 per lb (2,084,186); at 120 per lb (2,282,631) **TOTAL 5,459,041**

1818 Blanks for cents United States Mint **TOTAL 2,006,635**

1819 Boulton Memorial Medal 'Inventas' (BHM 976) **64mm; 55mm Pidgeon**

1819 Blanks for cents United States Mint **TOTAL 2,799,955**

1820 Death of George III Medal (BHM 991 and 992; Eimer 1121) **48mm after Küchler**